Dr Stafford-Clark is Physician-in-Charge of the Department of Psychological Medicine, Guy's Hospital, and is also on the consultant and postgraduate teaching staff of the Bethlem Royal and Maudsley hospitals, and of the Institute of Psychiatry of the University of London. During the war he served in the Royal Air Force, became a medical parachutist, and was twice mentioned in dispatches.

Dr Stafford-Clark's book, *What Freud Really Said* has recently been published as a Pelican. In addition to his books and numerous professional papers and articles he has also published poetry, and has undertaken pioneer work in closed-circuit colour and black-and-white television for psychiatric teaching and demonstration in his own and other hospitals. He designed and directed a number of programmes in this field in public television, including the B.B.C. 'Lifeline' and 'Brain and Behaviour' series, and the recent 'Mind and Motive' series for B.B.C. 2, as well as a special programme commemorating the twentieth anniversary of Freud's death, for the Independent Television Authority. He was medical consultant to John Huston's film, *Freud*.

PSYCHIATRY TO-DAY

DAVID STAFFORD-CLARK

PENGUIN BOOKS

Penguin Books Ltd, Harmondsworth, Middlesex, England
Penguin Books Inc., 3300 Clipper Mill Road, Baltimore, Md 21211, U.S.A.
Penguin Books Australia Ltd, Ringwood, Victoria, Australia

—

First published 1952
Reprinted 1953, 1954, 1956, 1959, 1961
Second Edition 1963
Reprinted 1965, 1967

—

Second Edition copyright © David Stafford-Clark, 1963

—

Made and printed in Great Britain
by The Whitefriars Press Ltd
London and Tonbridge
Set in Monotype Times

CONTENTS

The author gratefully acknowledges the courtesy of the following authors and their publishers in permitting him to quote from their books: Dr C. P. Blacker, *Neurosis and the Mental Health Service*, Oxford University Press (Medical Publications), 1946; Mr Rex Warner, *The Cult of Power*, John Lane (The Bodley Head) Ltd, 1946.

FOREWORD

This book deals with matters of fact and matters of opinion. I have tried to present them as clearly and honestly as I can, and whenever an opinion is expressed, to indicate whether it is my own or someone else's.

The responsibility for the book is mine, but several people encouraged me. I am particularly grateful to Sir Allen Lane, who suggested that it be written, and to Professor Aubrey Lewis, who suggested that I should write it. I have also been fortunate in my friends in this country and in America and Canada, who never interfered but who were generous when called upon for criticism and sensible advice.

In prospect the book seemed a difficult and terribly responsible job; in retrospect, I am all too aware of its shortcomings. It cannot claim to be complete; indeed, in one sense any book of this kind remains inevitably perennially unfinished. But the writer must lay down his task before the reader can begin, and now that point has been reached; it only remains for me to hope that something of the idea behind the book will have found its way into the pages.

D.S.-C.

London, July 1951

There is surely a piece of Divinity in us. Something that was before the Elements and owes no homage unto the Sun. Nature tells me that I am the Image of God, as well as Scripture; he that understands not thus much, hath not his introduction or first lesson, and is yet to begin the Alphabet of Man.

THOMAS BROWNE: *Religio Medici*, 1643

—

I conclude that man as a whole is a larger affair ... than any single method of minute inquiry – be it chemical, physical, pathological, microscopical, or psycho-physical – will ever unfold. ... There is work enough for as many methods of study of mind as are rationally based: have the definite aim of a concrete mental organization to be studied, and work definitely and progressively for it by observation of facts, exclude not one another, but know that in the end they must bring, and knowing, strive to bring their results into harmony.

HENRY MAUDSLEY: *The New Psychology*, 1900

One Way of Beginning

IN the presence of physical disorder man has a precious natural humility. Most of us, if we see someone afflicted with a crippling illness or injury, feel an instinctive sympathy, a desire to help or comfort at least as far as we can. Yet this feeling is not universal nor, in the majority of those who experience it, is it always unmixed; for example a dread of infectious diseases, or an involuntary repugnance and disgust at some terrible mutilation or disfigurement, can complicate or even overcome the compassion and sympathy which otherwise we might expect to feel. Sick or injured people are a challenge to our emotions as well as to our communal responsibility; but mankind has not always treated this challenge in the way which alone seems permissible now. A Prussian law still existent in the year 1230 included this statement:

Be a man laden with sick women, children, brothers, sisters, or domestics, or be he sick himself, then let them lie where they be, and we praise him too if he would burn himself or the feeble person.

Such an attitude sounds utterly barbarous, callous, and inhuman to us now, but we are separated from it by nothing more substantial than time, and a mere seven hundred years at that, only a fragment of the span of human history. None the less, the change which has taken place in people's approach to bodily illness, and to the art and science of medicine which seeks however imperfectly to relieve it, is of vital importance; moreover, in so far as it reflects a profound concern for the individual, it is indispensable to any kind of civilization worthy of the name.

In contrast to the relatively smooth and sure development of medicine in the sphere of tangible physical disorder, the story of affliction of the mind and personality is indeed appalling, charred with countless burnings at the stake, chequered with violence, cruelty, and remorseless persecution, and dark not only with the gloom of ignorance and superstition, but also with the despair of unlit solitary cells, stocks, bars, chains and brands, and all the sickening paraphernalia of torture. Why should this be? There is an echo of this attitude to mental illness in the heart of every one of us, however little we may care or be able to acknowledge it, but before we can understand it better we shall need to examine as honestly and objectively as possible something of the problem of mental illness itself.

Words are important here. In *Through the Looking Glass* Alice found herself involved in rather a trying conversation with Humpty Dumpty, who at one stage without apparent reason remarked :

'There's glory for you.'
'I don't know what you mean by "glory",' Alice said.
'I meant "there's a nice knockdown argument for you".'
'But "glory" doesn't mean "a nice knockdown argument",' Alice objected.
'When *I* use a word,' Humpty Dumpty said in a rather scornful tone, 'it means just what I choose it to mean – neither more nor less.'

Alice was justifiably irritated by this, and we can share her feeling from personal experience, although of course most of us at one time or another do precisely what Humpty Dumpty did, usually without recognizing or acknowledging it. We do it, for example, if like Mr Evelyn Waugh, an indisputable master of language, we object to the very terms 'mental illness' or 'mentally ill people', preferring the more robust and traditional 'madness', 'lunacy', 'madmen' and 'lunatics'. For these older words carry with them a strong and in some ways more satisfying emotional charge of contempt, or horror, or derision, or at least condescension, according to the way in which they are used. They have acquired this emotional flavour from the time when such a constellation of feelings was almost universal among sane people towards those less fortunate than themselves. That these same feelings maintain their place in the minds of many honest and far from inhuman men and women to-day is shown by their assertion that the terms 'mental illness' and 'mentally ill patients' are mere euphemisms or polite fictions. It is of course true that to describe someone as mentally ill is a less forceful and vivid statement than to say that he is mad or a lunatic; but what really determines what we say in such a case is not primarily a preference for accuracy in the first instance or gusto in the second, but rather whether our attitude towards madness is fundamentally one of contempt, of rejection of the lunatic as someone essentially separated from us, with whom we desire as little contact and for whom we acknowledge as little responsibility as possible, or whether we can accept his plight as an illness and him as a sick man with a claim upon our sympathies. The basis of the distinction is therefore an emotional one: and this in turn will govern our choice of words. In a dispute of this kind it is the emotional attitude of the participants rather than the facts which are at variance. This of course is true of most disputes, particularly the more heated ones.

Let us try to agree then at the outset that the problem we have to examine includes the whole range of disturbance of human emotion, judgement, action, and personality, whenever this disturbance is sufficiently profound to be considered abnormal. This range will extend from excessive anxiety, tension, unhappiness, fear, or confusion without apparent cause at one end, to the most bizarre forms of insanity at the other. Somewhere along it must be found a place for simple failure of mental development, failure to meet the requirements of society, sheer personal inadequacy, and the various short-lived but violent disturbances known as deliria: it must also include some other disturbances of consciousness and memory whether due to structural disease or damage to the brain or not. This aspect of human suffering in all its manifestations we shall call mental illness. It is with all this that the psychiatrist of to-day is concerned.

We must now turn back for a moment and remind ourselves that our first object in examining the problem of mental illness was to gain an understanding of its history, in which, as we shall see, violence has played so tragic a part, while the more decent and humane aspects of medicine have been all too often eclipsed despite the isolated efforts of outstanding individuals throughout the centuries. Why do normal people find it so hard to accept and understand the mentally ill? Why do the very words 'neurosis', 'idiocy', 'madness', or 'lunacy' call up such intensely hostile feelings by comparison with words like cancer, tuberculosis, poliomyelitis, or amputation? Granted that in the most primitive attitude of all men to all sickness there is to be found a blend of fear and hatred with sympathy and understanding, why have we been able to resolve this so much more readily in the case of physical illness than of mental?

We can gain some insight into this question by returning momentarily to Alice and Humpty Dumpty. Humpty Dumpty bewildered and finally annoyed Alice by refusing to accept the conventions of normal speech. Whatever his reasons, the ultimate effect of this was to make Alice feel she could not maintain contact with him at all. She was of course perfectly correct in this feeling: if everybody followed Humpty Dumpty's example all the time, we should soon all lose touch with each other completely in so far as we depended on words for our understanding. A similar necessity to accept objective as opposed to purely subjective standards, reality as opposed to fantasy, impresses itself upon us all. We normally make a realistic adjustment between our hopes and desires and fears on the one hand, and our experience of life as it actually is on the other, by means of our resilient emotional and intellectual equipment. A failure of this process, whatever its primary cause, is an essential feature of every form of mental illness. It follows from this that a refusal or inability to accept some or all of the demands of reality is characteristic of such patients, and it is this above all that separates them from their fellow men and provokes the hostility and antagonism which they still encounter. Gregory Zilboorg, in an epilogue to his *History of Medical Psychology*, puts it this way:

Every mental patient either aggressively rejects life as we like it – and he was therefore thought of as heretic, witch, or sorcerer – or passively succumbs to his inability to accept life as we see it – and he was therefore called bewitched.

This was the basis on which such people were burned, tortured, or imprisoned. Even after the era of persecution ceased, the residual hostility showed itself in harsh restraint, neglect, indifference, or exploitation. In the real world it would seem that grown men, unlike Alice, have taken a terrible revenge on Humpty Dumpty.

•

Every study that has been made of primitive peoples in no matter what part of the world, every attempt to pierce the mystery of the beginnings of the human race, has shown that primitive man has always believed in the existence of supernatural beings in the world about him. He heard their voices in the sighing of the wind among the trees, in the sound of the rivers and the rain, the roaring of the sea, the crash of the thunder. Some, like the sun or the moon, were visible to him; but most were invisible, mysterious, uncountable but all-powerful and everywhere, sometimes inhabiting animals or other men, sometimes condescending to dwell in temples or holy places, some good, some evil, some even more powerful and therefore more to be feared or worshipped than others; a whole hierarchy of gods and devils, benevolent or malignant but inescapable.

The sense of another presence – of not being alone – has occurred repeatedly to solitary travellers and explorers, to mountaineers on lonely heights, to men alone in vast deserts. An echo of this feeling at a more mundane level has occurred to most of us: who has not been into a wood and felt himself surrounded by eyes?

The less man knew about his world, the less subject to his control or understanding were the events which surrounded him, the more readily and completely did he explain them to himself as the direct result of action by these good or evil spirits, who might in turn be induced to favour him, or at least spare him the worst misfortunes, could he but find some way of propitiating them, or borrowing their power. The men most gifted in this activity in a tribe, who could predict or seem to bring about success or failure of crops or hunting expeditions, confer fertility on marriage, or cast out sickness, were the priests or medicine men. In a system of belief in which innumerable gods and demons, frequently warring among themselves, were responsible for literally everything that happened, from an earthquake to the opening of a flower, the more mysterious and terrible an event, the more awful and powerful must be the spirit who produced it, and the more extreme the measures to be adopted by the medicine man to deal with it or prevent its recurrence.

For a long time this probably applied equally to every form of disease or personal misfortune; but sickness or injury which gave rise to physical disability or pain led to the sufferer's demand for relief and help, and so even on this crude basis an empirical system of physical treatments and drugs gradually evolved, and the role of the medicine man or priest in relationship to the sick man became that of healer. It was not so with mental illness. Here the disturbance was all too often in the realm of behaviour and in the patient's relationship with others: he might make no complaint of his health but rather blame himself or others for his fear or anguish: he might seem different, a changed man, for whose transformation the work of a devil who had entered into him seemed at once the most obvious explanation. Or he might appear inspired and ecstatic – in a divine frenzy; in this case he had become the prophet or mouthpiece of some god who chose this method of making the sacred truths apparent. In this way the ancient Greeks came to regard epilepsy as 'the Sacred Disease'. Patients of this kind were often treated with great respect and carefully protected in the name of the god believed responsible. But in societies who believed in demoniacal rather than divine possession, those inhabited by devils would be attacked and tortured, squeezed or crushed, to drive out the fiend by making his temporary physical abode too uncomfortable for him. The fate of those of undeveloped or defective intelligence was apt to be less severe: they were either ignored or treated with some of the indulgence but by no means all the affection commonly displayed towards children. They were the harmless natural idiots, the simpletons, neither inspired nor accursed. When they died it was from neglect rather than persecution as a rule.

This then was the pattern underlying the response of primitive peoples to mental affliction. Yet at every stage in human history there were men whose vision and sensitivity were ahead of their time, who saw through the conventional acceptance and popular support of this attitude to the dreadful cruelties and callousness it covered, and who possessed the courage to challenge it in the name of truth and compassion.

Even before the blossoming of Greek civilization, with its medical tradition which has survived to this day, there is abundant evidence of attempts to understand and treat mental illness. The shamans, or primitive medicine men of tribal society, actually trephined some of their patients to release the devils from their heads; the remains both of the primitive instruments and of the perforated skulls have been found by archaeologists. The medical system of ancient India, whose records are to be found in the literary heritage of the Vedas as well as in other famous treatises, included not only the belief in demoniacal possession as a basic cause of mental disturbance, but also the views of Susruta which even to-day remain in advance of much of contemporary medical thought. Susruta held that passions and strong emotions might cause not only mental illness, but even bodily ailments for which surgery might be required. The evidence available in support of this amounts now to proof. But despite his remarkable shrewdness in this particular contribution to the problem of psychophysical relationships, Susruta like many more conventional men of his time could not escape the compulsion to think of the soul at least partly as a material thing, a sort of extra physical organ. He and his colleagues in the fifth century B.C. considered that the soul dwelt within the body in the cavity of the heart, that it possessed an essential faculty or essence which they called *manas*, and that this *manas* was bound up with the act of breathing, called *prana*, believed by them to be spiritually as well as physically significant. At death, with the last breath the living soul left the body and could then return after entering into another living creature.

About a hundred years later, in another and seemingly separate civilization, the idea of the *prana* was to appear in the writings of Hippocrates, who thought that the breath, *pneuma*, was the source of intelligence and feeling, but was distributed to the rest of the body by the brain. Other ideas on the nature and seat of the soul, some strikingly similar to the more mystical speculations of the Indian philosophers although not including the conception of the transmigration of souls, characterized the later works of Plato and his pupil Aristotle. But while Plato and Aristotle were philosophers, and their interest in psychology was traditional and scholastic, Hippocrates was essentially a physician, and a practising clinician at that.

Up to this time in Greece, medicine had been wholly concerned with physical suffering; psychological disturbance, although widely recognized in the rich mythology of the race, was not considered the special concern of the physician at all, but rather that of the priest or seer. Even so, treatment was sometimes remarkably empirical: there is a story that the daughters of Proetus, the king of Argos, brought down upon themselves the wrath of the Goddess Hera, by stealing gold from her statue. She afflicted them with madness, so that they believed they were cows, and ran wildly about lowing and mooing in the fields. A seer called Melampus, who lived about three centuries before Homer and had apparently established his reputation by curing Hercules of a similar attack of madness, was called in to treat them. Drawing on his experience with goats, whose violent purgings after eating white hellebore he had often observed, he gave hellebore to the royal patients, who were then chased vigorously about the fields by stalwart retainers. When they had reached complete exhaustion he had them bathed in the fountains of Arcadia, and pronounced them cured. Hellebore became a recognized specific for madness, and purging and cold baths have died hard as a method of treatment.

This story, although over three thousand years old, has a curiously modern flavour. Disturbance of the mind is still frequently felt to be a sign of guilt or shame rather than an illness: and even when it is accepted as an illness, the more demonstrably physical and spectacularly drastic the treatment, the more respect it is liable to command. But between the days of Melampus and our own the problem of mental illness remained for most of the three thousand years the almost exclusive province of the seer, and later of the philosopher: the physician, even if he were bold enough to venture into this vast and troubled field, could expect no welcome but rather resentment and contemptuous abuse. Even in the late eighteenth century Immanuel Kant could still berate the physician for displaying a professional interest in mind; yet out of the Greeks' love for reason, and from their passionate search for truth and justice, sprang the genius of Hippocrates whose observations on the medical nature of mental disturbances were to endure long after the very civilization of which he was so great an example had completed its insidious and terrible decline.

The nature of Hippocrates' special contribution to psychological medicine was threefold: he recognized the importance of the brain as an organ of mind, he sought a physiological explanation of the various temperaments, moods, and emotional disorders he encountered in his patients, and he attacked vigorously the conception of divinely ordained and therefore unalterable illnesses. It seemed to Hippocrates, as to present-day physicians, a greater blasphemy to ascribe to God the deliberate imposition of mental and physical suffering than to attempt by human means to relieve such conditions. Perhaps the best example of this is his attitude to 'the Sacred Disease', or epilepsy, which he considered 'in no way more divine, or more sacred than other diseases, but having a natural cause ...'. Inviting the student to examine the brains of epileptics after their death, he said '... in this way you will see that it is not a God which injures the body, but disease'. Of the 'purificators' who treated epilepsy by 'purifications and incantations' he wrote '... it seems to me, they make the divinity out to be most wicked and impious. ... Such persons thus use the divinity as a screen for their own inability to afford any assistance.'

He described with care and accuracy a case of puerperal insanity, another of psychoneurosis with morbid fears, still called by the Greek name of phobias to this day; he recorded the details of the deliria in malaria and tuberculosis, of loss of memory in a case of dysentery, and of acute confusion after a severe haemorrhage.

His view of temperament and constitution was founded on the theory that phlegm and bile were the body fluids responsible for emotional attitudes; a surfeit of black bile for example, $\mu\epsilon\lambda\alpha\gamma\chi o\lambda i\alpha$[1] in the Greek, producing depression. It was Hippocrates who gave us the mental picture of the melancholy man, and of the sanguine and phlegmatic temperaments. In later chapters

---

1. $\mu\epsilon\lambda\alpha\gamma\chi o\lambda i\alpha$ = melancholy.

we shall see how prescient was the view that body fluids are important in the regulation of our moods.

Hippocrates seems to have been the first man to strive to free medical psychology from the speculative theories of the philosophers and the mystical approach of the priests of his day, and to place it upon an essentially objective basis. In his attempt to do this he was without the aid of any more facts about mental illness than he was able to observe at first hand himself. The opposition to this way of regarding disturbances of mind and of behaviour, although less severe and harsh than it was to become in succeeding centuries, was perhaps more formidable than is generally realized. The whole weight of public opinion was against Hippocrates when he began his study of psychological problems; and despite the tremendous impact of his teachings almost one hundred and fifty years were to pass before another physician dared to do more than echo what he had said or to attempt to pursue further the line of thought which he had begun.

Of his immediate successors in the realm of psychiatry none were physicians and only one, Plato, shared the view of Hippocrates that the brain was important in mental life. Aristotle, Epicurus, and all their disciples stoutly maintained that it was the heart from which proceeded thought, feeling, and the springs of action. They maintained this by discussion and disputation, essentially a pastime for philosophers and a scholastic rather than a scientific procedure; sincere and passionate seekers after truth, they none the less ignored the experimental and observational methods which alone had enabled Hippocrates to lay foundations upon which they no longer cared to build despite their reverence for his ability. The whole of medicine once more became diverted into purely speculative channels and the factual basis of psychiatry sank again into oblivion.

Plato alone preserved a fragment of the Hippocratic foundation. He believed that reality was twofold, made up of two essentially distinct and almost incompatible members, mind and matter. 'Mind is the true reality, the thing of most worth, that to which everything owes its form and essence and the member of law and order in the universe; the other element, matter, is secondary, a dull, irrational recalcitrant force, the unwilling slave of the mind which somehow, but imperfectly, takes on the impress of the mind.' Plato believed that the soul consisted of two parts, the rational and the irrational; the greater of these was the rational soul, immortal and divine, with its seat in the brain. The irrational or animal soul was mortal; it was the source of feelings, of impulses, of all that most bound man's mind to his body, and it was scattered all over the body which it served. Its seat was in the chest, anger and courage dwelt in the heart, hunger in the navel, and lusts and passions raged in the belly. In considering madness Plato divided his allegiance between the humoral theory of Hippocrates, whereby the bodily juices were responsible for many disturbances of feeling, and a new idea of his own; this was that the rational soul might in some circumstances prove too powerful for the frail, dull, unwilling body, which might then be consumed while the balance of mind and body was overthrown. Plato also reopened the door to the idea of sacred and profane forms of madness: in this way he foreshadowed the massacres and torments inflicted upon sick and neurotic people in the Middle Ages, which he himself would have utterly condemned.

Aristotle was a pupil of Plato and the son of a physician. He had great respect for the objective approach of Hippocrates, and tried to combine this with his studies and teaching of philosophy. He probably knew more than any other man alive in his time, and he studied every branch of knowledge that existed. He laid the foundations for logic and the application of pure reason to all problems, and so it is perhaps understandable that for him, as for millions of intelligent men who have followed him, the concept of pure reason as something absolute, and beyond the range either of emotion or physical decay, was complete. The implications of this are that it is never possible for a man to misuse his reason except deliberately; and this is to this day the basis of the legal view of mental illness. If a man knows what he is doing, and knows that what he is doing is wrong, neither despair nor frenzy, even if unquestionably due to mental illness, can be accepted as extenuating his guilt or even as relevant to the plea. The laws which embody this principle were formulated in 1846 and are therefore comparatively modern; the suggestion that such progress in our understanding of mental and emotional processes as has taken place during the past one hundred and six years might provide a basis for revising them, is as stoutly resisted to-day as it would have been in the time of Aristotle.

Aristotle retained only partial support for most of Hippocrates' theories. The body fluids he considered essentially as conductors of heat and cold; the soul could not live without warmth. He gave no place whatever to brain in psychological matters, but his objectivity compelled him to acknowledge its size and to accord it some importance in bodily functions. He believed that it condensed, 'by means of its cold consistency, the hot vapours which arose from the heart'. These condensed vapours formed a dew which fell and refreshed the heart, making it more temperate. It would be interesting to know how many Victorian ladies, suffering from the vapours, suspected that they were at least in part disciples of Aristotle.

In this brief review of Greek thought in its relation to psychological medicine one more important fact must be mentioned. Hippocrates, the physician and founder of objective and empirical medical thought, was far from being a materialist in the modern or even the nineteenth-century sense of the word. Nor was he a man without faith in God. The fragment of his personal ethic and philosophy which is best remembered, and which has provided the medical profession throughout the world with a standard around which it can still gather the shreds of its dignity and courage, is the Hippocratic oath, which begins with the words 'I swear by Apollo the physician . . .' Apollo was the god of healing: the basis of medical ethics, as of all morality, was essentially spiritual.

＊

Aristotle's system of thought was the last incursion into psychology to be made in the great days of Greece. The Peloponnesian War, which ended in the fall of Athens in 404 B.C., had preceded his birth; and during the latter part of his life the cultural centre of the world moved from Athens to Alexandria, where it became established a little before 300 B.C. The military power of the ancient world came to lie now in the hands of Rome, but Roman physicians turned to the inheritance of Greece for their inspiration. Nevertheless the followers of Hippocrates were unable to maintain the standards of their master, unable even to preserve the essence of his views and methods unclouded by their own prejudices. With the passing of time and the further shifts of political power in the Mediterranean area, three systems of thought began to contend for acceptance as the basis of all knowledge both philosophical and scientific. These were the philosophy of early Christianity with its central belief in one God and its emphasis upon that God's concern for the individual; the religious systems of the East with their several differing concepts of God and their differing philosophies; and the pagan philosophy of the Romans, whose religious attitude was open-minded but whose political convictions and belief in an imposed law and order overruled all other considerations. It was still a liberal time for philosophers and physicians. Provided that they kept themselves free of political entanglements they did not have to choose between becoming persecutors or persecuted, a choice which in the Middle Ages was to confront them inescapably. Little contribution was made to mental science until the middle of the first century B.C. when Asclepiades, a physician, made his mark upon his time.

Asclepiades began his career as an orator and turned to medicine later in life. He was essentially a controversialist and dismissed the whole of Hippocratic teaching as a meditation of death. His writings have been lost but his views have been preserved by one of the earliest medical historians, Caelius Aurelianus. From these we learn that despite his contemptuous rejection of almost all the positive gain of his greatest predecessor, Asclepiades was a keen and gifted clinical observer. He differentiated deliria due to fever from the more chronic and subtle forms of mental disturbance, not simply on physical but also on psychological grounds. He is quoted as despising the term insanity as being a vulgar and popular rather than scientific and accurate description. He described the difference between delusions, ideas firmly held on a mistaken basis, and hallucinations, which are perceptions of the senses which do not correspond to external reality. No one else was to pay much attention to this important distinction until the beginning of the nineteenth century, when the

French psychiatrist Esquirol included it in his contribution to medical psychology.

Asclepiades considered that mental illness proceeded largely from intolerable emotional disturbance, which he called a passion of sensations. Here again he was tremendously in advance of his time. Nor did he confine himself to description but took original and active interest in the treatment and happiness of individual patients. He thought of many ways of making his patients more comfortable, from swinging hammocks to 'a hundred different kinds of baths'; he prescribed music and harmony and pleasant company for disturbed and unhappy people, and was the first doctor to go on record as condemning the cells and dungeons wherein such patients were confined. Patients, he said, should be kept in well lighted places; darkness leads to terror and terror increases the misery and the madness. He also had a vigorous comment to make on the prevalent treatment of bleeding, which despite his strictures was to survive him by well over fifteen hundred years. He saw little difference between bleeding and strangling, and added for good measure that, whatever the Greeks might claim for this method of treatment among their own people, it was hardly likely to benefit the Romans, who were already depleted by debauchery. He was probably a spectacular rather than a popular physician.

Laymen continued to outnumber physicians in outspoken concern about the causes and treatment of mental illness. Cicero and Plutarch both believed that only the soul could cure the soul, but favoured philosophical disputation as a means of reasoning with a sick soul, a procedure which has always proved somewhat sterile as a therapeutic technique. About the time of the birth of Christ, Celsus, who could perhaps be described as a medical journalist, surveyed the medical knowledge of his time. Dealing with the methods of treating madness he joined issue with the philosophers. The philosopher, he said, may have great knowledge of words, but these may not affect the sick man; if philosophy were the key to such problems the philosopher would be a better healer than the physician. However, when he goes on to describe the methods actually in use one is left with the impression that it might very well have been better to have been treated by a philosopher, for restraint, harshness, and violence all formed part of the management of disturbed patients.

Writing of what we might now consider as mania Celsus remarked: 'When he has said or done anything wrong, he must be chastised by hunger, chains, and fetters. He must be made to attend and to learn something that he will remember, for thus it will happen that by degrees he will be led to consider what he is doing. It is also beneficial in this malady to make use of sudden fright, for a change may be effected by withdrawing the mind from the state in which it has been.' This tendency to treat patients as though they were ultimately responsible for their actions and could be bullied, tortured, or frightened out of their perversity is not characteristic of any one period in history, but is with us always. When, nineteen hundred years later, the great physician, Philippe Pinel, had the chains removed from patients in the Bicêtre hospital in Paris, both his colleagues and the populace at large were exceedingly alarmed and convinced that he would be set upon by the dangerous mob of near animals whom he had released, and for whom no gentler treatment was desirable. Yet even Pinel himself believed that fear might be valuable in the treatment of certain cases.

Descriptive psychiatry received far-reaching contributions from another physician, Aretaeus of Cappadocia, who also recognized that certain types of illness, such as depression, carried a potentially favourable outlook and could be expected to recover spontaneously in the course of time. Towards the end of the first century A.D., Soranus, also a doctor, was writing about treatment and, while confirming much of what Celsus had already noted, had the courage and originality to challenge the whole conception of cruelty as a method of control.

Soranus was a pupil of Asclepiades and like him has left no trace of his original writings. Once again it is Caelius Aurelianus who has recorded what he thought. Soranus broke with every other disciple of Asclepiades in his attack upon violence and savagery in treatment. Of his contemporaries and their methods he has this to say: 'They prescribe placing all patients in darkness ... without ascertaining whether or not this measure adds another burden ... rather than being themselves disposed to cure their patients, they seem to be in a state of delirium; they compare their patients to ferocious beasts whom they would subdue by deprivation of food and the torments of thirst. Misled no doubt by this error they advise that patients be cruelly chained, forgetting that their limbs might be injured or broken and that it is more suitable and much easier to restrain the sick by the hands of men than by the weights of often harmful iron. They even advise bodily violence, like the use of the whip, as if such measures could force a return to reason; such treatment is deplorable and only aggravates the patient's condition; it stains the body and limbs with blood – a sad spectacle indeed for the patient to contemplate when he regains his senses.'

Soranus felt deeply the barbarity and uselessness of the measures he condemned. This, by contrast, is his own advice for dealing with maniacs. 'Maniacs must be placed in a moderately lighted room, which is of moderate temperature and where the tranquillity is not disturbed by any noise. No paintings should adorn the walls of their habitation; the air should enter through elevated openings. The patients should be placed preferably on the ground floor, for the majority of them are not infrequently disposed to jump out. Their beds should be solidly fastened and placed in such a manner that they do not see persons who enter; a variety of irritations is thus avoided. If they are in a state of agitation such that they cannot be given any bed other than straw, the latter should be carefully chosen, prepared and stripped of all hard substance . . .

'If any part of the body has suffered from the patient's restlessness, warm applications, held by soft and very clean material to the head, shoulders, and chest, are useful. It is necessary to employ fomentations of mixed warm oil, a light decoction of tallow or of linseed oil being preferred because of its softening qualities. Frequent comings and goings, especially on the part of strangers, should be forbidden, and the attendants should be rigorously advised to limit the excursions of the patients so that they will never be exasperated by too much vivacity. Nevertheless, it is equally necessary to avoid increasing their unreasonableness by too much activity and resulting feebleness.

'Much tact and discretion should be employed in directing

attention to their faults; sometimes misbehaviour should be over-looked or met with indulgence; at other times it requires a slightly bitter reprimand and an explanation of the advantages derived from proper conduct.

'If patients are agitated or struggle against restraint, or if they are exasperated by seclusion, they should be controlled by a num-ber of attendants, who should take care that their purpose is dis-closed as little as possible. Thus, patients may be approached as though frictions were to be given, and thereby unnecessary resistance will be avoided. If the sight of men irritates them, restraining bands may be employed, a measure which is seldom required. These bands must be soft and of delicate texture and all joints must be carefully protected. The greatest precautions must be taken in order to avoid shock, for the careless applica-tion of restraining bands increases or even produces fury instead of appeasing it.'

The impression which emerges from this detailed and careful prescription is that here was a physician who loved not only medicine but also men, even when they were estranged, bizarre, and a frightening challenge to the peace of mind of all who saw them. In this respect he was an unusual man and it is noteworthy that his chronicler, Caelius Aurelianus, was unable fully to share his tolerant attitude. Caelius found himself particularly distressed by sexual perversions. Writing of the general cult of sensuality, which at that time was undoubtedly widespread and often un-critically accepted, he called it 'the most malignant and fetid passion of the mind.' It was perhaps this strong feeling which led him to turn in the direction of superstition, already increasing its hold throughout all sections of the community in which he lived, in ascribing certain types of madness to possession by demons.

He wrote a treatise, *De Incubone*, in which he gave the stamp of his own authority to the existing view that there was a special kind of demon, taking on the appearance of a man, whose business it was to seduce women sexually and thereby gain control of their souls. A complementary conception of the incubus was the succubus, a female demon who performed the same function for men. Here was the shadow of a small cloud upon the horizon, heralding the onset of sixteen hundred years of demonology in which hundreds and thousands of men and women were to be tortured and murdered in the name of exorcism and expiation.

Before the Dark Ages closed on medicine there was to be one final torch blazing against the deepening shadows. This was the contribution of the physician Galen. In the seven hundred years which had elapsed since the time of Hippocrates the principles which he had enunciated had fallen gradually into progressive decay. As we have already seen, his successors had found it impossible to preserve intact the full impact of his discoveries because so few of them were prepared to follow his methods of objective observation and the dispassionate acceptance of the facts observed, seeking rather to combine the fruits of his work with the product of speculation and dispute which all too often drifted away from the actual study of living man. The best that had been done had been to preserve something of classical learning and tradition, and to combine this in a body of knowledge which drew on all available schools of thought without committing itself exclusively to any one. This was the philosophy of eclecticism. The weakness of eclecticism, which persistently dogs the system although it is not inherent in it, is the tendency towards stagnation. This can only be combated by a constructively critical attitude towards the pool of knowledge already gained, combined with a positive search for fresh discoveries to add to this pool. This was perhaps Galen's greatest distinction. By no means all his conclusions were valid; some of them in the light of modern knowledge were fantastic; but he re-established the brain as the seat of reason and went further by adducing experimental evidence in support of this conclusion. He exposed the brain and heart of a living pig and showed that while compression of the heart affected only the blood vessels, compression of the brain produced unconsciousness and paralysis. From this he argued that the brain and not the heart was the seat of the rational soul. In the course of this experiment Galen was actually stumbling on the threshold of another great medical discovery, the circulation of the blood, but this in fact he never made, nor was it made until 1628, when William Harvey deduced it from experiments on living animals without the aid of the microscope, which had not yet been invented and which was to provide the final link in the chain by demonstrating the actual course of the finest vessels.

Galen also recognized the dependence of the personality upon physical health; while leaving as an open question, beyond the authority of the physician, Plato's concept of the immortality of the soul, he emphasized that the soul in its outward expression was dominated by the body in so far as morbid humours could produce changes of mood and reason; the young brain of the child was weak in reason and the old brain of the dotard forgetful and confused. He attempted a rather ambitious correlation between brain substance and mental performance. 'The keenness of the mind depends upon the fineness of the brain substance. Slow thinking is due to heaviness...its firmness and stability produces the faculty of memory. The shifting of opinions is produced by the mobility of the brain.'

The modern medical historian, Gregory Zilboorg, to whose work so much of this chapter owes its inspiration, sums up the achievement of Galen by saying that while he contributed nothing new to either the therapy or the clinical description of mental diseases, his total contribution was monumental. It was a kind of summary of the classic Greco-Roman period in medicine, as well as that period's epilogue. He remarks that whereas political historians divide ancient history from the medieval period by emphasizing the decisive invasion of Rome by the barbarians in the latter part of the fifth century, the Dark Ages in medical history began with the death of Galen in A.D. 200.

*   *   *

In the history of medical psychology during the period of demonology, which lasted roughly from A.D. 200 until the latter part of the eighteenth century in Europe, it is easy to blame Christianity and the Universal Church of Rome for a great deal of the cruelty, intolerance, persecution, and terror of the times. Indeed, there were not lacking teachers and scholars who could quote the Bible in support of many of the terrible things which were done. To seek out and kill mentally abnormal people in the belief that they were witches or inhabited by devils came to be regarded as a religious duty; in Exodus xxii. 18 occurs the sentence 'Thou shalt not suffer a witch to live.' There is an even more specific injunction in Leviticus xx. 27 'A man also or woman that hath a familiar spirit or that is a wizard shall surely be put to death: they shall stone them with stones; their blood shall be upon them.' It seemed to matter little or nothing that Christ Himself had specifically taught that many of the more bloodthirsty laws of the Old Testament should be abandoned. Had He not Himself cast out devils?

The intolerance and persecutory fervour which gripped the Middle Ages was consistent, not truly with Christianity, but rather with the recurring pattern of a totalitarian orthodoxy which bears the same sickening and horrifying characteristics whenever it is seen throughout history, and whatever the creed around which it is constructed. There are always the sincere fanatics who elevate absolute conformity above individual worth or the dignity of man; and for their henchmen, willing bullies and torturers are never found wanting. There is a picture by El Greco in an art gallery in Budapest which perfectly illustrates the tragedy and the irony of this situation. It shows Christ about to be crucified, standing in the company of three other figures. One is an executioner, a savage and unreflecting man who is gripping and twisting his victim's arm; the second is a soldier, a representative but not the instigator of authority, who is plainly disgusted by this treatment of a helpless man but who has his orders to obey; and the third is a scribe, who seems to be proclaiming that all this is due and necessary, that the end, however hypothetical, will justify the means no matter how horrible and vile. The superstition, ruthlessness, and terror of the Middle Ages thrived in an atmosphere in which ignorance of psychological medicine was almost complete. To-day knowledge has increased but intolerance has not everywhere diminished. What we condemn in the history of the Middle Ages we have yet to eradicate completely in the twentieth century.

For some time the almost universally accepted belief that the delusions of disturbed minds were in fact reliable accounts of consort with the powers of evil, led to complicated attempts to exorcize these powers with charms and prayers. Similar exorcisms were applied to cure disturbances such as hysteria, which was believed to be due to the wandering of the womb about the body. Here are some passages from such an invocation. 'To the pain in the womb. In the name of God the Father, God the Son, and God the Holy Spirit Amen Amen Amen. O womb womb womb, cylindrical womb, red womb, white womb, fleshy womb, bleeding womb, large womb, neufredic womb, bloated womb, O demoniacal one . . . stop the womb of thy maiden and heal its affliction for it is moving violently. I conjure thee O womb, in the name of the Holy Trinity to come back to the place from which thou shouldst neither move nor turn away . . . to return without anger to the place where the Lord has put thee originally. I conjure thee O womb by the nine choirs of angels and by all the virtues of heaven to return to thy place with every possible gentleness and calm . . . ' and so on.

But the time and forbearance necessary to treat all mental illness in this way, and particularly to treat the more truculent, querulous, resistant, violent, or deluded patients, were bound to lead to more drastic and final methods of disposing of them. The first formal execution of a witch took place in Europe somewhere about A.D. 430. How many hundreds of thousands were to follow will never be known, but in the reign of Francis I of France alone well over one hundred thousand are said to have been killed. Five hundred were burnt at the stake in Geneva within three months in the year 1515. As time went on the practice of denouncing witches spread until it was no longer the prerogative of misguided but fanatically devout priests, but became the resort of malicious neighbours or the profession of enterprising charlatans. One such man, Matthew Hopkins, known as Witch-finder General, secured the execution of over one hundred witches in the years 1645–7 in England.

Before the Reformation the principal authority for the entire practice of the persecution of the insane or neurotic was a treatise by two monks, Henry Kramer and James Sprenger, entitled *Malleus Maleficarum* – The Witches' Hammer. They had been entrusted by Pope Innocent VIII with the duty of preparing this treatise so that Christendom might be purged of a tremendous invasion by demons, witches, succubi, incubi and the like. The Pope had issued a bull on 9 December 1484, appointing them supreme inquisitors, empowered both to inspect the existing arrangements for controlling heresy and witchcraft and to advise upon their improvement. The *Malleus* has been described by latter-day historians as 'a heavy volume in quarto, so insane, so raw and cruel, and leading to such terrible conclusions, that never before or since did such a combination of horrible characteristics flow from human pen.' It contains three main parts; the first a collection of arguments in support of the existence of witchcraft and witches, leading to the conclusion that to doubt such things is to be a deliberate heretic and blasphemer; the second part describes the various kinds of witches and how they may be identified; and the third is concerned with their treatment. The second part dealing with their recognition traces many phenomena which we now know to be important in the diagnosis of certain forms of mental illness; for example, the occurrence of areas of anaesthesia on the skin which can be decreased or diminished by the suggestion of the examiner. In the section devoted to treatment the tone is one of consistent cruelty, scorn, and malevolence. The legal forms enabling victims to be removed from all secular protection and the detailed techniques for torturing and burning them are all faithfully recorded.

After the Reformation the position was if anything worse, because the Protestants vied with the Catholics not only in persecuting heretics but in destroying those possessed of devils. Nor were physicians wiser than their generation. Even Ambroise Paré, the father of modern surgery, and the outstanding medical man of the sixteenth century, believed that the only proper treatment for a man claiming magical powers was execution.

Exceptions to the general conformity did however occur. One of the most notable was Paracelsus, an original and unconventional physician of vast influence and penetrating genius who cast vigorous scorn on the idea of demoniacal possession. 'Mental diseases', he said, 'have nothing to do with evil spirits or devils . . . one should not study how to exorcize the devil but rather how to cure the insane . . . the insane and sick are our brothers.' He was in all things a fearless innovator and controversialist whose ironic fate it was to be killed in a tavern brawl in 1541.

About the same time a more quiet but a deeply sincere religious man, Juan Luis Vives, published a whole series of religious and philosophical works contesting the whole basis of the *Malleus Maleficarum* and insisting upon the natural basis of mental illness. He also made a number of notable contributions to normal psychology, including the first account of the processes whereby ideas become associated with each other in human thought.

Yet another trenchant champion of the ideas which had lain forgotten and abandoned since Hippocrates was Cornelius Agrippa of Nettesheim, who began his career with a study of astronomy and alchemy, supremely important subjects in the view of contemporary scholars. His keen critical ability led him to attack the whole basis on which these subjects rested and his life was to become a series of battles with the oppressive intolerant orthodoxy of his day. Agrippa fearlessly denounced the Inquisition in the course of his duties as an advocate in the city of Metz. He was forced to leave Metz in the end, but not before he had proclaimed that the torture of women in the name of religion was the work of the anti-Christ rather than of Christianity. He died alone, penniless, despised, and reviled. His sole companion seems to have been his black dog, which his detractors insisted was the devil himself constantly communing with Agrippa. But three years before his death he had inspired a young student named Johann Weyer with the ideas and principles which were to enable him to make the greatest contribution to psychiatry of the Renaissance.

Weyer was more adroit, more composed, and more successful than his erstwhile teacher, but he was no less sincere. He became the personal physician of Duke William of Julich and was protected by this position despite the challenging nature of his views, which he expressed with a remarkable facility and irony. In his studies of mental illness he was inevitably brought into collision with the Inquisition. Of this he said, ' It is highly unpleasant to see how people in order to kill errors are busy killing human beings.' He was equally impatient with the boundless credulity which accompanied demonology, which, as he remarked, 'prejudiced the life and safety of medicine, the most ancient, the most useful, and the most necessary of all sciences.' He proved in one famous case his ability to restore to her family as a normal little girl, a child who had been widely believed to have the miraculous power of existing without eating. Maintaining her under his personal and kindly observation he was able to discover that she did in fact devour occasional scraps of food and eliminate them just like anybody else. Her parents were not altogether pleased because they had enjoyed the reflected glory of her fame. But Weyer's reputation gained even more from his originality in questioning the phenomenon than from his success in explaining and treating it.

He took great pains to describe the various types of delusions and disturbances of behaviour which he had seen among patients and compared them in detail with that part of the *Malleus Maleficarum* devoted to the diagnosis of witches and demons in human form. The breadth and vision of his insight into the whole problem of mental illness laid bare for those who could accept it the preposterous nature of demoniacal theories and the effect of these theories on the treatment of patients. For the first time since Hippocrates had dared to assail the conception of the Sacred Disease, a physician was able to claim the realm of mental illness as a part of medicine, rather than of theology or law, without suffering total eclipse or defamation as the price.

Weyer was a religious as well as a deeply humane man; but his wisdom and courage made it possible for him to say that even the confessions of people accused of witchcraft were often no more than symptoms of their illness, expressions of a fantasy which coloured their own beliefs as well as those of their judges.

Of course, Weyer was attacked on all sides by the legal profession. The criminal code of Saxony published in 1572 referred to his books in this way: 'In the course of the past few years many books have appeared in which sorcery is considered not a crime but a superstition and a melancholy, and even insist violently that it should not be punished by death. Weyer's reasonings are not very important for he is a physician and not a jurist.' Among other legal arguments devoted to the refutation of Weyer's teachings were those of Jean Bodin, one of the leading jurists of the Middle Ages, who maintained that Weyer was a very wicked man, a protector of witches, who was even disposed to question such undeniable truths as that witches eat babies' flesh, and that women are peculiarly prone to sorcery and witchcraft, being liars, having larger intestines than men, and being half way between men and wild beasts.

That the views of Bodin and the judges reflected powerful trends of public opinion may be judged from the fact that over one hundred years after the death of both men two hundred and fifty people were arrested and tried in Salem, Massachusetts, in the infamous witch hunt of 1691–2. The power of suggestion and the authority of credulous judges can rarely have been better exemplified than in this tragic passage from the record of the Salem trials, after which nineteen victims were executed and one tortured to death. One of those condemned to hang as a witch was Martha Carrier. Her daughter Sarah, aged eight, was interrogated by the judges and it was her evidence upon which they chiefly relied.

'How long hast thou been a witch?'
'Ever since I was six years old.'
'How old are you now?'
'Near eight years old.'
'Who made you a witch?'
'My mother. She made me set my hand to the book.'
'You said you saw a cat once. What did the cat say to you?'
'It said it would tear me to pieces if I would not set my hand to the book' [that is, the 'Devil's Book'].
'How did you know that it was your mother?'
'The cat told me so, that she was my mother.'

Based upon the carefully worded and closely reasoned testimonies of Weyer there was published in 1584 another treatise designed to discredit the superstition of witchcraft, written by one Reginald Scot, whose work so incensed King James I that he ordered it to be burnt, and proceeded straight away to publish a book of his own entitled *Daemonologie* in support of the existing system. Scot's work had perhaps even less influence than Weyer's; probably because while Weyer paid lip service to the idea of demons, even estimating their number in the universe as something over seven million, but insisting that neither the insane nor those who might even seem to be possessed were to be blamed for their possession but rather treated, Scot contemptuously dismissed the whole system of belief as a compound 'of erroneous novelties and imaginary conceptions'. People were not ready for the truth, could not accept it, and would not have it. It was not until 1736 that the laws against witchcraft were repealed in the United Kingdom, or until the latter part of the nineteenth century that any substitute was devised by the medical profession for the incarceration and neglect of the mentally ill which followed public indifference to them, once they were no longer believed to be supernaturally possessed.

Psychiatry Yesterday

AN enormous increase in the knowledge of the external world was the outstanding feature of the Renaissance period. In medicine it brought a number of important discoveries, and above and beyond them all it restored the principle that man was a wonderful creation, worthy of study in his natural as well as his spiritual aspects. But the shackles of the superstition and confusion of the past were not loosed from the problems of the mind, and in a period of history of medicine and science in which the invention of the microscope, the discovery of the circulation of the blood, and the rotation of the earth round the sun were made, and the foundations for the whole of modern physics up to the time of Einstein were laid by Newton's discoveries, the mental and emotional aspects of human life were almost entirely left out of the sphere of medical curiosity. Once again there were exceptions, such as Felix Plater, who made an individual study of patients with mental illness, visiting them in their hundreds in the dungeons and dark cellars where they were kept, often chained to the wall. But while his observations led to yet another careful classification of their symptoms and characteristics he seemed to see nothing intolerable in their treatment nor to conceive of any possible alternative. On the theoretical side, concern with the activities of the mind remained traditionally in the hands of philosophers, but among these were numbered such outstanding men as Descartes, Hobbes, Spinoza, and Locke, of whom the last was also a physician. Descartes sought the essential principle of life in the power of thought; other and simpler conceptions of a life force abounded, and indeed the basic conception of such a force persists to this day and has been the inspiration of later writers and physicians. The life force was believed by philosophers to be common to all forms of life; it differed in this way from the soul, whose possession distinguished man from all other living creatures. The study of the life force, or vital principle, was to pave the way for the emancipation of medical psychology from the tortured disputes of theology and scholasticism.

Clinical medicine in all its other branches leapt ahead. The prestige of the physician increased with his heightened understanding of natural phenomena and his power to treat physical disease; it was perhaps not altogether surprising that a realm of human suffering and distraction so baffling, alarming, and unattractive as mental illness should be tacitly segregated from the triumphant advance which it might otherwise have embarrassed, in just the same way as the deranged patients were themselves locked away or ignored. The practical physician, although by now increasingly sceptical of demonology, had little to offer the maniac or the patient stricken with intolerable grief or despair, or those deluded or hallucinated. Medicine was advancing so swiftly on other fronts that on grounds of strategy no less than expediency this one was for a time abandoned. Weyer's insistence upon patient and detailed study of the individual mind was swept aside in an era in which the body received just this attention. Preoccupation with anatomy, physics, and chemistry, did, however, lead to a growing understanding of what we now call organic mental disorder: structural damage or degeneration in the brain, cerebral tumours, and other physical disturbances which could be correlated with mental symptoms.

Thomas Willis, the great anatomist and student of the nervous system, dissected the brain and worked out its blood supply in detail. His attitude to the treatment of disorders of mental function may seem the more surprising in this light: 'the primary object is, naturally, curative . . . discipline, threats, and blows are needed as much as medical treatment . . . truly nothing is more necessary and more effective for the recovery of these people than forcing them to respect and fear intimidation. By this method, the mind, held back by restraint, is induced to give up its arrogance and wild ideas and it soon becomes meek and orderly. This is why maniacs often recover much sooner if they are treated with torture and treatments in a hovel instead of with medicaments.'

Another trusted stand-by was blood letting. Patients were literally bled to death; nor does Harvey's discovery of the circulation of the blood seem to have affected the current attitude to exsanguination as a method of treatment, except perhaps to have encouraged it.

With the gain in medical understanding at the expense of witchcraft it remained necessary for those physicians who were interested in mental illness to find some alternative explanation for the aberrations of their patients. Sexual preoccupation, hitherto completely explained by the activities of incubi and succubi, was treated by a French physician, Jacques Ferrand, by simple explanation of the natural desires of the patients. He described how the Lord cured through his remedies two young wives of the conviction that the devil lay with them every night while their husbands slept. After recovery they were able, he said, 'to recognize that it was all a depravity of their imagination ...' This observation has been claimed as the first recorded instance of patients gaining what we now call insight for their delusions as a result of medical treatment.

Later in the seventeenth century a return to the Hippocratic objectivity led to further attempts to find empirical means of treating mental illness. Blood transfusion took the place of blood letting, the blood of young sane men being used in the treatment of old madmen. As has always happened, a single cure received the fame and recognition denied to a thousand failures. The desire to treat mental illness by purely physical methods is a natural one and has led to the success of malarial therapy, insulin, and electro-convulsive treatment, as well as to the blind alleys of massive surgical removal of various organs, and to the latest advances in brain surgery, whose value is undoubted but whose range and scope has yet to be clearly defined.

In opposition to much of the purely physical approach was the concern of certain physicians with the vital principle, mentioned a little earlier. A German doctor, George Stahl, who became Professor of Medicine in the University of Halle and later moved to Berlin, emphasized that however valuable detailed anatomical knowledge might be, the body's function in life was something greater and beyond the sum of its material parts. He believed that an understanding of how the soul and the vital force worked together in the body was more important even than a knowledge of physics and chemistry; this was a revolutionary proposition for his day. He called attention to 'the stupendous sudden and quick effect of the so-called passions and affects (feelings and moods) on the body.' He maintained that disturbed emotions could interfere with physical health and with the recovery of the body from physical disease. He even recognized that dreams occasionally reflect the trend of physical illness. He was in fact the outstanding disciple of what is now called psychosomatic medicine; the inseparable unity of mind and body in their effect upon each other, and the equally essential need to study both and not merely one or the other. His influence was important in establishing the propriety of medical concern for mental disturbance.

Early in the eighteenth century this principle had gained some guarded acceptance. It was possible for a physician to say that 'the mind and body exercise on one another a reciprocal power, the extent of which we do not know.' Yet it was also possible for physicians who specialized in the treatment of disorders of the nervous system, such as John Brown in England, Benjamin Rush in America, and Johann Christian Reil in Germany, to champion physical and mental torment in all sincerity. Reil specialized in what he called 'non-injurious torture'. This consisted in flinging patients into water, firing cannons, and confronting them with physicians and keepers garbed as 'judges, angels, the dead newly risen from their graves, which in accordance with the needs of various patients should be played to produce the illusion of utmost verisimilitude.' The scenery for these theatrical displays, designed to harmonize with the patients' delusions or hallucinations, was to include lions' dens, places of execution, and operating rooms. Benjamin Rush some hundred years later clung to the idea of ducking as a specific. The more inventive physicians designed apparatus such as twirling stools and trap doors which, giving way, precipitated the patient into an icy plunge. These essentially practical incursions of physicians into the sphere of psychological medicine did not improve their credit with the philosophers, who studied it with more refinement. Kant insisted that psychiatric testimony in the courts of law should never be entrusted to a doctor, but always to a philosopher.

In 1733 an English physician, George Cheyne, M.D., Fellow of the Royal Society and of the College of Physicians at Edinburgh, published a treatise on nervous diseases of which the outstanding feature was a case report based on his own experience when mentally ill. In this he showed not only tremendous courage but a pioneer spirit of self-effacing honesty. When, almost two hundred years later, Sigmund Freud was to illustrate his brilliant theory of the psychology of dreams by recounting and then interpreting many of his own dreams and inner feelings, his work was greeted by many with shocked indignation. Yet a physician who cannot acknowledge and accept his own frailties and humanity, at least to some extent, can have nothing to offer those whose sufferings he must understand in all their aspects.

The implicit assumption of personal superiority made by almost all doctors and laymen of those days when they considered patients with mental illness, an attitude still widely taken for granted to-day, was perhaps more responsible for the appalling inhumanity and neglect of these patients than even the more obviously aggressive but now outmoded cult of demonology and persecution. It may well be that the very motive force of persecution, as we have already hinted, was the hostility provoked by this type of abnormality, a hostility whose outlet might be either violence or at least an attitude of withdrawal and disdain. Whatever the explanation it remains true that until almost the end of the eighteenth century, over one hundred and fifty years after the superstitious persecution of the insane had been forbidden by law, there were no real hospitals or institutions to care for them on a humane basis, far less a medical one. The places where they were kept were essentially prisons, open to the public to display the antics of the captives. Going to Bedlam, the Royal Bethlehem Hospital for the Care of the Insane in London, was an entertainment in the late eighteenth and early nineteenth century comparable to going to the zoo now. Writing of the conditions to be found in the French asylums, the great psychiatrist Esquirol said: 'I have seen them naked, or covered with rags, and protected only by straw from the cold damp pavement upon which they were lying. I have seen them coarsely fed, deprived of fresh air, or water to quench their thirst, and of the most necessary things for life. I have seen them delivered and abandoned to the brutal supervision of veritable jailers. I have seen them in squalid, stinking little hovels without air or light, chained in caves where wild beasts would not have been confined. These unfortunate beings, like the criminals of the state, are cast into dungeons or into dark cells into which the eye of humanity never penetrates. There they remain to waste away in their filth under the weight of chains which lacerate their bodies. Their faces are pale and emaciated; they await only the moment which will end their misery and conceal our disgrace. They are exhibited to the public gaze by greedy keepers who make them appear as rare beasts. They are huddled together in disorderly manner with no known means of maintaining order among them, except terror. Whips, chains, and dungeons are the only means of persuasion employed by keepers who are as barbarous as they are ignorant.'

In the course of an investigation of the York asylum undertaken in 1814 in response to public pressure after the death and disappearance of several patients whose relatives had been forbidden to visit them, and the subsequent destruction by fire of the records of the hospital, Mr Samuel Tuke, a member of the famous Quaker family who were to found the York Retreat, the first humane mental hospital in England, recorded these particulars: 'There were not any day rooms with contiguous airing courts. There were but two airing courts for all the classes of patients, except the opulent, who took their exercise in the garden. All the other classes of men were turned into one court, and the women into the other. There was no provision in either court for shelter against the rain or heat. Very few of the patients were allowed hats, and shoes and stockings were not unfrequently wanting. In this state, you might see more than 100 poor creatures shut up together, unattended and uninspected by any one; the lowest paupers and persons of respectable habits, the melancholic and the maniac, the calm and the restless, the convalescent and the incurable. It is needless, and it would be painful, to enumerate the evils and the dangers resulting from this system of indiscriminate association. The danger of patients injuring each other, was also very great, from their being shut up in considerable numbers in their day rooms, without any attendant or inspector. Nor must we forget, in this short sketch of the domestic evils which existed in the Asylum, that utter neglect of ventilation and cleanliness, which rendered so many parts of the place alike disgusting and unwholesome. It is almost impossible to conceive any place in a more damp and offensive state, than that part of the building called the low grates. The light, in several of the rooms, was obstructed by the erection of pig-styes, and other disagreeable offices; and the little air which was admitted, passed immediately over these places. The upper galleries suffered in some degree, from the same causes as the lower one. Their elevation prevented them from being damp; they were, however, with some exception in favour of that part occupied by the opulent, as gloomy as ingenuity could devise to make them, and as defective as possible in ventilation.'

*

These revelations led to a public outcry and in 1815 a select committee was appointed under the chairmanship of James Birch Sharpe, a member of the Royal College of Surgeons, to 'consider of provision being made for the better regulation of madhouses in England.' These are some excerpts from its report:

Concerning the York asylum: evidence of G. Higgins.

'. . . I went into the passage, and found four cells, I think, of about eight feet square, in a very horrid and filthy situation; the straw appeared to be almost saturated with urine and excrement; there was some bedding laid upon the straw in one cell, in the others only loose straw. A man (a keeper) was in the passage doing something, but what I do not know. The walls were daubed with excrement; the air-holes, of which there were one in each cell, were partly filled with it. In one cell there were two pewter chamber-pots, loose. I asked the keeper if these cells were inhabited by the patients, and was told they were at night. I then desired him to take me upstairs, and show me the place of the women who came out of those cells that morning; I then went upstairs, and he showed me into a room, which I caused him to measure, and the size of which, he told me, was twelve feet by seven feet ten inches; and in which there were thirteen women, who, he told me, had all come out of those cells that morning.

'I then desired the Governors to come with me to see those cells; and then I discovered, for the first time, that the cells were unknown to the Governors. Several of the committee, which consisted of fifteen, told me they had never seen them; that they had gone round the house with his Grace the Archbishop of York; that they had understood they were to see the whole house, and these cells had not been shown to them. We went through the cells, and at that time they had been cleaned as much as they could in so short a space of time. I turned up the straw in one of them with my umbrella, and pointed out to the gentlemen the chain and handcuff which were then concealed beneath the straw, and which I then perceived had been fixed into a board newly put down in the floor.

'The day after my examination of these cells, I went again early in the morning to examine them, after I knew that the straw could have been used only one night; and I can positively say, from this examination, that the straw which I first found there must have been in use a very considerable time. When Colonel Cooke, of Owston, was in one of the cells, he tried to make marks or letters in the excrement remaining upon the floor after it had been cleaned, and fresh straw put upon it; which he did without any difficulty, and which he will be ready to state to the Committee, if required.'

This Colonel Cooke subsequently confirmed. Asked whether any subsequent visits had revealed any improvement, Mr Higgins replied:

'I saw them some time after that, and I think their situation was not mended; the second time I visited the house, three patients were chained in one bed; two were lying lengthwise, and one across the other two.'

Concerning Bethlem Hospital: evidence of E. Wakefield.

'At this visit, attended by the steward of the Hospital and likewise by a female keeper, we first proceeded to visit the women's galleries: one of the side rooms contained about ten patients, each chained by one arm or leg to the wall; the chain allowing them merely to stand up by the bench or form fixed to the wall, or to sit down on it. The nakedness of each patient was covered by a blanket-gown only; the blanket-gown is a blanket formed something like a dressing-gown, with nothing to fasten it with in front; this constitutes the whole covering; the feet even were naked.

'In one of the cells on the lower gallery we saw William Norris; he stated himself to be fifty-five years of age, and that he had been confined about fourteen years; that in consequence of attempting to defend himself from what he conceived the improper treatment of his keeper, he was fastened by a long chain, which, passing through a partition, enabled the keeper, by going into the next cell, to draw him close to the wall at pleasure; that to prevent this Norris muffled the chain with straw, so as to hinder its passing through the wall; that he afterwards was confined in the manner we saw him, namely, a chain passed to a ring made to slide upwards or downwards on an upright massive iron bar, more than six feet high, inserted into the wall. Round his body a strong iron bar about two inches wide was riveted; on each side the bar was a circular projection which, being fashioned to and inclosing each of his arms, pinioned them close to his sides. This waist bar was secured by two similar bars which, passing over his shoulders, were riveted to to waist bar both before and behind. The iron ring round his neck was connected to the bars on his shoulders by a double link. From each of these bars another short chain passed to the ring on the upright iron bar. We were informed he was enabled to raise himself, so as to stand against the wall, on the pillow of his bed in the trough bed in which he lay; but it is impossible for him to advance from the wall in which the iron bar is soldered on account of the shortness of his chains, which were only twelve inches long. It was, I conceive, equally out of his power to repose in any other position than on his back, the projections, which on each side of the waist bar inclosed his arms, rendering it impossible for him to lie on his side, even if the length of the chains from his neck and shoulders would permit it. His right leg was chained to the trough; in which he had remained thus encaged and chained more than twelve years. To prove the unnecessary restraint inflicted on this unfortunate man, he informed us that he had for some years been able to withdraw his arms from the manacles which encompassed them. He then withdrew one of them, and, observing an expression of surprise, he said that when his arms were withdrawn he was compelled to rest them on the edges of the circular projections, which was more painful than keeping them within. His position, we were informed, was mostly lying down.'

Concerning the Surgeon to Bethlem: evidence of J. Haslam the Apothecary, under examination by the Committee.

'Do you remember the case of a person who died a few years ago of a constipation of the bowels?' 'I know no particulars of it.'

'Do you remember the case about which Mr Crowther, who was the surgeon of the Hospital, made some observations as to the cause of his death?' 'I do.'

'Do you know what those observations were?' 'Knowing the situation of Mr Crowther at that time, I paid no attention to it. Mr Crowther was generally insane, and mostly drunk. He was so insane as to have a strait-waistcoat.'

'What situation did Mr Crowther hold in the Hospital?' 'Surgeon.'

'How long had he been so?' 'I do not know; he was surgeon when I came there.'

'How long did he continue so, after he was in a situation to be generally insane, and mostly drunk?' 'I think the period of his insanity was about ten years ago.'

'And the period of his drunkenness?' 'He always took too much wine.'

'How long is it since he died?' 'Perhaps a month ago.'

'Then for ten years Mr Crowther was surgeon to the Hospital: during those ten years he was generally insane; he had had a strait-waistcoat and was mostly drunk?' 'He was.'

'And during that period he was continued as surgeon to the Hospital?' 'He was.'

'Did he attend the patients?' 'Yes, he did.'

'Did he attend the patients as surgeon?' 'Yes, till a week before his death; from his incapacity to officiate as surgeon, he frequently brought some medical professional man to attend.'

'But he did sometimes attend himself without assistance?' 'Certainly he did.'

'Were the Governors of the Hospital acquainted with the fact of his incapacity?' 'I should think not. His insanity was confined principally to the abuse of his best friends; he was so insane that his hand was not obedient to his will.'

The report dealt also with various private hospitals operated under licence, and with the Admiralty establishment at Hoxton where the 'Naval Maniacs' were confined. They were all characterized by a similar reliance upon chains, by straw and filth or at best often bare boards for beds, and by overcrowding and under-ventilation which eventually led to the death of a number of the patients.

It may seem beyond belief that physicians could contemplate other human beings naked, cold, crusted with their own excrement, chained and starving in the dark on stone floors, without pity and without remorse. But they could, and they did, and it is only by the exertions and the example of exceptional men that our own standards have been raised above this appalling state. The importance of a decision made as early as 1793 by Philippe Pinel, physician superintendent of the Bicêtre Hospital in Paris, to unchain his patients, can therefore not be exaggerated. He was an outstanding and a fearless physician who succeeded in keeping his head during the turbulent days of the French Revolution and published works on the subject of mental illness which are classics of observation and humanity. He was as enlightened in treatment as he was in abolishing restraint. He forbade blood letting, ducking, and every form of violence; and he introduced a moderation in the use of drugs which remains exemplary to this day. The same tendencies were to be observed in all civilized countries sooner or later, but in studying the history of psychological medicine it is the era of Pinel and Esquirol in France which points the way to that real concern for the patient as an individual, indispensable to what we now regard as the theory and practice of psychiatry.

*

In the same year in which Pinel came to Paris there arrived in this city another man whose name was to gain an even wider if less wholly estimable fame. This was Anton Mesmer, the discoverer of 'animal magnetism'. This was essentially the technique of hypnotism practised with a great deal of additional paraphernalia and suggestion, in all of which Mesmer himself probably believed, although he has often been regarded as an enterprising, aggressive, and quick-witted charlatan. His theories embraced astrology and rested upon the assumption that the universe was filled with a magnetic fluid which permeated everything and conveyed the influence of the stars. Mesmer claimed to be able to manipulate the balance and effects of this fluid by personal power. He constructed an apparatus like a cauldron from which projected iron rods. These, grasped by the patients, who could then hold each other's hands, brought them under the influence of Mesmer's magnetic wand which he waved about in conducting the treatment.

In 1784 the Academy of Sciences in France investigated Mesmer's activities and came to the conclusion that 'imagination with magnetism produces convulsions and that magnetism without imagination produces nothing.' This infuriated Mesmer, who was always keenly conscious of his own dignity and position, but although scepticism and ridicule were employed against him with a powerful effect his personal prestige remained, and the effects which he produced continued to receive careful study by individual physicians. Furthermore, mesmerism fulfilled an unquestionable need of the times. It was in fact the only available treatment for neuroses, since the medical profession were little interested and had nothing to offer, and the priests and lawyers had withdrawn from the scene with the ending of the era of persecution. The work of Pinel, the Tukes, and Benjamin Rush and others in America was still essentially dedicated to the demonstrably insane; but the proportion of the population afflicted with mental illness outside the new mental hospitals was probably not a great deal smaller than it is to-day, and sought, as it still seeks, relief wherever it might be found.

In the nineteenth century the development of hypnotism from Mesmerism received a considerable stimulus from its use in surgery. Operations were performed under hypnotism before the discovery of anaesthetics, and the knowledge of sub-conscious mental processes to which this was leading might have owed more to surgery than to medicine had not the successful use of ether and chloroform during the first half of the nineteenth century removed the impetus to further work with hypnosis in this field An English surgeon, James Braid, remained interested in hypnosis for its own sake, which he still knew by the name of mesmerism. After careful study he became finally convinced that the whole conception of magnetic fluid, magnetism, and magic was false, but that the phenomena of sleep, anaesthesia, automatic obedience and so forth were consistently produced by psychological processes which remained obscure only because they had not been sufficiently studied. He wrote a paper on the subject, in which he introduced the new terms hypnotism, hypnotize, hypnotic, and hypnosis.

Thereafter hypnosis was studied by a number of physicians in France, England, and America. It was used by Liebeault, a country doctor, to relieve his patients of many of the ills which hitherto had been beyond medical skill. He had faith in this method of treatment, sought every occasion to practise it, and made it popular among his peasant patients by offering it to them free of charge while continuing to request a modest payment for bottles of medicine. Liebeault found that most of his patients could be readily hypnotized, although he told an English doctor who visited him that the 'nervous and hysterical were his most refractory subjects.' He was an honest and modest doctor who worked alone among the villages where his patients lived and made very little money. He did not court publicity and it was in Britain rather than in France that his work first received attention.

In the latter part of the nineteenth century the great French physician, Charcot, established hypnosis as a major clinical attraction of his famous clinics at the Salpêtrière Hospital in Paris. He was a brilliant clinical neurologist, who examined his patients in detail and was able to demonstrate the difference between the signs of paralysis induced by hypnosis and that due to organic disease of the nervous system. From this, however, he drew the somewhat misleading conclusion that it was only in patients capable of producing hysterical illness spontaneously in response to extraordinary stress, that the phenomena of hypnotism could be induced by the physician. This led him to the view that hypnosis itself was a pathological entity and the capacity to be hypnotized a sign of abnormality. It was this doctrine which separated the views of Charcot from those of Liebeault; it had also the effect of confining the use of hypnosis in Paris to demonstrations rather than to treatment, and despite the greatness of Charcot as a physician it seems now indisputable that the effect of his work with suggestible patients at these demonstrations was almost without exception to make them worse.

Some of the concepts arising from this approach to the phenomenon of hypnosis were also misleading; one of these was the diagnosis of hystero-epilepsy, which was divided into major and minor according as to whether there were or were not spectacular convulsions. Charcot himself knew that hystero-epilepsy was not another form of true epilepsy, but only resembled it on superficial observation. None the less the term was convenient and has died hard. The age-old belief that the uterus was responsible for hysteria, the belief which gave the condition its name, cropped up again in this anatomical age in the designation of certain conditions and excitement in women as ovarian mania. Removal of the ovaries was even prescribed and carried out for such afflictions.

In 1885 a pupil arrived at the Salpêtrière on a travelling fellowship, to study under Charcot, who was destined to perform for psychological medicine a feat of illumination which has been compared to that performed by Newton for Physics. This was Sigmund Freud, who came as a neurologist and neuro-pathologist from Austria and stayed to learn all that he could of hypnosis and the study of individual patients by this powerful method. The reception accorded to some of his observations when he returned to his own country is singularly revealing. Freud had described some cases of hysteria which he had studied in men. The President of the Viennese Society of Medicine declared that this was incredible, and Dr Meynert, a leading neurologist of the time, challenged Freud in a friendly but incredulous fashion to discover a single case of hysteria in men in Vienna. Freud records that he tried to produce several such cases to the Society, but the senior physicians in whose departments he discovered them refused to allow him either to observe the patients or to work with them. The basis of their refusal was epitomized by one old surgeon, who protested 'But, my dear Sir, how can you talk such nonsense? Hysteron means the uterus. So how can a man be hysterical?' This statement was made at a time when the brain as the organ of mind was fully accepted by contemporary physicians. None the less the study of hypnosis and of hysterical patients both at Nancy by Bernheim, who followed the teachings of Liebeault, and in Paris under Charcot, led to an approach to mental illness of overwhelming importance in which Freud was to become an outstanding pioneer.

This was the scientific study of the workings of the mind in health as well as in disease and the recognition of the relationship between normal mental processes and those which could be observed in the disturbed or insane. The acceptance of neurosis as an illness rested finally upon work of this kind. Bernheim succeeded in convincing the medical world that hypnosis was possible in completely normal people, something which Charcot had long disputed. He went further by maintaining that the symptoms associated with gross hysterical states differed in degree rather than in kind from those seen in less disturbed but unquestionably ill or unhappy people. It was by the study of the borderland population of neurotic patients that insight was to be gained not only into the mechanism of mental illness but also into the motives of much of the behaviour of ordinary people.

Bernheim, addressing humanity at large, remarked 'In truth, we are all potentially or actually hallucinating people during the greatest part of our lives.' He meant by this that each one of us makes his own compromise with reality, accepting only as much of it as is bearable and living in an inner world of imagination as well as an outer world common to others: and just as our resources for dealing with reality vary, so are our actions and beliefs influenced by our capacities. Freud was to put all this upon a logical basis by his intuition, his experimental work, and his remarkable success in finding a technique for therapy and for research which remains a major influence in psychiatry to-day.

Up to the time of the establishment of the schools of Salpêtrière and Nancy, qualified doctors had literally no training whatever in psychological medicine. There was no agreed basis for such study and every physician started, as it were, from scratch. The tradition implicitly established was that possession of a general medical qualification embraced all reliable knowledge of mental life. This, too, is a tradition which has died hard. Even to-day there are eminent, sincere, and respectable physicians and surgeons who consider themselves competent to deal with neurotic illness which they have never studied and which they do not understand. Charcot and Bernheim were both great teachers and their schools represented the first centres of post-graduate study to be established in this branch of medicine. The genius of Freud came as the first fruit of this remarkable innovation.

Before considering any further the remarkable contributions of Freud to psychological medicine the work of some other physicians deserves mention. Dr Brodie recorded the alternation of hysterical behaviour with physical symptoms, which he realized were of similar origin. He concluded that 'fear, suggestion, and unconscious simulation are primary factors in the production of such symptoms.' He was undoubtedly right. Pierre Janet made a number of exceedingly penetrating studies of hysterical patients and even recognized that some of the mental processes involved in their illness remain permanently outside the consciousness of the patients themselves. This might have led him to the conception of the subconscious mind as an essential part of normal mental equipment; a keystone to Freud's later discoveries. But while Janet's brilliant and original views include the concept of dissociation of an idea or group of ideas from consciousness, so that some hysterical symptoms could be regarded as the product of isolated and unconscious mental activities, he did not develop the dynamic implications of his theory, being more concerned with description in terms of physical analogies. He was also interested in neuro-anatomical explanations of the production of diseased states of mind, and in the possible significance of a constitutional weakness of the nervous system as a predisposing factor. When Janet spoke of unconscious mental acts he meant that these acts were automatic, in the same way that the reflex action whereby the pupil contracts under the stimulus of light is automatic and unconscious. Freud was to propose that much of mental life which is unconscious has a far greater range of variability and is infinitely more amenable to alteration through treatment than are the established reflexes of neuro-physiology.

The use of hypnosis in the treatment of patients along far more dynamic lines than those envisaged by Janet or Charcot was propounded by Bernheim before it was carried further by Freud. Bernheim conveyed this brilliantly when he said that the treatment of hysteria was not so much the production of suggestion (that is, ideas accepted upon an emotional rather than a critical or rational basis), but rather the removal of the harmful effects of suggestion previously accepted by the patient at an unconscious level. The motives for this acceptance, and indeed the mechanism whereby it could take place, remained for Freud to discover. The essence of this discovery was that conflicting desires and forbidden, painful, or threatening emotions beneath the surface of consciousness, can both call forth and shape responses which emerge as symptoms of illness, or abnormal actions and attitudes of mind.

A general survey of the progress of psychiatry throughout the latter part of the nineteenth and beginning of the twentieth centuries demands attention not only to outstanding individuals, but also to the important trends in public policy which have already engaged our attention. The whole basis of institutional care had changed fundamentally. We have seen that this was due partly to outstanding individuals like Esquirol, Tuke, and Higgins, who shook and then shaped the public conscience, and partly to occasional open scandals in the existing asylums, of which the institution at York provided the first example.

Following the appalling revelations of the public enquiry in 1815, to which we have already referred, public indignation was thoroughly inflamed: yet this fervour was not maintained, and, despite a number of salutary changes in the asylums, popular clamour waned and was diverted before all the abuses had been removed: ignorance and apathy threatened once again to prevail.

Some twenty-six years later an American woman, Dorothea Lynde Dix, who was a retired school teacher, started her campaign for improvement of conditions in mental hospitals in the latter half of her life without influence or authority of any kind at first, and achieved the most tremendous results in public education and reform by sheer courage, determination, and enthusiasm. Her energy was staggering and was harnessed to a singleness of mind which enabled her to travel tens of thousands of miles in America and in England and to gain a hearing in the United States Congress and in the Houses of Parliament. She encountered and defeated enormous opposition and established her own reputation as a champion of the mentally ill by disregarding personal prestige completely and by devoting herself utterly to those whose helplessness and despair she felt so deeply.

The English medical superintendent of the Hanwell Asylum, John Conolly, who had abandoned the professorship of Practical Medicine at University College when all his efforts to introduce psychiatry into the teaching curriculum were obstructed, removed all forms of mechanical restraint from the patients and proclaimed publicly his intense opposition to such methods. Once again this aroused considerable opposition; Isaac Ray, one of the foremost American medical superintendents and himself a pioneer and a humane man, gave it as his opinion that while non-restraint might work with Europeans, who, whether sane or mad, seemed to have the habit of obedience, it could never be adopted for Americans, whose belief in liberty would lead them when insane to violent and dangerous assertions of the principle.

The travels and writings of the French psychiatrist, Esquirol, have already been mentioned; whatever the practical difficulties of managing disturbed patients, the indictment he had prepared against the existing methods was unanswerable. Another outstanding contribution made by Esquirol on the basis of his prodigious experience was the application of statistical methods to clinical study. He made a list of what he called psychological causes of insanity, for example disappointment in love, worries about money, and other external factors which would be regarded to-day as precipitating rather than basic elements in breakdown, and then proceeded to count the number of times which they appeared in the histories of many hundreds of patients whom he had studied. He also established a prize for the best essay on mental diseases by students of the subject. In the course of his travels he was once shown a new hospital for the insane by no less a person than the King of Italy, who asked him for his candid opinion. Esquirol gave it: to his credit the king accepted it and the hospital was used only as an armoury, a more suitable establishment being built to Esquirol's own specifications.

Pinel's successor at the Bicêtre Hospital, Dr Ferrus, accomplished the final separation of the insane from the criminals who had previously been confined with them after sentence in the courts. He was particularly concerned for the criminal insane, for whom he demanded special provision which should combine humane detention with medical and physical treatment. He also organized working parties among the less disturbed patients in the Bicêtre to rebuild some of the more antiquated and appalling sections of the hospital, and finally succeeded in constructing a large farm for the benefit of the patients and staff. This was the first example of occupational therapy of any kind and the first constructive and productive use of the patients' time and energies. The farm included a dairy, workshops, and animal sheds, and must have been a comparatively happy place. Its example was widely followed in the United States, but soon after the departure of

Ferrus the whole project fell into decay and was abandoned in France.

A further outcome of the importance and development of mental hospital service was the return to the Hippocratic tradition in the study of mental illness. This, as we have seen, had taken place at least a hundred years earlier in other branches of medicine, again in response to improved facilities. Patients could be studied objectively, and each individual patient could be observed over a long period of time, since now survival and even a reasonable degree of peace and security was possible for him. The idea that mental diseases might have a characteristic beginning, course, and outcome gained acceptance. Research in various centres became correlated through the medium of numerous journals published in Britain, Europe, and America, wherein the ideas of men like Daniel Tuke, Dr Bucknill, and Dr Conolly in England, Drs Isaac Ray and Benjamin Rush in America, Esquirol, Pinel, and Ferrus in France and, later, Krafft-Ebing, Griesinger, Alzheimer, and Nissl in Germany, could find a wider circulation.

Krafft-Ebing's contribution was particularly important because in one sense it tended to give a reactionary turn to psychiatric progress. Krafft-Ebing discovered the relationship of an illness, at that time called general paralysis of the insane, to syphilis. He proved his point by inoculating patients suffering from this condition with syphilis and showing that no new infection took place. The implications of this discovery were that an illness whose manifestations were often chiefly psychological had an essentially organic cause. The temptation to regard all mental illness as nothing more than a by-product of physical disease, and approachable solely along material lines, was reawakened. But the more balanced view that, while brain and mind are indissolubly linked, not all brain lesions produce psychological symptoms and not all psychological symptoms originate from brain damage, had to prevail. Morel, a French physician who died in 1873, had begun his career by maintaining that psychological study was being neglected in favour of anatomical and pathological research. He became friendly with Claude Bernard and C. Renaudin, whose own view was that there was 'an essential psychosomatic duality in man' into which the concept of mental illness must be integrated. But Morel parted from this wider view and ended his life maintaining that physical degeneration was the basis of all mental illness. There is an echo of this in the attitude of Charcot, and it was not until the days of Bernheim that it was finally overthrown.

In Germany the developing interest in mental illness largely took the form of a passion to classify accurately on a descriptive basis. Here the impact of the materialistic approach upon European psychiatry as a whole received a salutary modification from the work of Henry Maudsley, the great English psychiatrist, who founded the famous London hospital which bears his name, and whose interest turned him towards 'a philosophical history of insanity...not content to occupy itself with a catalogue of appearances...' While Maudsley was indeed impatient of metaphysical or even of introspective speculations in psychiatry, his regard for the brain as the organ of mind had far wider implications than those of purely deterministic materialism. Believing indeed that structural and physiological processes were indissolubly linked with both normal and abnormal mental function, he ascribed the whole interdependence of mind and body to one purpose...'the will of God...manifest in its highest form and with least obscuration in the temple of man's body.'

Working within this framework, he paid assiduous attention to all possible sources of physical and constitutional contribution to mental illness, particularly heredity and individual structure; although treating of the latter, he remarked: 'The intimate chemical and molecular changes which are presumably the conditions of mental disorder go on in a domain of nature the subtleties of which far exceed the subtleties of observation.' Here, despite our recent discoveries in the realms of microbiology and the electrical patterns of brain activity now available for study in neurophysiology, we can still only echo much of what he said. The changes, although beginning to emerge within the field of experimental observation, remain as yet far more subtle than our techniques for recording them or our capacity to understand them.

But in his attention to the bodily element in the body–mind relationship Maudsley did not neglect either the influences of environment or the possible effects upon structure of abnormal function. Indeed, by precept and example he laid the foundations for that comprehensive approach to the individual patient which remains to this day the most reliable method in clinical practice.

The value of this approach lay not so much in its philosophy or classificatory skill as in its insistence upon detailed historical and clinical studies of every single patient; a method which was to have its widest development in the twentieth century in the hands of Adolf Meyer, the famous American psychiatrist, who was born in Switzerland, emigrated to the United States in his early twenties, and founded there his famous school of psycho-biology, the method of approach whereby everything that could have influenced the life and development of the individual, from heredity, through physical and emotional stress to the details of day-to-day existence, was meticulously studied.

In 1882 Drs Tuke and Bucknill published their monumental text-book, *Psychological Medicine*, which summarized much of the English-speaking world's knowledge of this subject at the time. From then until the early part of the twentieth century the enthusiasm for classification remained paramount among psychiatrists. In retrospect this may seem to have been almost a sterile period from the point of view of progress in therapy and understanding. But probably a longer view will reveal that it was a breathing space in which the known territories of psychiatry were more carefully mapped and the ground prepared for the tremendous and explosive advances which were to take place between 1900 and 1950. The men whose names are most vividly associated with the period of detailed observation, masterly clinical description, and the long-term view which could be erected on this basis, are Emil Kraepelin and Eugen Bleuler. Others, such as Kahlbaum, who had coined the word cyclothymia for the alternating moods of elation and despair characterizing a particular form of mental illness, must be mentioned; but Kraepelin and Bleuler were the giants of the period which immediately preceded the avalanche of discoveries made possible by the work of Freud and Jung.

Kraepelin based his work on the assumption that mental illnesses were distinct entities to be separately studied so that their predetermined secrets might be made known. He regarded the outcome of such illness as essentially fixed. One type of illness would naturally recover. Another, equally naturally and inevitably, would have a progressively downward course. The whole process was subject in his view to natural laws which, once understood, would give the key to prognosis and thereby provide the classification with an essentially practical basis. His meticulous observations led him to differentiate two major groups of mental illness: one, in which the personality progressively deteriorated and disintegrated, he called dementia praecox and regarded as a progressive madness starting characteristically at puberty; the other, a profound disturbance of mood which was fundamentally the alternation between elation and despair, called by Kahlbaum cyclothymia, he labelled manic-depressive and established as having an essentially favourable outlook. A third group of illnesses which he called paranoia were characterized by delusions of grandeur or persecution in an otherwise unclouded mind. Kraepelin's work was prodigious in amount and his attitude to therapy was not as passive as his deterministic attitude might suggest. Day-to-day management and care he regarded as most necessary. But as he based his system on the essentially unalterable nature of the diseases he described, he was bound to maintain that their ultimate outcome would be unaffected by treatment, although their course might be modified. The explosion of the whole basis of this theory, despite the maintenance of an undying respect for the tireless and patient work which had produced it and the wider gains to which it had already led, came in an epoch-making monograph on dementia praecox, published in 1911 by Eugen Bleuler, and probably derived fundamentally from the revolution in psychiatric thought to which Freud was the outstanding contributor, while Jung, Adler, Adolf Meyer, and Bleuler himself were all prominent.

Bleuler showed that the features of dementia praecox which Kraepelin had said were specific and essential, its onset in adolescence and its inevitable culmination in dementia, were secondary and inconstant manifestations of a much wider group of illnesses, whose fundamental characteristic was a breakdown of the normal associative bonds and integrity of the entire personality. He coined the name schizophrenia to cover this whole group of mental illnesses, whose detailed manifestations and outcome might vary considerably. Schizophrenia as Bleuler used it meant therefore a group of reactions rather than one disease entity, and his analysis of the various forms of disordered thought and feeling which might appear in the course of these reactions was as brilliant and penetrating as Kraepelin's broad classification had been striking and impressive. With the details of Bleuler's conceptions, based as they were in part on the psycho-analytic theories of Freud, we shall have to deal when we come to survey our modern knowledge of schizophrenia in all its manifestations.

In the same way, the whole body of psycho-analytic teaching and knowledge originated by Freud and developed by his followers, together with the works of Jung and of Adler, who broke away from the Freudian school to found their own analytical principles, and the teachings of Adolf Meyer, who could never wholly accept psycho-analysis but was too great a man to oppose it on personal or emotional grounds, and in fact was one of the founders of the American Psychoanalytic Association for its further objective study – all these are part of the present, part of psychiatry to-day rather than of the history of the psychiatry of yesterday. Probably there is no one living who can steer a wholly balanced course between these vivid and powerful schools of thought. The study of history shows us that all men are to some extent limited by the bonds of their time in assessing the merits of contemporary views. In modern psychiatry the objective study of history ends with the twentieth century. From that time on the brilliance and the blunders, the triumphs and disasters in the study of this vital subject, are too much with us for us to assess them with an historian's objectivity. Great things are happening, and we are surrounded with the excitement and confusion of further discoveries and the promise of further progress. It is this that we have now to examine, but no longer from afar. Now we are in the thick of it.

Normal Mental Life

WE have seen enough of the history of psychiatry to understand that the task which concerns the psychiatrist to-day is one whose roots are spread more widely than the foundations of medicine or even of pure science; yet from the time of Hippocrates onwards it has been the combination of scientific and objective study with a sincere interest in human beings as a whole, which has led to the greatest advances and the most sure methods in the practice of psychological medicine. At the back of the doctor's mind when he sees anyone who is ill is a conception, based partly on his own experience and partly on all the gathered fruits of the experience of others which have gone into his training, of what is the normal state of that person when he is well. The concept of normality is in fact fundamental to any study of the abnormal; and yet when we examine this concept we see at once that there are more ways than one of forming a judgement of what is normal in any field which we agree to survey. Our field here is the study of human personality, and the scientific basis for this, the theory and application of the science of human behaviour and experience, is called normal psychology. It bears the same relationship to psychiatry as physiology bears to general medicine and surgery; that is, it is concerned with the whole range of normal function and with the scientific assessment and evaluation of what the normal really is.

Now most people form their own conception of what is normal in human experience and behaviour without recourse to any such scientific approach, and there can be few words more cheerfully and regularly misused in the English language than the word 'psychology'. If we take a simple example from a study of human beings in which measurements are perhaps easier to make and more readily understood than they tend to be in psychology, namely the study of physical growth and development, the divergence between the two ways will become clear. A woman, asked what are the normal size, weight, and proportions of a six-months-old baby, will frame her answer naturally enough on her own experience of children. This may be wide and representative or it may not. An anthropologist, asked the same question, would suggest that the best way of answering it would be to take say one thousand babies of six months selected at random from the general population, to measure their height, weight, and general proportions, and to take an average of this. Probably the estimates reached in these two ways would not be significantly different, but they might be. If they were, it is not hard to see which, from the scientific point of view, would be the more reliable.

When we come to less easily measurable quantities, such as intelligence or behaviour or emotional development, the subjective element in any one person's estimation of normal increases directly in proportion to the difficulty in obtaining objective measurements. Again, most women feel that they know what is the normal stage in a child's development for him to sit up, stand, walk, talk, and cut his teeth; they feel on less sure ground when it is his capacity to learn to perform simple tasks, for example building with bricks, or to achieve emotional adjustments such as the ability to share things happily with other children, which is in question; but however definite are their ideas they are bound to vary considerably from one observer to another and to be based upon a fairly limited range of experience of a comparatively small number of children. This is why quite often sensible and conscientious mothers come to welfare clinics, worried about some real or imagined failure with regard to the development of their child, only to be reassured once they learn that their child's behaviour falls well within the range of normal, and that the wider experience of the nurses or doctor whom they consult includes many other such variations which are in no way outside the average. The scientific approach to experience of this kind is simply to collect it sufficiently widely, to ensure that it is representative, and to accept the consistent average as a reasonable basis for establishing what is normal.

We can now begin to see that differences between the subjective concepts of normality in human behaviour formed by different observers are inevitably bound up with the attitude and experience of the particular observer concerned, at least to some extent. As a general rule we tend to put ourselves a little on the credit side of normal in most of our judgements. So it comes about that a highly intelligent man who is not scientifically trained may spend a lifetime assuming that the average intelligence of the adult population among whom he lives is considerably higher than it really is; he makes an allowance for the discrepancy which he imagines to exist between himself and most other people, but it is just as likely to be too small as to be too great. Judges who deliver sound but sometimes advanced strictures upon simple people, whose conception and understanding of the law is exceedingly primitive, provide an example of this. Our tendency to centre our conception of what is normal around our own experience contains an essential error, which, carried to extremes, is exemplified in the remarks of Humpty Dumpty quoted in the first chapter. 'When I use a word . . . it means just what I choose it to mean – neither more nor less.' In much everyday conversation, no matter how intelligent, 'normal' and 'psychology' are Humpty Dumpty words.

To establish the normal scientifically and to study it objectively, academic psychology has had first to devise a number of ways of measuring the various aspects of human personality, behaviour, and experience. Three useful divisions which are quite arbitrary, but which tend to make the task of measurement and description less confusing than it might otherwise be, are these: intelligence, which we can define as the capacity to modify behaviour successfully to changing situations and to learn by experience; emotional adjustment, which is much harder to define but which is concerned with our capacity to accept, recognize, and be reconciled to our feelings about things; and that faculty of exerting decision, or taking and maintaining action in response to the promptings of intelligence or emotion or a combination of both, which we readily recognize in those whom we know but which is most elusive and complex when we come to describe it. It is an aspect of personality intimately bound up with determination and persistence: at one time psychology regarded it as a self-contained faculty to which the name of conation was given; conation meant much the same thing as will, but its use as a psychological term avoided the disadvantage of involving the user in the current and thorny philosophical question of whether free will really existed at all.

More recently, and possibly more wisely, psychology has been concerned rather with the objective fact that people vary both in their readiness to take action or exert effort in response to stimulation, and in the subsequent persistence which they show in maintaining such effort or action in the face of difficulty or discouragement. Moreover a start has been made upon the practical problem of measurement of this capacity under standard conditions. As for the other two aspects of personality already mentioned, while psychologists have found it comparatively simple to measure certain aspects of intelligence, the objective measurement of emotional adjustment or maturity, or even the intensity of the emotions themselves, has proved very much more difficult. It is constantly being studied and has in some degree been achieved; nevertheless a great deal has yet to be done before any finally agreed and valid basis for the measurement of human emotion and capacity for action can be established. Meanwhile it must remain much easier for the layman to use, for example, the term 'normal will power' with some confidence (which may be misplaced) that he knows what he is talking about, and that other people know this too, than it is for the psychologist.

Clearly, the possibility of establishing on a comparatively firm basis what is normal for human beings in these three spheres of personality is interesting as well as important. In the course of one of the many somewhat anxious discussions which must precede the writing of a book of this sort I was asked by someone whether I proposed to show how a standard concept of normality might be reached, and whether such a concept might differ according to the particular society in which it was observed; whether, for example, it might mean different things in a primitive society from those accepted as normal in an established civilization, or if the political nature of the society would affect it fundamentally.

The answer here, in the well-worn phraseology of the Brains

Trust, must surely be that it all depends on what you mean by normal. We have already seen that normality can be either a matter of measurement or a matter of opinion. In the instances quoted above it is also essential to realize that what are being measured, or providing the grounds for the opinion, can be either patterns of group behaviour established in a society, or individual capacities and tendencies to behave in certain ways. The former are predominantly the concern of anthropology and sociology, which, whether regarded as outgrowths of psychology or as kindred subjects borrowing heavily from the same source, are more concerned with communal than with individual behaviour.

By their methods we are able to recognize, study, and measure such communal patterns, to establish scientifically as well as subjectively what is normal for any particular group, and what is the range and distribution of deviations from such normality among members of the group. They are also concerned with the differences between the pattern in one group and another, and with the effect of varying backgrounds and circumstances upon the formation of these patterns. Regarded in this way what is normal for one group is indeed often abnormal for another, and the standards accepted by or imposed upon individuals belonging to different groups may vary very widely indeed. But the patterns of behaviour displayed by members of different societies tend to differ only in so far as they are acquired in response to environmental pressure; in this case the pressure of the cultural or political standards of the society concerned. The ultimate concern of normal psychology, as of psychological medicine, must be with the individual; with what is innate in him as well as with what is acquired; with what he is as well as what he does or is made to do, with his essence as well as with his performance.

The study of the individual conducted on this basis by the methods of normal psychology does seem to show that fundamentally man is one and indivisible; that whether he lives in a mud hut, an igloo, a prefab, or a penthouse, whatever the political yoke under which he thrives or is oppressed, whatever his colour, race, or creed, he is moved by essentially the same fundamental instincts and aspirations, hopes and fears, knows the same needs, and contains in varying measure the same capacities.

Strenuous opposition to this thesis may be expected from several quarters, not least from within the ranks of psychologists themselves. Some, for example, have held the view that the whole idea of the existence of any fundamentally consistent structure in human personality is an illusion, that there is in fact no essence to study, that all is performance, and that performance itself is merely a complicated pattern of inevitable responses to preceding stimuli. Control the stimuli enough, they say, and you control the whole nature of man: for he is nothing but the sequence of responses he displays. This was the position adopted by the Behaviourist group. Their leader, J. B. Watson, writing of his subject in the *Encyclopædia Britannica*, has said 'So far in his objective study of man no behaviourist has observed anything that he can call consciousness, sensation, imagery, perception, or will. Not finding these so-called mental processes in his observations he has reached the conclusion that all such terms can be dropped out of any description of man's activity.' The reader may at once enquire how, if this view were a valid one, the behaviourist could become aware of it himself, or conscious of the findings he claims to observe; he may also ask what *is* this observation on the part of the behaviourist if it does not depend upon the perceptions of observed phenomena occurring in a conscious mind? For myself I should prefer to leave those very reasonable questions for the behaviourist to answer.

It is only fair to add, however, that modern behaviouristic theories are infinitely more subtle and no longer so extreme. None the less, the underlying preference for an essentially mechanistic approach to mind, and to the role of consciousness and purpose in human behaviour, crops up again in some of the arguments adduced from the design and method of function of modern electronic calculating machines. These machines can be constructed to perform, within a few minutes or hours, series of complicated calculations which would take a human brain almost a lifetime, to store their results within a special memory system, and to embody these remembered results in the relevant stage of every subsequent calculation.

Such devices have been called 'electronic brains', or even more fancifully 'machines with minds of their own'. This is precisely what they are not. Despite their great rate and range of sorting and calculating ability, it has never been possible to get any performance out of them that was not first put into them, by being built into their design. They can evolve no new principles, nor outstrip their inventors in ingenuity, although they exceed them in speed of performance. The argument that because human ingenuity has devised calculating machines that can carry out some processes analogous to human thought, the human mind itself is nothing but the product of a bigger and better calculating machine, is certainly arresting. But it is already obsolete, and moreover even as an argument it lacks completeness. Another way of putting it may bring this out: 'I have designed this machine,' says the proud inventor, 'so that it thinks.' We, his audience, are naturally impressed. We may be even more impressed when he has put it through its paces. He tells us that it is possible to design another machine which can play a fair game of chess.

'It's almost human . . .' murmurs someone admiringly.

'On the contrary,' he says, not without some condescension, 'it is simply a machine; but then what else are human beings?'

We file out, preoccupied. It is a machine: but it thinks. We think: we are but machines. What a paraphrase of Descartes! But is it watertight? Men are machines which can invent other machines. How did they come to be invented themselves? We return to ask the inventor two further questions.

'Is it possible to invent a machine which in itself can invent another?'

'Yes,' he says. 'It is at least theoretically possible to do that.'

'And would such a machine *want* to invent another?'

He sighs, patiently: 'I am afraid that is a meaningless question in this context.'

We stand corrected; but it would seem that man's mind remains more wonderful than any analogy or working model of himself that he can devise, brilliantly ingenious though he may be. Perhaps we had better resume our humble study of him.

*

We already know a good deal about the way in which normal

development and growth of human personality take place. The sources of this information are very wide, but they mostly depend upon detailed studies made by doctors, psychologists, and anthropologists on various people at various times in their lives. In maintaining that the fundamental aspects of this process are probably the same in all human beings we have already acknowledged that what is *accepted* as normal, and what is produced in the development of patterns of behaviour in children by their upbringing, and in adults by the society in which they live, will of course vary widely from one community to another. None the less, the data which we are about to consider can be accepted as normal for all children, other than those who are separated from their parents (or from suitable foster parents) at an early age, whether by tribal custom, political interference, or the accidents of existence. These circumstances anyway cannot be considered as fundamentally normal.

From birth until about the age of four, the whole of the child's emotional needs and their expression and satisfaction are centred on the mother. It is as though the child were still in many ways contained within the mother, in so far as her personality and her feelings intervene of necessity between the child and his experience of any form of outside reality, and may powerfully influence his response to such experience. At birth that part of his nervous system responsible for delivering incoming messages in the form of sensations to his brain is relatively completely developed, but his capacity for correlating and interpreting them is negligible, and his ability to control the motor or expressive side of his mind and body is quite unformed even if he knew what he wished to do with it. But the continual bombardment of sensory experience to which he is subjected during his waking hours, and the constant and inevitable sorting and assimilation of these experiences for which his brain is equipped, leads him within a matter of months to recognize first that there is a part of life and experience which is permanently with him, and a part, constantly fluctuating, which is in some way beyond and outside him. The division which the child may be imagined to be making at this stage is between what is 'me' and what is 'not-me'. The most important single aspect of the part of experience which is 'not-me' comes to be recognized as a constant element against an inconstant background; and this soon turns into a recognition of the mother as another person, instinctively accepted as the indispensable link between 'me' and everything else.

This relationship is a fundamental one which has to occur if the child is to develop normally, although of course it can be made with any other individual who occupies the mother's place in the early life of the child. It is the mother's own special relationship to the child and her personal feelings about him which tend to make her the ideal person to fulfil this role.

From the age of about four to about seven there is a change in this relationship, occasioned by the child's growing capacity to form separate and enduring relationships with other people, although the support and influence of the mother are of supreme importance in forming the child's attitude to these relationships as well as to all else that happens to him. His relationship with his father will by this time have begun to be an important one; and even relationships beyond the family circle, dependent for both their quality and quantity upon the family structure and enduring only as long as the central relationship with the mother supports and encourages them, begin to be made. The normal child is by nature eager, hopeful, and accepting; but to say this is only to say that these qualities will emerge provided that the parents are themselves reasonably happy, confident, and accepting in their attitude towards the child.

None the less children are both remarkably plastic and remarkably resilient; they reflect with uncanny fidelity the moods and preoccupations and tensions of those nearest and dearest to them, often without realizing or understanding anything about these moods and tensions at all. But no matter how severe may be the impact upon a child of unhappiness, resentment, or insecurity in his parents, it is nearly always possible for that child to regain an emotional equilibrium within normal limits if the parental troubles can be removed or relieved. This is one of the most important discoveries of the branch of psychiatry known as child guidance, which we shall be considering in more detail later on.

Together with the developing emotional adjustment of the

child there is a progressive development of his intelligence. This was first studied and measured objectively by Professor Binet in the early part of the twentieth century in a series of pioneer experiments upon the children of Paris. His approach to this was extremely sensible. He and his colleagues devised a number of tests of performance and understanding which they guessed would be reasonable for children of varying ages from the pre-school stage to adolescence. They assembled a battery of these tests, which included for example the capacity to build towers of bricks, copy simple patterns, know one's own name and age and the names of simple objects, for the younger children, up to quite complicated arithmetical and vocabulary tests, and the solving of logical puzzles or the deduction of inconsistencies and absurdities in printed statements, at the senior end of the scale. They then set large numbers of children to work on these tasks, an activity which the average child hugely enjoys, and they were guided in their estimate of what were the appropriate tests for the appropriate age groups by their results. They were then able to calculate an average score for each age group and to discover the normal range of variability above and below this average score within the age group. This led them to the conception of a normal mental age as a readily ascertainable factor emerging from the examination of children by this method. For example, the average score of all the children aged five who were tested, and the tests found most suitable for their interest and capacity, were accepted as being appropriate to a mental age of five.

The tests started at a level appropriate to the age of two, and to score a mental age of five a child had to succeed in all groups up to the five-year level and to score a total within the limits of variation found in the majority of children of that age. The degree of development of a particular child's intelligence was then expressed as an intelligence quotient. This was obtained simply by dividing the child's mental age by his actual or chronological age. A child of four whose score gave him a mental age of five, and who was therefore presumably of above average intelligence, would have an intelligence of 5/4 or, expressed as a percentage, 125.

Just precisely what it is that is being measured here we do not know. But we do know that it bears a close and constant relationship to all other methods of assessing the general brightness of the child and predicting his ability to succeed at school and even in life, provided always that his emotional adjustment is sufficiently stable to permit him to make full use of the intellectual capacity he possesses. But of course this is not always the case, and it is probably true that unhappiness, anxiety, or boredom and frustration are more frequent causes of apparent dullness or backwardness at school than is sheer lack of intelligence.

The conception of intelligence quotient, or IQ as it is often called in abbreviation, has met with receptions varying between excessive respect and carping criticism. It is certainly not the sole or even the main answer to the question so often asked about unsuccessful people: What makes him fail? Why can't he learn by experience? Nor, on the other hand, is it an entirely sterile and meaningless finding.

A number of school teachers once objected that they could form a far better estimate of the intelligence of their pupils than could be gained by Binet's test. Invited in groups to make assessments of a reasonably large number of children known to them all and to score these assessments numerically, they did so only to find that while the general average of these assessments corresponded closely to the scores of the children on the Binet scale, the figure obtained for any particular child on the scale tended in many cases to be closer to the average of all the teachers' estimates than any one of them had been able to get. An example will make this clear: a particular child, John, aged ten, is regarded by ten teachers who know him as of more than average intelligence. Their numerical estimates of his intelligence, expressed so as to be comparable with a Binet score, range from 112 to 135. The average of these ten estimates is 123. His Binet score is 125 and the nearest individual estimates to the average of 123 made by any teacher are one of 127 and another of 119. The great majority of teachers now accept the Binet scale, and since its introduction a great number of other methods of measuring intelligence have been devised, standardized, and put into general practice.

Particularly interesting are those tests whose performance calls for no previous educational knowledge of any kind, and which are therefore suitable for testing people of different cultural backgrounds and different races and languages. Some of the best-known and most reliable of these are the progressive matrices designed by Professor Raven. The principle underlying this test is the capacity to perceive first a logical sequence of events in successive diagrams, then the principle underlying this sequence, and finally to apply this principle to completing the last diagram in a further series of similar sequences.

These various studies of intelligence, which have reached a reasonable degree of precision, have told us something else of considerable interest about the development of human mental capacity. This is that, while intelligence tends to increase from birth throughout childhood, and both the rate of increase and the degree of development reached at any stage are susceptible of measurement, the peak of development appears to be reached somewhere between the ages of fourteen and sixteen. Thereafter, although judgement and experience and the wisdom which results from their combination will continue to develop, the faculty of intelligence remains constant until in the latter half of life it gradually, although at first imperceptibly, declines. This decline again tends to be offset in terms of individual performance and, in the assessment of the casual observer, by the accumulation of judgement, experience, and wisdom already mentioned. But it can be detected by methods of testing similar to those outlined, long before its more manifest appearance in the evening of life.

The measurement of emotional development is a far more difficult undertaking and rests as yet on a far more speculative basis than does the measurement of intelligence. It is of necessity bound up with the idea of maturity, and it is in the continuing study of the developing individual that its importance emerges most clearly.

Between the ages of seven and eleven the child has become an independent individual who is learning to make his own terms with life. It is no longer possible for him to gain every satisfaction in life from his mother, or indeed to gain it completely anywhere at all. The earlier frustrations and disappointments inseparable from growing up have now to be met on a more solitary basis, and the conflicts which occur between desires and possibilities, or even between one desire and another, he has to begin to solve to some extent by himself.

The way in which such conflicts occur can be described without plunging at this stage into the more detailed theories of subconscious mental life, most of which we owe to Freud. We can think of the developing human being as being equipped with the capacity to make responses both to the stimuli of the outside world and to those arising from within. These responses we call behaviour, and in their most simple form in early life they appear to be entirely automatic. The physiological basis of such automatic behaviour has been studied most intensively by Professor Pavlov, and it is based upon the mechanism of what is called reflex action. This means the production of a constant effect, which may be the secretion of a gland, the contraction of a group of muscles, or some comparatively complicated piece of behaviour, as the unvarying reaction to some incoming stimulus which travels from the sensory nerve endings which receive it to a nerve centre in the body from which it is relayed through motor nerves to produce the characteristic response. Reflex action is therefore essentially an unvarying pattern of stimulus and response, and the means by which it is achieved is an incoming nervous pathway bearing information, with central connexions whereby impulses are relayed to outgoing nerves, producing an effect. This particular functional unit in the nervous system is known as a reflex arc, and it is upon millions of such arcs that the structure of the nervous system is founded.

Pavlov found that reflex responses can be made to appear to new forms of stimuli if these are introduced at the same time as the original stimulus and the effect allowed to follow a number of times. Ultimately the new stimulus alone will produce the effect. This process, whereby established patterns of reflex response could acquire new operative stimuli to produce them, Pavlov called conditioning; and he built up an elaborate theory of behaviour on the basis of conditioned reflexes. Such a theory, it will be observed, has no need to invoke conscious participation in the explanation of behaviour; and reflex action, whether conditioned or not, need not be accompanied by awareness, still less by emotion. It follows that a conflict between two stimuli whose reflex responses may be contradictory or mutually exclusive will be solved automatically without the need for any conscious decision.

An example of this is a conflict which can easily be produced in a dog between the reflex response of scratching, produced by tickling the back in a certain place, and the response of extending the hind leg to stabilize the body when the other leg is lifted gently from the ground. If you tickle your dog's back on the left side, while lifting his right rear leg from the ground, the normal scratch reflex which would lead to his scratching the tickled area with his left leg will not appear. Instead the stabilizing reflex will overrule the other response, which will then be said to be inhibited. Experimentally it can be shown that this result is achieved even when the dog's brain is separated surgically under anaesthesia from the lower part of his body so that no conscious decision is involved.

That part of human behaviour which is served entirely by reflexes is concerned chiefly with balance, automatic protection – such as blinking the eye when an object approaches it closely or touches the eyeball – and the whole regulation of internal processes such as digestion and breathing. None less it is possible to control some reflexes consciously, at least to some extent, as for example when we hold our breath deliberately or stifle a sneeze before it takes place. When we perform this latter feat by pressing beneath our noses we make use of the capacity of one reflex to inhibit another at an automatic level.

More complicated patterns of behaviour which are still essentially innate and, although not automatic, may depend only to a small extent on conscious deliberation or control, are known as instincts. We can define an instinct as an innate tendency to behave in a certain way which is characteristic of a whole species, which does not have to be learnt and which leads to patterns of behaviour which are relatively perfect at their first performance. As a general rule the more highly organized the living creature the more widely variable and subject to conscious control are its instinctive patterns: thus the spider, who spins a perfect web without having to acquire the skill or the technique by any process of learning or imitation, can vary the essential plan of construction scarcely at all, whereas birds building their nests in response to a similar instinct can use a great variety of materials in widely different ways according to what is available.

Human beings are born with a number of powerful instincts which develop during childhood and adolescence. The most important are the instinct for self-preservation, the sexual instinct, and, probably, what has been called the herd or communal instinct. The patterns of expression of these instincts in man are very widely variable indeed, and they are mediated by the exercise of intelligence through consciousness to a greater extent than in any other living creature.

This brings us back to the concept of emotion and its overwhelming importance in human behaviour, for the way in which we become aware of the promptings of an instinct is by the urge or tension of the feeling which we have, and which we seek to discharge in any way that will serve the pattern of instinct producing it. When a feeling becomes sufficiently intense to demand action of some kind for its discharge, whether such action is in fact possible or not, it is invariably accompanied by certain characteristic bodily changes; for example, the feeling of fear is accompanied by pallor, quickening of the pulse, and dryness of the mouth, and by increased muscular tension which may even lead to trembling; the physical accompaniments of anger are somewhat similar, while grief tends to be associated with flushing of the face and the appearance of tears in the eyes. It is this combination of feeling and physical change to which we give the name of emotion.

We can begin to see then that while it is one of the functions of intelligence to enable us to choose ways of responding to our environment which are most appropriate and most likely to gain those ends which we desire, both the experience of desiring them and the driving force behind the response which we make belong essentially to the realm of feeling. Every decision which we make must depend ultimately upon the evaluation of our feelings about the factors involved. The more intelligent we are the more quickly and accurately are we able to perceive these factors, but no matter how clear or accurate our perception, our feelings about them will still finally be decisive for us. If those feelings are sufficiently strong they may even interfere with the degree of clarity and accuracy with which we are able to accept the results of our more abstract intellectual examination of the problem. And so it is true to say that while intelligence provides a screen or filter for experience, the means of storing its results and the most consistent way of assessing them, yet the springs of action are essentially emotional, and in the exercise of decision it is feeling which provides the ultimate force.

In the life of the mind, therefore, conflict must mean in the last analysis emotional conflict. Intellectual questions, as for example where there appear to be several possible answers to an abstract problem, can always be resolved without tension unless there are emotional issues involved: doubt, indecision, frustration, and anxiety enter upon the scene only under these circumstances, and it is perhaps an added illustration of the overwhelming importance of emotions in human life that personal decisions which do not involve conflict of any kind are exceedingly rare.

We have left our child between the ages of seven and eleven facing conflicts of this kind: shall he do his homework or shall he go out and play? Shall he spend all his pocket money to-day or save some of it for to-morrow? Large or small, baffling or comparatively simple problems of this kind ceaselessly confront him. What are the normal mechanisms for dealing with them?

It seems to every conscious human being that he has some freedom of choice in these matters; and even in those in which he has not, and must accept a disagreeable solution imposed on him by external circumstances, he can still decide to some extent what adjustment he will make. He hasn't much pocket money left; he will still save some of it. He has already spent the lot; he will look forward to next week, when some more is due. When the solution in practice is unsatisfactory he can imagine happier circumstances or pretend that things are better than they are. This kind of solution of the conflict between desire and reality may be realistic, if hope for the future or acceptance of the present form its basis. Even if it is not realistic the compensatory fantasy of being richer, or happier, or braver, or better-looking, or more successful than one really is, is a natural and normal device, available to all of us and particularly favoured by children. Its only drawback is that, by releasing some of the tension of emotion without achieving the ends towards which that emotion is directed, it may eventually weaken what we have called the springs of action.

As the child grows older, between eleven and about sixteen, a whole avalanche of increased tension and conflict floods his life. The sexual instinct, present from birth but hitherto existing in a far more vague, diffuse, and but dimly perceived form, and lacking until now the full development both of the physical means for its expression and the stronger drive towards this expression to which such bodily development gives rise, now dominates the emotional development of the child, who has begun to be a child no longer.

This can be a most turbulent and a most unhappy time. The individual feels himself to be beyond the old safe, secure, and at least partly explored boundaries of childhood experience, to be venturing into a no-man's-land leading to adult independence and power which still seems magically remote, yet he is without the confidence or the experience of adult life, from which he feels himself still excluded and which he tends to envy and to resent. He has reached the frontier, and the gates of childhood are closing behind him, but he has no passport and 'they' won't let him through. 'They' tend to be exemplified by his unfortunate parents at this stage, whose own sexual relationship is one which all too often he finds hard to acknowledge or tolerate in the light of new feelings and misgivings which possess him: and yet in some ways he needs his parents more than ever before.

Many people find themselves quite unable to remember this period of their lives in any detail. For those who can remember it it is seldom a particularly happy memory, although all of us, lest we be too disturbed by the resurrection of past shames, uncertainties, fears, disappointments, or humiliations, tend to remember no more than we can bear. The average adolescent is comparatively indifferent to children, essentially divided in his attitude towards grown-up people, and alternately fierce and tender towards others like himself. He is bewildered by his feelings, by their intensity and by the moods which they produce in him, and he is thrown back upon introspection and fantasy for much of his time. We shall see later how the decidedly chaotic pattern of this stage of normal development influences profoundly the way in which those who find its stresses more than they can tolerate display their distress. Adolescence is always a period of turbulent emotion, sometimes of disturbed behaviour, and a time when love, tolerance, and imaginative understanding were never more in demand and yet never harder wholly to accept. This is, of course, not to say that normal adolescence is a period of unrelieved gloom and despair, but rather that the many consolations, pleasures, and excitements of these remarkable years tend to belong either to what we have brought over with us from childhood, or to what we anticipate in full maturity.

After the age of sixteen or thereabouts the period of entering upon maturity has begun. In the normal person all the instincts and their attendant emotions with which he will be called upon to deal have made their appearance, and, despite the increasing complexity of the struggle for existence in the outer world, the most explosive phases of adjustment to his inner life, to himself, and his relationship to others, have been completed. By now the patterns which he has laid down for dealing with success and failure, the capacities which he has formed for loving or hating, trusting or suspecting, accepting or rejecting other people, are in essence already formed. Modification, of course, remains possible; but, as we have seen, modification in the light of experience is not simply a matter of reason and intelligence; it depends far more upon the extent to which new emotional responses with their attendant risk of new and perhaps painful adjustments can be tolerated.

Everyone knows how difficult and disagreeable it can be to give up even a simple habit once it is formed. If the habit is connected with the satisfaction of some desire it is even harder; that the desire may itself be acquired rather than innate, as for example smoking, makes no difference. How much harder still it is to give up a habit of emotional response which has become ingrained during the most sensitive and formative years of childhood, in the course of that child's relationship with those most close to him. In this way, for example, a child whose relationship with his father has been unhappy, whose need and desire to respect, admire, and love the father has been thwarted and replaced by resentment, jealousy, or a sense of betrayal, will find every relationship with older men, or those charged with authority, an exceedingly challenging and difficult one. Sometimes a lifetime will not be enough to enable such a person to make a better adjustment to this emotional predicament, which burdens him constantly with the threat and the shadow of far-off, half-remembered days whose present impact he may well deny.

This tendency to build up patterns during emotional development, and to use them thereafter repetitively and without consciousness of their origin, is essentially a normal one. But when these patterns are particularly morbid or unsuccessful they form the basis for all the wide and protean manifestations of neurotic illness. One way of looking at the neurotic patient, and a good one, is to regard him as a person whose patterns of response have started by being abnormally unsuccessful, and have produced subsequently a series of increasingly intolerable situations with correspondingly intolerable emotional experiences, to which his desperate and increasingly unsuccessful response is a further repetition of the original pattern.

This is a good way of regarding such a patient because it enables us to keep clearly in mind the similarity of neurotic behaviour to normal behaviour, as well as its difference. When in a difficult, anxious, and troubled world most of us contrive to be reasonably happy and moderately stable people most of the time, it is because our basic patterns of behaviour are normally sound and because our capacity to modify them is not abnormally limited. This is one way of expressing the concept of emotional maturity, and it is not hard to understand why it should be such a difficult thing to measure. None the less, as we saw earlier in the chapter, emotional no less than intellectual development deserves and has received the attention of normal psychologists.

There are in existence a number of ways of testing people both for their degree of emotional maturity and their tendency towards neurotic patterns of behaviour, which rest upon a similar foundation to that already described for tests for intelligence. Large numbers of people selected at random have undertaken these tests and provided what are known as control results. These can then be compared with the results obtained when the tests are given to groups of other people selected on the basis of recognizable neuroses or the agreed opinion of psychologists, psychiatrists, and other physicians that they show clinical evidence of immaturity. While it would be early to say that conclusive results have been obtained, or that the reliability of such methods of objective assessment compares with those now generally accorded to the majority of intelligence tests, yet some valid correlations between some types of response to the test and certain groups of people selected as potentially neurotic or immature have emerged. The value of this from a medical standpoint is that it confirms the view that psychiatric diagnosis, even at the least severe and dramatic levels, is something more valid than just the opinion of one person about another, or the agreed verdict of a body of self-styled experts upon other people, whose complaints are varied but whose underlying patterns of behaviour and development are the same.

*

This account of the growth and development of normal human personality has been made with only one reference to the work of Freud. This virtual omission, which many colleagues of mine might regard as heretical, has been deliberate. The contribution of Freud to this as to so many other subjects in psychology and psychological medicine has been profound. But it has also been controversial, and the reader may find it easier to form his own opinion of the place of the Freudian contribution if that is added after the main body of more generally accepted current opinion has been outlined. This is what I have tried to do in this chapter so far.

It now remains to say something of the special additional contributions which Freud has made, while recognizing that much even of what has already been written owes a great deal to the approach of Freud and his method of study. Quite apart from the division between 'me' and 'not me' in the mind of the child, he postulated a further division in the 'me' element; a subjective awareness of self, which he called the ego, and an unconscious reserve of primitive instincts striving to influence this ego, to which he gave the somewhat unprepossessing name of the Id. The interaction of Id and ego produced the behaviour of the individual, whose emotional energy sprang from a particular source in the Id, called by Freud the libido. He assumed that this libido was a fixed quantity in any particular individual, which was related to the strength of that individual's instinctual drives, and might be invested in varying degree in a number of channels of activity, but was derived in the first instance from the impulse to love and to obtain gratification through loving.

This might not seem a particularly revolutionary idea, still less a disgusting one, but the terms in which it was originally represented led a large number of people to believe and maintain that Freud's conception of libido was precisely equivalent to the adult sexual instinct. From this there arose the familiar gibe that Freud says 'everything is due to sex'. Freud did in fact say that the impulse to love and to obtain gratification through loving found its most natural expression in the mature individual in sexual fulfilment; he also said that its progress towards this natural expression began from the time of birth, and that in the development of the infant the love which the child felt first towards the mother's breast and then towards the mother herself when she became recognizable to him was, at an infantile level, a combination of emotion and physical gratification, not essentially dissimilar from the adult sexuality which one day the individual would achieve.

His response to being vigorously attacked was to maintain this principle with corresponding vigour and force, and he went on to divide the physical expression of love in childhood into a number of stages. These stages were, however, complicated by his recognition of and insistence upon another hotly contested principle, that loving and hating, cherishing and hurting, are no more separate in the relations of childhood than they are in those of adult life. Here again his views were regarded with horror and disgust. People who saw nothing particularly abnormal or distasteful in such protestations of young lovers as 'I love you so much I could kill you' or in the assertion of some women that if their husbands stopped beating them they would fear that they had stopped loving them, took grave exception to the suggestion that babies might bite their mothers' nipples for pleasure or might occasionally enjoy being smacked by someone whom they loved.

Freud developed his theory about the development and canalization of these feelings in children through successive stages. In the first he postulated that all the infant's love and interest was lavished upon himself and his gratification was essentially with his own body. The zone most sensitive at this time was the mouth, and the pleasure most eagerly sought that of sucking and later of biting or chewing. To return to the phrase used in an earlier description, the child's concern at this stage would be exclusively with 'me'. With the recognition of the mother as a separate person the child's natural feelings would be divided between extreme love for the mother when she satisfied and comforted him and equally extreme resentment when she kept him waiting or frustrated him. It seems almost inconceivable that anyone who has ever watched a baby with his mother can doubt the truth of at least this observation.

With increasing awareness of the body and the rest of the world another zone of sensitivity and importance in emotional development was the anus, for Freud maintained that the child would experience normal satisfaction in emptying his bowel, and would regard this too as a performance which he could give proudly and happily to his mother. When in a more resistive frame of mind he could refuse this performance and gain another sort of gratification from the physical and emotional sensations occasioned by this refusal. A later stage, still located in infancy, would be the development of awareness of physical gratification from the sexual organs. Freud never suggested that the child would have a developed adult conception of their use, but rather that he would discover that they were a source of simple physical pleasure which would already be connected with the experience of loving, as was all other physical gratification. The fact that physical manipulation of their own and each other's bodies occurs quite spontaneously in young children is again incontestable: nor was it Freud who disputed the innocence or naturalness of this procedure. It was his opponents to whom the idea was intolerable and whose interpretation of it was obscene.

However, few children who do handle their bodies in this way escape detection and rebuke. If this is sufficiently pointed and charged with emotion on the part of the parent, the anxiety and guilt aroused in the child's mind in this connexion are considerable. Freud maintained that children shamed and rebuked in this way developed great fear about their parents' attitude towards their bodies. He linked this with the developing jealousy which young children tend to feel for their father when his influence with their mother conflicts with their own, and on this basis constructed the famous theory of the Oedipus complex. This, named after the Greek myth about the prince who unwittingly murdered his father and married his mother, assumes that children of both sexes at first, and boys throughout their childhood, have to face a conflict between their love and admiration for their father on the one hand and their desire to be rid of him so that they may have their mother to themselves on the other. Behind this crucial conflict lurks the fear of talion punishment from the father for the forbidden wish to do away with him.

Freud considered the whole of this intense crisis of loving and hating and fearing to be understandably too much for the child to handle. He believed that it was at first denied and then repressed – that is, banished from consciousness in a way which we shall have to examine later – so that by the age of five these conflicts although unresolved were beneath the surface, and between five and about eleven the child's emotional life remained comparatively tranquil, at least in so far as these more fundamental impulses were concerned. He called this period the latency period, and it is certainly true that violent jealousies and disturbances of behaviour centred around the parental relationships arise more commonly in the period of life up to the age of five, or between eleven and sixteen, than they do during this so-called latency period.

With the coming of adolescence the whole of this buried explosive material is assumed to erupt again on to the surface. This provides a dynamic explanation of the adolescent turmoil to which we have already referred. During this period the further canalization of libido has to take place, and the concluding stages lead through a period in which emotional fulfilment is sought no longer with the parents but at first with members of the same sex and later with those of the opposite sex. This final stage is accepted as the culmination of normal development, while completely insoluble crises at earlier stages may lead to what Freud called a fixation of libido at this particular level. In this way he was able to explain the genesis of various types of neuroses, of homosexuality, and of what we now call immaturity of the personality, on the basis of an arrest of the normal process of emotional development at an intermediate stage.

We shall have to consider other aspects of Freudian theory later on: but this extremely condensed account of one part of it has, I hope, reflected something of that intense interest in human beings and keen observation of them which characterized Freud himself. This, combined with a genius for speculation and hypothesis, ensured that while practically everything he wrote was striking and original, and much of it brilliant, almost all his views have at some time been not only vigorously attacked, and defended, but misquoted, misinterpreted, and misunderstood. The reader sufficiently interested to turn to his original writings, now available almost without exception in translation, will be well rewarded.

The more general views expressed in this chapter were based largely on the work of Professor Piaget of Geneva, Dr Leo Kanner of the Henry Phipps Psychiatric Clinic, the Johns Hopkins University, Baltimore, and Professor Gesell of the Yale Clinic of Child Development, Hartford, Connecticut.

Abnormal Mental Life

AT one point in Chapter 1 we agreed that the problem of mental illness should include for the purpose of this book the whole range of disturbance of human emotion, judgement, action, and personality, whenever this disturbance was sufficiently profound to be considered abnormal. It is evident that such disturbance of normal mental life can be caused in a great variety of ways: it can be due primarily to structural disease or damage in the nervous system; to failure of the nervous system to develop fully, still on a purely structural basis; it can arise in the course of other physical illness or it can appear apparently spontaneously and without the demonstrableco-existence of any physical cause. This is not to say that even in those disorders of mind and emotion which are most characteristically psychological rather than physical in their apparent origin there is ever a complete absence of accompanying physical change. To maintain this would be to come dangerously near to propounding a contradiction in terms, since we have already seen that it is part of the very nature of an emotional state that certain physical changes should accompany it. When that emotional state becomes abnormal in intensity, in duration, or in its comparative inappropriateness to the stimuli which have elicited it, as in certain types of anxiety reaction where extreme panic may be produced by apparently harmless situations, the physical changes accompanying it will be correspondingly excessive or protracted.

An examination of the phenomena of mental illness, even when conducted from the standpoint of the intelligent layman who is presumed to be reading this book, rather than from the approach of the textbook which is of necessity entirely different, must still include an elementary system of classification. The one I propose to use is based upon that designed by Professor Aubrey Lewis in his contribution to *Price's Text Book of Medicine*. It divides the headings under which mental disorder may be considered into an organic group, embracing all those forms of mental illness which are directly related to and dependent upon some distinct bodily disorder, and a functional group in which the disorders, while still in many cases almost certainly due to some disturbance of bodily processes, display a form and pattern which is recognizable on a psychological rather than a physical plane, and for which no characteristic structural basis has as yet been discovered.

This second group can be further divided into the disorders of emotion, such as excitement, depression, or anxiety, disorders characterized by a profound disturbance of the capacity for normal thinking, feeling, and maintaining contact with external reality, those in which firmly held morbid false beliefs, known as delusions, dominate the clinical picture and the behaviour of the patient, and finally disturbances of behaviour, using the term in its widest sense. These disturbances of behaviour may either be conscious and even resisted, as for example when repetitive rituals or ruminations obsess the mind of the patient to the detriment of all normal activity; such conditions being known as obsessional or obsessive compulsive states; or they may occur outside the normal level of consciousness as in the various forms of hysteria where symptoms such as paralysis, anaesthesia, loss of speech or hearing or other disturbance of sensation, may incapacitate the patient threatened by an unpleasant situation which may thereby be modified or avoided.

There is yet another group of disorders in which behaviour disturbance predominates. This group includes both behaviour disorders and delinquency in childhood, which will be separately considered in another chapter, and also that complex and important aspect of human maladjustment which gives rise to what has been described as psychopathic personality. Here the impact of the disturbance is primarily at the level of the patient's interaction with his environment rather than in the sphere of his conscious feeling or intelligence. He tends to be regarded and to regard himself as the black sheep or the weaker brother in the community rather than as a sick person. This in itself is a tremendous problem, and like a number of others in medicine it has yet to be solved.

*

In studying the first group of mental disorders, those with an organic basis, our determined emancipation from the aims and standards of the textbook enables us to concentrate on principles rather than upon detail. The characteristic features of this group are, in the cases where the structural change has been sudden and acute, a mixture of confusion, delirium, and a true loss of previously existent intellectual power which is known as dementia. In cases where the damage has been more insidious the most striking features tend to be a sort of irritable, hypersensitive, almost peevish weakness and fatigue with subjective lassitude; failure of attention, concentration, and memory combine to produce a more general underlying dementia in which a progressive scattered dilapidation of the patient's earlier knowledge, judgement, and intelligence are manifest. The term structural change needs to be interpreted, however, in its widest sense when dealing with the acute organic disturbance, since many of these are completely reversible. Examples are the states of acute delirium and excitement seen in the course of infectious fevers and sometimes after haemorrhage; a more specific agent in producing such an acute disturbance is alcohol.

There is no need to describe the phenomenon of acute alcoholic intoxication, and as the insidious changes of chronic alcoholism owe something to the structure of the underlying personality, as well as to the physical and mental effects of the alcohol, they will be discussed in that part of the chapter devoted to personality disorder. But the acute delirium which follows prolonged and intensive consumption of alcohol when the physiological tolerance of the body and its capacity to deal with the drug have become exhausted provides a vivid example of the acute type of organic mental disturbance.

The patient begins to display an increasing restlessness, agitation, and suspicion which tend to increase with the coming of night. Orientation, the capacity to know where one is in space and time, may be soon lost, and then the grip upon reality weakens and all manner of strange and disturbed beliefs and sensations overwhelm him. Hallucinations, particularly of hearing, frequently of the sense of touch so that he imagines animals or insects are leaping or crawling upon his body, make their appearance; there may even be visual hallucinations, although these are far less common than mis-identification in which he takes doctors or nurses or those attending him to be prominent figures in his family circle or earlier life. There is often an occupational flavour about all this, so that the railwayman worries and cries out about the signals and the points, the actor strains for his cues or cringes from a hostile audience, the housewife worries about the children or hears the footsteps of burglars upon the stair. Underlying the whole course of the delirium there is suspicion and alarm and through it there is sustained a note of terror. It seems to be a product of confusion and emotional over-reaction. The underlying dementia is there, but it is rarely accessible to testing, and when the condition recovers, as with proper treatment it nearly always does, the dementia also disappears unless the chronic effects of alcoholic poisoning exist to maintain it.

The more subtle and insidious but equally profound changes seen in association with slowly growing damage or disease vary to some extent with the nature of the lesion. The whole group of degenerative disorders of the brain, the senile and presenile dementias, tend to be characterized primarily by a loss of intellectual function of which attention, concentration, and recent memory have already been mentioned as particularly striking, with a comparative retention of the memory for earlier days. These features are often linked to a developing shallowness and sometimes fatuity of emotional expression; tears or cackles come readily and with little apparent meaning, although there may be outbursts of spiteful rage or piteous weeping in response to quite minor disappointments or frustrations. Such patients, particularly when these changes overtake them in the evening of their lives as a result of a progressive failure of the blood supply to their brains through tired and choked arteries, may well suffer far more than their failing powers of expression allow them to convey; for them too the night is a time of added stress, for they sleep little and poorly, and it is then, as in the acute forms of organic disturbance, that reality and fantasy seem to become more confused and they tend to wander muttering about the house. They may even fall and injure themselves or set fire to their rooms in their restless pottering.

Space-occupying lesions in the brain, such as tumours or abscesses which are only slowly increasing in size, produce in the psychological sphere a gradually progressive dementia without as a rule delirium. Emotional change tends to be confined to blunting or to some increase of lability and shallowness of response. Accompanying the psychological manifestations there are often signs and symptoms along the borderland of neurology and psychiatry; disturbances of speech and the special aspects of memory and intellectual function concerned with remembering names, functions of objects, and ways of doing things.

There are other diseases of the nervous system in which organic neurological change is accompanied by profound disturbance of psychological function, which may vary from simple failure of intellectual capacity on the one hand, to profound emotional disorder such as despair or an unrealistic elation on the other. Syphilis of the central nervous system, among its many and varied neurological manifestations, produces a type of mental disorder to which the name of general paresis of the insane has been given. This condition, while including the ultimate confusion and dementia common to all groups of progressive organic disorder, presents a number of special features which enabled its clinical separation and subsequent correlation with syphilitic infection to be made.

The essential change is a blunting, coarsening, and deterioration of the entire personality, which is most apparent in the early stages to those who know the patient well; a moderately successful façade may be maintained in the presence of strangers, but whether the emotional tone of the patient's prevailing mood is one of grandiose elation or gloomy and sullen despair, behaviour becomes increasingly inappropriate and ultimately bizarre.

A patient of my acquaintance insisted on presenting me with a cheque for nine million pounds in recognition of services rendered. Similar donations were made to all the nurses, in gratitude not only for their treatment of him but for their co-operation in stabling seventeen of his racehorses in their dining room. At the same time he was angry, querulous, and suspicious because his wife was being consistently unfaithful to him, either with me or with the bank manager, and despite her lavish allowance was forging his Post Office savings book and thereby involving him in considerable trouble and expense.

The cheque he presented was an almost meaningless and indecipherable scrawl upon a dirty piece of paper; but two weeks before his admission to hospital and before some of his more unacceptable ideas had emerged in conversation, he had passed among his casual acquaintances as being no more than a tired and slightly irritable man. The key to early diagnosis in such cases is, of course, careful observation and prompt laboratory examination of the blood and spinal fluid; untreated, dementia is progressive and death inevitable.

*

The general group of conditions which come under the heading of mental deficiency can be considered as belonging under the organic group. The brains and the bodies of all inherently mentally defective people are in some degree abnormal in structure; this abnormality is naturally enough largely a matter of inadequate development, and what distinguishes it from all other forms of impairment of mental function on an organic basis is that by definition a mentally defective person is someone who has never developed the same degree of intellectual and emotional capacity and maturity as his more fortunate fellows. In short, the patient with dementia has lost what once he had; the mentally defective patient has never possessed in full the normal assets of mental function.

We have already seen enough of the development of intelligence to realize that there is a wide range on either side of normal in the endowment of human beings. Intelligence indeed tends to follow what is called a normal curve of distribution, with a comparatively small proportion of the population appearing at one end of the scale as sub-normal to the point of mental defect, while another small proportion at the opposite end are endowed with such excessively high intelligence as to be abnormal in the opposite sense; these are the men and women of genius in our midst. The vast bulk of the population remain fairly evenly distributed around the mid-line. It is therefore necessary on a purely administrative basis to postulate some definition of what constitutes mental defect, to divide it from what may be called normal stupidity.

The official definition for this purpose in Britain is 'a condition of arrested or incomplete development of mind existing before the age of eighteen years, whether arising from inherent causes or induced by disease or injury.' There are, of course, theoretical objections to this as to any other definition, official or otherwise, but in practice it works reasonably well. A further subdivision on an administrative basis is made between idiots, imbeciles, and feeble-minded people.

Idiots are defined as those who are too defective to be able to guard themselves against common physical dangers such as falling into the fire, upsetting boiling water over themselves, or becoming lost when unattended, while imbeciles and feeble-minded people are those who require special care because by themselves they can neither manage their affairs nor profit by normal instruction. The distinction between them rests upon their capacity to earn a living or gain something from special education in schools designed for this purpose. Imbeciles cannot do this, but feeble-minded people can become, within their limits, productive and useful citizens.

The intelligence quotients (see Chapter 3) roughly corresponding to these three divisions are as follows: idiots have a quotient of less than 20, imbeciles between 20 and 50, and feeble-minded people between 50 and 70. The imperfections inherent in the necessarily limited approach of formal intellectual testing must never be forgotten, however; there is an essential difference, for example, between a normal child of, say, ten years of age and a mentally defective adult with a mental age of ten. There is a similar difference between mentally defective children and mentally defective adults, the difference depending in the main upon the element of sexual development and the physical and emotional changes characteristic of adolescence and adult life. Mental defect never occurs without some involvement of emotional maturity and, as has been mentioned, in the more severe cases physical development may be obviously impaired. It follows from this that the mental symptoms are combined of a lack of intelligence coupled with such stresses and limitations as are imposed upon the individual by his mental and physical inability to lead a normal life, and the response which an already immature emotional system has to make to these circumstances.

Idiots are wholly dependent. They cannot be taught to feed themselves, or to keep themselves clean, nor can they recognize other people or communicate with them except in the crudest and most primitive way. They are in fact considerably less intelligent than domestic animals. Their habits are simple and unformed and their emotional responses crude in the extreme. When frustrated they may bite or scratch themselves. They tend to pull out their hair and eat it. Unlike imbeciles, whose emotional state is usually readily apparent, they appear to be neither happy nor unhappy in the accepted sense of these descriptions.

Imbeciles, while being by definition unable to learn in the ordinary sense of the word, may acquire certain striking accomplishments on a purely automatic basis. For example, they may be able to memorize simple mathematical procedures such as the tables in arithmetic and produce answers to questions put purely along these lines with startling rapidity and accuracy. However, they are unable to apply these feats to any general purpose and their capacity for dealing in abstract thought is negligible. They tend to be happy dependent creatures who appreciate affection and care, and respond with docility and obedience to kind and sympathetic handling. The immaturity and instability of their emotional and intellectual balance, however, may be brought out disastrously by their response to sexual or aggressive impulses. Allowed to roam about without care or supervision they may commit murder, rape, or arson with as little concern or appreciation of the nature of their actions as they show towards some minor delinquency. A high proportion of the ranks of prostitutes, vagrants, and petty recidivists are found on examination to suffer from a degree of mental defect.

E. O. Lewis has pointed out that the personality of imbeciles varies widely, some being docile and kindly, others being rough, deceitful, and vindictive. With them, as with everybody else, a great deal depends on their upbringing. He records that with the best available type of upbringing less than 10 per cent of all defectives show antisocial or troublesome behaviour. But the capacity of even the highest grade defectives, those feeble-minded persons who can be taught a simple trade for example, depends as much upon their character and personality as upon the level of their intelligence. All defectives are prone in childhood to profound disturbances of behaviour, largely arising out of the handicaps in adjustment which they face, and in adult life they may exhibit the swings of mood and occasionally either the deliberately grotesque or hysterically exaggerated behaviour seen in other forms of mental illness, such as schizophrenia, again probably as compensatory mechanisms. On the other hand some may show a remarkable capacity for social adaptation in adult life, provided the stresses and demands are not pressed too far. A mentally defective girl with a lick of lipstick, a flick of powder, and a cheerful fluency no matter how shallow or stereotyped, can often deceive potential employers and even magistrates into forming a considerable over-estimate of her basic intellectual powers.

There are two forms of inherent mental defect which deserve special mention. One is due to deficient secretion of the thyroid gland and is known as cretinism; the other is associated with profound and consistent physical changes, notably obliqueness of the eyelids, breadth of the nose, and fissuring and often comparative enlargement of the tongue so that it protrudes between the lips. These features produce in the individual a characteristic appearance to which the name of Mongolism has been given. Mongols are usually placid and happy idiots whose whole bodies bear ample evidence of the widespread constitutional nature of their abnormality. They have lax joints, short fingers, bulging bellies, and often congenital abnormalities in the heart and other bodily organs and in the central nervous system. There is no special relationship between this condition and those members of the human race who inhabit the Mongolian plateau, despite the superficial facial resemblance. On the other hand, it has been said that so characteristic is the syndrome of Mongoloid defect that when a child exhibiting this happens to be born to a Mongolian parent there is no difficulty in distinguishing its appearance, quite apart from its subsequent behaviour, from the rest of the children.

Cretinism is a variety of dwarfism, in that all physical development is delayed, as well as the development of mental function. Untreated, cretins rarely rise above the level of idiots, achieve no degree of self-sufficiency, and do not mature sexually. In contrast with the comparatively rosy and attractive appearance of the Mongol, the cretin has thick skin, dull, lacklustre eyes, and an apathetic expression. However, unlike the Mongol, the cretin can be treated and to a large extent relieved, although rarely cured, by suitable administration of extract of thyroid glands.

In general the consideration of mental defect underlies what can never be ignored in any study of the mental life of human beings; namely that a severe handicap or impairment in one sphere of function, in this case intelligence, is usually accompanied by some degree of impairment and handicap in all the other spheres both physical and mental. This is because man is essentially a body-mind unit, functioning in an environment which both affects him and is affected by him. Even when the primary impairment cannot be demonstrated in more than one sphere, the repercussions it causes on the organism as a whole can be expected to produce responses in all related areas. The mentally defective patient displays not only impairment of intellect and physical change but also some degree of emotional instability, an explosive, volatile, and fluctuating pattern of behaviour in response to stress, and even an altered susceptibility to infection.

* * *

When we come to consider the functional group of mental disorders the problem of classification immediately becomes difficult and disputed. There are, for example, two distinctly divergent schools of thought on the question of whether there is an essential difference in kind between one entire group of mental disorders which are called neuroses and another which are called psychoses. Whether its fundamental validity is accepted or not, no one denies that in practice this distinction is a useful and convenient one. Under its terms the neuroses are those disorders of emotional or intellectual functioning which do not deprive the patient of contact with reality; the psychoses, on the other hand, are characterized by a fundamental disturbance in the patient's appreciation of the nature of his environment and his response to it. Dr T. A. Ross in his admirable book *The Common Neuroses* draws the distinction in this way:

> The psychotic lives, in so far as he is a psychotic, in a world of fantasy; the neurotic lives in the real world; its difficulties are greater by far for him than they are for normal people, but they are the same difficulties which all of us have. The difficulties of the psychotic arise from the fact that he is living in quite another world, in one which is not subject to the ordinary physical laws.

The contrary view postulates no difference between what are called neuroses and what are called psychoses save one of degree, and holds that the decision in any particular case is bound up with the severity of the symptoms, the type of treatment required, and the extent to which the patient will co-operate in such treatment. On this basis the psychotic patient is one who cannot be relied upon to co-operate in treatment, and who may therefore require special arrangements for care and protection, such as certification: this tends to make the grounds for distinction essentially administrative or legal rather than clinical or scientific. If this is accepted, the sooner the use of the terms is dropped altogether the better, since we can already speak of a mental illness as certifiable, potentially certifiable, or not certifiable, without the need for synonyms carrying an altogether different implication. In practice most doctors use the terms in the sense proposed by Dr Ross, and succeed in understanding each other fairly well.

The way in which this works out in practice will perhaps best be illustrated by describing the main groups of functional mental disorder under the headings which we agreed to adopt at the beginning of this chapter, and indicating in the case of each one whether it normally presents as a neurotic or as a psychotic type of illness. This procedure will have the further advantage of enabling the reader to decide for himself to which school of thought he chooses to belong.

The first group to be considered are the disorders which occur primarily in the sphere of emotion. These are called affective disorders, and the two most commonly encountered are states of anxiety and states of depression. The anxiety state is characterized by a persistent feeling of tension and anxiety for which the patient can recognize no fundamental cause. He is apt to say that he feels worried about everything, but he is often not at all sure why he finds everything so worrying. Another description which he may use is that he is afraid, but he does not know what he is afraid of or why he is afraid of it. An eminent neurologist has described anxiety as 'fear spread out thin'; it is this condition of constant gnawing fear without discoverable cause which is so singularly striking in a patient with an anxiety state.

The quality of the anxiety is not essentially different from that experienced by normal people in the face of some appropriate stress. It is accompanied by the characteristic changes familiar to us all; for example, by a raised pulse rate, by recurrent dryness of the mouth, dilated pupils, and by a subjective feeling of distaste for food and of being uncomfortably 'keyed up' all the time. Sleep is disturbed in characteristic ways, the patient being unable to get to sleep for hours, tossing and turning restlessly and finally falling into a broken slumber often disturbed by vivid and terrifying dreams from which he may wake tense, sweating, and trembling.

During the day he may experience paroxysms of increased tension and anxiety amounting to attacks of panic; in such attacks the feeling of panic may be accompanied by the physical sensation of choking or suffocation, the tremulousness and sweating may increase and the patient may fear that he is going to die. In this general setting of emotional tension, external events are fully appreciated but tend to be interpreted in the light of the prevailing mood, while all actually or potentially disagreeable experiences in everyday life take on a heightened and more unpleasant tone. Any ordeal becomes harder to bear and any stress tends to provoke an increase in the existing discomfort. Sometimes the patient will be aware that certain types of situation or certain general threats to his happiness or security with which his life confronts him are particularly related to his symptoms and particularly difficult to bear. In other cases he may claim complete ignorance of any possible provocative factors in his life, and may attribute the symptoms to some entirely physical cause such as a 'strained' or 'weak' heart, or a state of 'nervous exhaustion' due to overwork. We shall see in a later chapter that the degree of insight which the patient has for the nature of his symptoms can be important both in his readiness to accept treatment and in his ability to get help from it.

Some patients who suffer predominantly from anxiety may display this anxiety mainly or exclusively in response to certain specific stimuli. For example, they may feel utterly unable to face travelling on an underground train or going in a lift, or they may be acutely afraid of venturing out alone on the one hand or meeting people or going into a crowded place on the other. Specific fears of this nature are described as phobias, and the so-called phobic states can be regarded as a variety of anxiety states in general. In practice it is most rare for any phobia to be so restricted to a specific type of experience that the patient remains free of anxiety under all other circumstances. What usually happens is that the underlying and persistent anxiety is heightened to an unbearable degree by the activation of the particular phobia concerned.

Anxiety states are on the whole probably the commonest type of emotional illness to be encountered in practice. In the terms of the neurosis/psychosis distinction the anxiety state is essentially a neurosis, and the diagnosis of anxiety neurosis a synonym for anxiety state.

*

Depression, like anxiety, is of course an emotional condition with which practically all normal people are familiar. Many of us are subject to swings of mood, being at one time on the top of our form, and at another time somewhat under the weather both in spirits and in our sense of physical well-being. Severe depression in a normally well person tends to follow only upon some correspondingly severe cause for grief, such as bereavement or intense disappointment in some aspect of life. It is when the depression exceeds both in severity and in duration what can normally be regarded as appropriate to the individual's life situation that it is regarded as a form of mental illness. Occasionally the distinction has to be almost arbitrary; for example, the period during which intense grief and mourning are felt by a normally sensitive person after bereavement may vary between several weeks and several months, or even a year. But when this condition persists for over a year and colours the person's whole attitude and approach to external life and his relationship with other people, there comes a time when it must be regarded as a form of mental illness and treated in this way.

The illness of depression may in fact follow stress of this kind, or it may come apparently out of the blue, or be displayed as an excessive and abnormal counterpart of the more widely experienced fit of the blues common to so many of us. When a depression appears to be related to some recognizable stress in the patient's life, it is often spoken of as being a reactive depression. The other type, in which the source and origin of the patient's mood remain obscure, has been given the name of endogenous depression. Both types tend to have in common, in addition to the sadness which characterizes the patient's subjective feelings, some blunting and withdrawal of interest from the outside world, a general slowing up of mental and physical activity so that the patient thinks and responds to questions only with difficulty and after a struggle, and may even display a hesitation and retardation in movement as well as in thought.

The general experience of someone in this condition is so unpleasant, and the tendency to despair so strong, that such patients tend very frequently to feel that there is no hope and that life is no longer worth living. Most of them contemplate suicide at one time or another during the illness and many of them succeed in carrying it out. The physical symptoms of depression and the disturbance in general health tend also to be characteristic. The patient's facial expression is mournful or pathetic, his appetite is poor, he loses weight steadily, is often constipated, and suffers a particular type of disturbance in his sleep whereby he tends to wake early in the morning and to lie awake for several hours with his mind actively dwelling upon the most gloomy preoccupations, unable to get off to sleep again until perhaps a little before the dawn, only to awake tired and intensely miserable later in the morning.

Some patients complain rather of a loss of the power of feeling than of specifically painful or unhappy feelings all the time. They will say that they have lost the capacity to care about themselves or about those whom they love; they will describe this loss of feeling as a dreadful experience for which they may blame themselves, but their description is flat and matter-of-fact and the examiner is made aware that they simply cannot convey the depths of their despair because of the inertia, retardation, and general deadening of emotional response which has them in its grip.

In some cases this may go on to a condition of complete stupor wherein the patient sits or lies motionless and unresponsive, completely aware of what is going on around him but no longer able or disposed to do anything about it. Patients in this state may have to be dressed and undressed, washed, fed, and even in extreme cases may require nursing attention for their bladder and bowel functions which they no longer spontaneously manage for themselves.

Characteristic of most depressive illnesses is an element of withdrawal from reality, of immersion in despair, and acceptance of a feeling of helplessness and self-denunciation going far beyond the bounds of reality, which justify us in considering them even in their milder forms manifestations of psychotic illness. But there are some depressions in which the reactive element is predominant, and in which the depressive mood is mixed with anxiety in response to the stresses of external existence, and these can be described as neurotic disorders. Patients with this type of affective illness tend to blame others, or circumstances, rather than themselves, and to demand help rather than to consider themselves beyond it or unworthy of it.

It must be clear that the distinction drawn here is based upon the conception of Dr Ross already quoted, rather than upon grounds either of severity or of the need for special care and protection. But it is also true that even a severe neurotic depression, despite sincere protests of despair and of intolerable suffering, will be less likely to end in suicide than one in which the fundamental relationship to reality, and therefore to the possibility of help and the hope for ultimate recovery, has been lost.

Depressive illnesses may occur at any stage during life although they are exceedingly rare in children. They may, as we have seen, be largely reactive or largely endogenous, although they nearly always contain elements of both types, and they may occur only once or several times during the course of a lifetime. There is a classical type of recurrent depression with intervening periods of elation or even of excitement, which has been given the name of manic depressive psychosis. This is not particularly common in its classical form but is so striking when it does occur that it has earned recognition and clinical description by many observers throughout the history of psychological medicine. The nature of the depressive swings is characteristically endogenous, and retardation, self-reproach, and well-marked suicidal tendencies are very common. The manic and depressive phases may vary in duration from days or weeks to months or even years, and they may be separated by intervening periods of apparent normality, or may alternate gradually or violently without such normal phases occurring at all.

Another type of depressive illness which tends to show a distinct and characteristic pattern is that which occurs during or after the involutional period of life in men and women. This has been given the name of involutional melancholia, and some psychiatrists maintain that this diagnosis should be reserved for illnesses appearing for the first time in this period of life without evidence or history of previous depression. It is perhaps more consistent to make the diagnosis when the time of onset and nature of the illness conform to the clinical pattern, whether or not the previous history contains evidence of mood swings or frankly depressive illness.

Involutional melancholia is a particularly severe form of depression in which agitation is often a predominant feature. Such agitation, expressed by repeated importunate complaints of bodily or mental suffering, by wringing of the hands, restlessness, and lamentation, may take the place of retardation in the general picture. Hypochondriacal ideas, frequently of delusional intensity, such as those of a patient who said 'my bowels are blocked and everything inside me is going rotten and festering and poisoning me; my brain has gone and there is nothing inside my head any more; my skull has become an empty tank ...' are comparatively common.

Such patients, while often demanding or imploring help, will at the same time ceaselessly insist that nothing can be done for them, that they are unworthy to be saved, that they have committed an unpardonable sin, are truly damned and will bring grief, horror, and decay upon all connected with them. Sometimes they develop ideas of persecution, always with a strongly punitive and threatening flavour. While sitting in a ward or in the doctor's consulting room they await in terror the arrival of the executioner, or the torturers, or the van which is calling for their bodies after they have been murdered. Such ideas may be accompanied by actual hallucinations in which they hear the clank of chains or are tormented by voices accusing them, and prophesying the doom which they expect and dread. Not all these manifestations are present in every case, but the general nature of the disturbance, and above all the almost total severance from reality seen in the worst cases, and yet unaccompanied by any failure of abstract intellectual processes apart from those involved in the acceptance of delusions and hallucinations, are characteristic.

Such illnesses may occur insidiously in women at or after the menopause, in men at a corresponding time of life, exceptionally in the early forties, more commonly after the age of fifty, and they may appear to have been precipitated by some external crisis or physical illness or accident, or to have begun spontaneously. Their duration, untreated, may be confined to months, but often extends to years, and in a small proportion of cases recovery does not occur at all. These are essentially psychotic illnesses and the risk of suicide is ever present; particularly when retardation, which so often impairs the patient's capacity to take sudden and violent action, is replaced by agitation, of which such action is often the outcome. The physical changes do not differ essentially from those of depression at other times of life; the agitation differs from anxiety as an accompaniment to depression in that the pulse is slow, the skin dry rather than moist and sweating, and the patient's concern riveted upon his own preoccupations rather than expressed in a tense and startled response to outward reality.

•

The other side of the coin of depression is abnormal elation which may go on to a state of true mania. This is a very much less common form of mental illness than depression although, as we have seen, there is one form of periodic disturbance in which the two states alternate. Like depression, elation is part of the normal experience of human beings, and often only gradually and imperceptibly emerges therefrom into an abnormal degree of intensity, but when the sense of well-being and confidence not only exceeds all degree of appropriateness to the patient's life, but begins to colour and to cloud judgement and responsibility to a point at which the capacity to adjust to reality and manage affairs becomes impaired, then it constitutes a condition of illness no matter how little the patient may complain.

The mildest form of such illness is called hypomania. By contrast with the depressed, retarded, inert, apathetic patient, the person afflicted with hypomania shows elevation of mood and an acceleration and extension of his stream of thought whereby every idea is rapidly associated in his mind with a whole host of others, some relevant and logical, some linked by rhyming, punning, or alliterative connexions which in fact interfere with normal thought processes. Such a patient may say 'Yes, doctor, I see you have a watch, watch me, I'm Scotch, do you like Scotch toffee, or coffee?... What a lot of nonsense this is, but really you know I think too rapidly, it's marvellous how I do it but I do it, I knew it, I knew I'd do it...' interspersing this type of conversation with winks and giggles and often displaying a gaiety which, at first infectious, may rapidly become tiresome or exhausting. This flight of ideas is accompanied by a pressure of talk and often of action.

The patients are restless and excitable, cannot sleep, will often not be bothered with food and must always be busy, dashing purposelessly about, taking up one activity after another. Such a patient may plan or launch a hundred tasks and then, constantly abandoning one to embark upon another, finish none while seeming to thrive upon the mounting chaos of his own contrivance.

In more severe cases complete physical collapse from lack of sleep and nourishment may follow, unless treatment controls the situation. While gaiety and good will often form the superficial characteristics of the patient's mood, irritability and exasperation are apt to be provoked by the slightest attempt to control or restrain him. Great tact is therefore necessary in handling such patients.

The severest form of the disorder is mania, wherein the patient is uncontrollably excited, while flight of ideas and pressure of talk may render him incoherent. Violence and exasperation may lead to homicidal assaults by such patients upon those who endeavour to control them, and in these extreme conditions hallucinations and delusions are again apt to occur. Maniacal excitement is, however, a comparatively rare condition, and the term maniac one which springs far more readily to the mind of the layman than to that of the doctor.

Far more common in everyday practice are states of anxiety and depression of various kinds, although it seems possible that in more primitive societies the incidence of manic or abnormally elated and excited states approaches that of states of depression. The inference sometimes drawn from this remarkable preponderance of states of anxiety and depression over wild excitement or senseless glee in modern civilization may not be misleading. But in assessing the significance of observations of this kind at least as much attention must be paid to the creed and traditions of a society as to its more recently acquired cultural standards and present way of life. Moreover, even when the form taken by an illness is manic or hypomanic, the provocative stresses will almost always be found to have been unpleasant, rather than enjoyable for the patient: no one in fact ever goes mad with joy.

*

The second great group of functional mental disorders includes all those illnesses which approach more closely the layman's idea of true madness. The generic name for this group of disorders is schizophrenia; and we have already seen that this was the name coined by Bleuler in 1911 to designate all cases of functional mental disturbance with the exception of the affective mental disorders already described. In his subsequent monograph he actually narrowed this concept considerably and thereby gave it increased usefulness and meaning. It superseded entirely dementia praecox, which had been used by Kraepelin to cover a vast collection of mental illnesses which he believed could be characterized by their onset at or about adolescence, and their uniformly progressive and ominous course ending in dementia.

The word schizophrenia is derived from two Greek words, $\sigma\chi\iota\zeta\omega$ and $\phi\rho\acute{\eta}\nu$, and means a splitting of the personality. The first Greek root is familiar in the word schism, and the second originally meant the diaphragm, which as we have already seen was regarded at one time by Greek physicians as the bodily seat of feeling. The kind of splitting of the personality envisaged by the term schizophrenia is therefore essentially one of feeling, a disintegration of the emotional stability of the patient, and it is impossible to imagine any single term which could better indicate and exemplify the process of this disease.

Schizophrenia can best be regarded as a form of mental illness displayed by human beings subjected to various kinds of stress and meeting it with various constitutional handicaps which even now are not fully understood. It may appear in childhood or in adolescence, as Kraepelin believed: but it may also appear later in life, and what are called syndromes characteristic of schizophrenic illness, that is, collections of symptoms presenting a picture identical with developing schizophrenia, may be produced by some forms of organic illness or temporarily by certain drugs such as mescalin. This makes it possible to regard schizophrenia as a vast collection of morbid reactions of a particular kind, in the same way in which we now regard epilepsy as a collection of forms of normal response of mammalian brains to abnormal stress. There is, however, this difference. The epileptic convulsion can be evoked from every living creature possessing the mammalian type of brain, under suitable stimulation, as well as appearing spontaneously in a small proportion of all such creatures; schizophrenia, on the other hand, seems to be a form of morbid reaction not inherent in all human beings but possibly dependent for its production upon certain specific constitutional or hereditary factors without which the full picture will not develop, its place being taken by some other form of mental illness such as an affective disorder.

Besides those illnesses running their course through mental and emotional disintegration to dementia, singled out by Kraepelin as characteristic, Bleuler recognized that a single attack of the illness could occur and be followed by complete recovery. His own words were: 'This disease may come to a standstill at any age, and many of its symptoms may clear up very much or altogether, but if it progresses it leads to dementia of a definite character.' What is most common to all forms of schizophrenia is a progressive deterioration of the entire personality, involving most strikingly emotional life and displaying itself by disorder of thought, of feeling, and of action. Except in the terminal stages formal intelligence is not impaired when the co-operation of the patient can be secured for its testing. What have been described as the basic symptoms of schizophrenia (Lewis) are (1) disorder of thinking, (2) emotional incongruity, (3) hallucinations, (4) disturbed impulses or conduct.

The disorders of thinking may be many, and may so interrupt or influence the mental life of the patient as to make contact with the examiner or with friends and relatives almost impossible. These patients can become totally inaccessible to the normal processes of inquiry or conversation, not only because they themselves are no longer interested in or able to accept the words and attitudes of others who seek to communicate with them, but also because their own mental processes have become so bizarre and extraordinary as to defy completely the normal efforts of imagination, whereby we put ourselves in the other fellow's place when holding a conversation and interpreting the replies we receive. What is fundamental in approaching the problem of schizophrenia is the necessity to appreciate that the schizophrenic patient lives in a totally different world to our own, and even those aspects of objective reality which he still perceives may have quite a different significance for him to that which they have for us, and for those whose minds and feelings we understand.

One example of thought disorder which will illustrate this

consists in what are called ideas of reference. These are notions which, for the patient, have the certainty of complete conviction, that virtually everything that is going on relates to his own life and feelings in some special way. The smoke from the neighbouring chimneys is a signal to his friends or his enemies; a paragraph in a newspaper dealing with a cattle show is a subtle and deliberate attack on the reputation of his wife and children; the advertisements on the buses, the visits of the postman to other houses, the sound of traffic and the ringing of bicycle bells are all woven into the substance of some vast incomprehensible cosmic plan directed entirely towards his own life and problems. Small wonder that these patients display perplexity and bewilderment as they contemplate their extraordinary fate.

Another form of interference with their thinking is known as thought blocking. Their stream of thought may be suddenly cut off so that they forget completely what was in their minds and either experience a sensation of subjective blankness or receive an entirely new and apparently unrelated idea which may have the force of a revelation. This shows itself in conversation by constant interruption in the flow of talk with a resumption along totally different lines. The associations of normal thought are impaired and become distorted by all manner of haphazard connexions, some of which resemble the punning and rhyming associations of mania, others leading to the most remarkable incongruities and non-sequiturs in the course of conversation; for example, a patient said: 'There is coffee for breakfast this morning so I need not wear my stockings.' Another remark made with evident concern was: 'If I were to go away from here you would arrest me after I had gone and then there would be no more peas in the river. I am conscious of things but if you stretch words too far they become paralogs. There are too many boxes to put in the coffin.' The more abstruse and complicated these thoughts become the more necessary it may be for the patient to coin new words to symbolize a meaning for which his experience can find no parallel. Such neologisms, as they are called, are frequent in the speech and writing of schizophrenic patients, and bear a striking resemblance to the work of some modern poets.

One of the consequences of thought disorder is the formation of delusions which may be elaborate and systematic, or as bizarre and incongruous as the words in which the patient describes them. They have in common the same tendency already exemplified by ideas of reference, to relate always to the patient, and to bring all events into some connexion bearing upon him. They tend also to bear some relationship to previous fears or knowledge and to include often elements of popular prejudices or preoccupations; for example, activities attributed to the Jews, or the Jesuits, or the C.I.D., or the Nazis, or the Communists, may form the background to some of the more commonplace ideas of persecution. Similarly the feelings of influence may be ascribed to electricity or more recently still to radar or the atomic bomb. There are often areas of consciousness uninvaded by delusions at least for a time. Dealing with these, the patient may seem perfectly sensible and logical. The degree of conviction with which the delusions are held varies considerably, as will be seen when we mention some of the more specific types of delusional illness such as paranoia. The more ill the patient, the more disintegrated his personality, the more disordered, unrelated, and chaotic are his delusions likely to be.

Emotional incongruity is often a most striking feature. Apart from his bewilderment and perplexity already mentioned, the patient may show astonishingly little concern about the uncanny nightmarish life which he describes as his own. Ominous revelations, often delivered by hosts of hallucinatory voices constantly intruding upon his thoughts, manipulation of his body and sensations by electricity, witchcraft, or telepathy, and even the constellation of the whole universe being brought to bear upon his single and defenceless mind, may produce not despair or even violent alarm so much as querulous irritation or a certain aloof suspiciousness. He may announce some terrible disaster, such as the boiling and subsequent eating of his parents or children, with quizzical blandness, or upon learning of the actual death of some loved person may giggle and say 'Serve her right, she always was careless about her shoes.' There is often a shallowness, but sometimes an alarming depth and intensity of mood, which seems unrelated to the patient's thoughts or ideas in so far as he is able to reveal them. But the outcome of suspiciousness or persecutory delusions may sometimes be impulsive murderous attacks, just as the response to some mysterious vision or message may be a state of ecstasy striking and evident, but transcending the power of the observer to share or in any way experience.

Hallucinations themselves are common although by no means essential in the clinical picture. Most frequently they take the form of voices repeating the patient's thoughts, explaining, praising, criticizing, abusing, or ridiculing his actions even before he acts, thereby often distracting him so much that no outward action follows; but visual hallucinations including quasi-mystical experiences are not particularly rare. Sensory hallucinations are probably responsible for the common delusions of electrical or radio-active stimulation, and may lead to belief that the patient is being erotically caressed by invisible admirers. Such conditions may at one and the same time form the subject of vigorous complaints and obvious satisfaction. This preoccupation with a vivid but unreal world, of course, releases the patient from the demands and limits of normal existence, and this withdrawal from reality underlies almost all the symptoms.

We saw in an earlier chapter that it was part of the normal emotional response to be capable of both love and hostility towards the same person, although in the normal person such feelings are rarely fully present in consciousness in equal proportions at the same time. In the schizophrenic, love and hate, trust and suspicion, joy and sorrow, terror and confidence, may coexist or alternate so rapidly as to be indistinguishable in the patient's mind. It is not hard to see how such a chaos of mental and emotional existence can lead to impulsive action or eminently bizarre and incomprehensible behaviour.

When I was a child I remember being told by some companion, drawing presumably on vivid imagination rather than experience, about the inhabitants of the local lunatic asylum. One of them, I was informed, believed himself to be a hatstand, and stood about all day with raised arms desiring only that visitors would make use of him. Another was reputed to believe himself to be a teapot and to adopt a posture with the left arm curved like the spout before him and the right hand upon his hip as the handle. In this position he was said to squat, constantly asking to be poured out. There are no patients quite as conventionally mad as this, but it is among the chronic deteriorated schizophrenic group that we come closest to seeing bizarre and pathetic spectacles of this kind. For as their grip upon reality progressively weakens and the content of their minds becomes more and more primitive, jumbled, chaotic, and confused, they may in fact assume and maintain for years postures symbolic of some inner stress or experience, just as in the earlier and more acute stages of the illness they may seek to convey otherwise incommunicable feelings and ideas by fantastic gestures, speech, and action.

The underlying concept which will help to explain the whole picture of schizophrenia is one of withdrawal from reality, in which thinking, feeling, and action are no longer dominated by contact with other people or outside events, but are given over entirely to a world of fantasy whose only counterpart in the experience of normal people is the world of dreams. Professor Jung has said 'The schizophrenic is a dreamer in a world awake'; and just as in dreams we have only to fear or sometimes to desire some extraordinary event for it to take place, a closed door to open and reveal something utterly dreaded, yet inevitably approached, so, too, it would seem, is the schizophrenic both the creator and the victim of his own fantastic world. When he recognizes others they are made a part of it in his mind; when he does not, they are as a rule powerless to reach him.

One composite clinical picture may illustrate this sharply: A young man of twenty-seven who had always been rather shy and disinclined to mix, got engaged to be married and soon afterwards began keeping strange hours and became irregular and unreliable at his work. One day he locked himself in his room, kept the light on all night and was heard pacing and muttering before appearing at the window calling for help. When his family gained entrance to his room they found him alternately ecstatic and apprehensive, maintaining that his sins had been purged, that he was about to prepare a new heaven and a new earth. He had murdered his fiancée, so he said, and sacrificed her for the purity of all mankind, to overcome his enemies who were trying to debase him sexually with electric thoughts and waves of influence played upon his spine. He was not sure whether they were inspired by Buckingham Palace or by the Kremlin, but it was essential to take action at once to save the immortal hostages.

At first he resisted violently any attempt to remove him to hospital but later craved protection, and claimed that through the supernatural power granted to him, and the obedience of the doctor, the forces of light had triumphed over those of darkness, although the price that he himself might have to pay could not as yet be reckoned. Within a few days he had begun pursing up his lips and continually peering at himself in the mirror. For a time he would trust no one enough to confide the reasons for this, but eventually told the doctor in an interview that he had begun to turn into a wolf so that he might eat his young, shortly to be born to his fiancée whom he had brought back from the dead. This would complete his sacrifice and diminish the fuel cuts necessary in the Borough of Wandsworth.

He wrote pages of letters, advice, and petitions with many bizarre sentences and words of his own invention. He abandoned all care for his physical appearance, refused to shave because 'that would be exposing myself to the rays – I suppose that is why you want me to do it,' and on one occasion smeared his body and bed with excrement. After a few weeks he settled down, and, while he still spent much of his time in restless endeavours to escape the persecutory rays and the interference with his thoughts, adopting various bizarre postures to this end, he could sometimes contrive a few hours of peace during which he produced beautiful lettered drawings of inventions, such as a machine for dragging gold from the bottom of the sea with magnetic anchors. It was this which had excited the envy and admiration of Buckingham Palace and the Kremlin....

The subsequent course of such a patient's illness would be immensely modified by his response to modern forms of treatment, with which we shall be concerned in a later chapter. The purpose of this brief sketch has been to illustrate some of the processes already described, and to enable the reader by an effort of imagination to experience a little of that sense of mystery, horror, and alarm, an awareness of something altogether uncanny and grotesque, which such patients inspire in those neither trained nor able to accept their plight as the tragic illness which in fact it is.

There are a number of physical changes connected with schizophrenia which have been extensively studied and which continue to form the basis for one avenue of research into this subject. In so far as they are evident upon clinical examination and contribute to the descriptive picture for which this chapter is designed, they may be mentioned now. They include a lankness and drabness of the hair and often a greasy, blotchy complexion, with a sluggish circulation particularly evident in the extremities and leading to blueness or a purplish mottling of the limbs, tip of the nose, and ears. There may be variations from the normal in body temperature and there is often loss of weight in the acute stages with fatness if the illness becomes chronic. Menstruation in women is commonly disturbed as it is in many psychological disorders, and in some forms of schizophrenia stupor, more profound in effect than that seen in depression, but not necessarily involving loss of consciousness, may be seen.

In general, the schizophrenic tends to have a low blood pressure, and his heart rate and circulation time are slow; these findings have been regarded in general terms as defects of adaptive efficiency, which correspond to the failure of normal emotional response. It is, in fact, as though the schizophrenic patient were living at the most depleted level of exchange with his external environment which is possible for him; in his lowered metabolism, just as in his deficient or inappropriate emotional responsiveness, he is like a hibernating animal.

Of the clinical varieties of schizophrenia it is perhaps sufficient to mention the three main forms. The first includes the hebephrenic or simple types, which, varying in severity, are characterized by an early onset, a chronic course, and all too often an eventual dementia which may persist for many years, these being the types which earned from Kraepelin the name of dementia praecox. Kraepelin, however, did not distinguish this form from the two remaining main groups. The second group are called catatonic forms of schizophrenia and include the wildly bizarre postures and activities of the obvious madman, which may alternate with periods of complete stupor and withdrawal. They have the most favourable prognosis and a single attack may be over in a matter of weeks or months and never recur. The third form comprises all those disorders which at one time were considered entirely separately from schizophrenia and called paranoia.

Paranoid illness is distinguished by the pre-eminence of delusions of persecution which may be logical and systematic, and could even be accepted as entirely reasonable were their premises to be true. Such delusions may remain fixed and apparently unalterable without subsequent deterioration or disintegration of the personality; but far more commonly there is an eventual insidious and progressive disorder of thought and feeling, sometimes accompanied by hallucinations and a splitting up and crumbling of the existing delusions into diverse and inconsistent fragments so that the final picture resembles that of a comparatively well preserved hebephrenic form. To quote Lewis once again: 'The more bizarre the delusions, the more likely is affective emptiness to replace gradually the initial resentment and distress, but sometimes the patient passes into a chronic paranoid state, obviously schizophrenic to the psychiatrist but compatible with ordinary life outside a hospital.'

*

The reference made in the section on schizophrenia to paranoia virtually covers all we need to say on this subject. There are, however, experts in mental illness who favour the meaning given to this term by Kraepelin. He described paranoia as the endogenous insidious development of a permanent unshakeable delusional system, with complete preservation of clarity and order in thought, will, and action.

In point of fact such an illness with such a course is exceedingly rare. Moreover, the ultimate state reached by patients with this condition who neither get well nor succeed in encapsulating their delusional system sufficiently to be able to live with it in the external world, is one of schizophrenia. Minor forms of the paranoid attitude are seen in people who are not insane in the legal sense at all. It is a normal mechanism of the mental life of human beings, when troubled by doubts or shame as to their physical or moral integrity, or the nature of certain actions about which they are sensitive, for example, masturbation, to project these doubts and shameful or guilty feelings on to others in their environment and to come to believe that others are criticizing them for being puny or dirty or nasty. An example is the common, but of course totally false, belief on the part of any men who do masturbate that evidence of this behaviour is visible in their eyes to anyone who cares to look.

Similarly, it sometimes happens that desires as well as fears, particularly if these are not easy for the person to acknowledge even to himself, may become the subject of such ideas. The old maid who looks under the bed in fear or in hope that she may find a man hiding there is a classical if vulgar example of projection of this kind. Personal resentment or mortification is more often projected than accepted by human beings. One's troubles are usually someone else's fault. 'They' are responsible and we are not going to let 'them' get away with it. Some people become quarrelsome and even litigious and waste a great deal of their own and everyone else's time in pursuing outside themselves grievances whose origin is often within the structure of their own personality. The barrack-room lawyer forms an example. There is, however, no absolute dividing line between people of this kind and those who are sensitive to and detest injustice or inhumanity of any kind, and who will spare no effort to denounce and oppose it.

We have already seen that even the most bizarre and distorted mechanisms of schizophrenic thought and behaviour may have a common basis in the inherent response of human personality to excessive stress, just as more obviously the affective disorders are exaggerated and distorted manifestations of normal human emotional experience. So, too, paranoid mechanisms exist and can be activated in all of us to some degree. In some they may become part of a habitual response to difficulty, and in a few may become uncontrollable, self-perpetuating, and constitute a form of insanity.

*

A third great group of functional disturbances which await our attention can be regarded as including obsessional disorders, hysteria, and the whole array of what have been called character disorders and lumped together under the all-embracing term 'psychopathic personality'.

Obsessional or obsessive compulsive illnesses are those in which the patient develops ideas or impulses to behave in certain ways from which he cannot free himself, but which he recognizes both as abnormal, distasteful, and essentially to be resisted. Such ideas or impulses commonly have a somewhat ritualistic flavour; for example, the need to count the number of steps one ascends or descends every day, or to do everything three times or to repeat certain phrases before undertaking certain normal daily tasks. That this again is a mental mechanism in some degree inherent in us all becomes apparent when we remember how frequently, in childhood, games involving just such rituals appealed to us or even dominated our behaviour from time to time.

Such games as walking on all or none of the lines on the pavement, of touching every lamp post or every other lamp post as we passed, form part of the recollections of childhood of very many people. Sometimes a purely verbal injunction has to be repeated and may even be written out and placed where it can be seen. I remember a boy who occupied the desk in front of me when I was at school, aged about ten, who used to repeat every morning in a solemn voice a small incantation which he had prepared for himself to increase his efficiency. This was the phrase 'I must work, I must not shirk.' I was fascinated to observe this humble couplet pinned to the inside of his desk. So far from increasing his efficiency it seemed to trouble him and increase the difficulty which he already encountered in some of his lessons. It was in fact a minor example of an obsessional attitude with a particularly evident symptom, but he was a child and he may well have outgrown it or found other more fruitful and constructive ways of dealing with his disinclination for certain aspects of his life.

Obsessional ideas may be replaced by mental images; these may reflect some particularly horrifying or disgusting scene against which the patient rebels but which, like the fancied man under the old maid's bed, may in fact represent a forbidden wish. This wish may be obscene or simply rebellious, and, although the patient's authorship of the wish cannot be denied, his opposition to it and his distress when it is thus conveyed to him in symbolic form by his own mind is absolutely sincere and unfeigned.

Obsessional impulses may be even more alarming. For example, a nurse may feel a recurrent impulse to strike or stab children entrusted to her care. It is characteristic of the illness that she will always be able to control this impulse although it may become so strong and so disturbing as to render her completely unfit for work or even normal existence while it persists. It is in this way that the obsessional patient differs from the schizophrenic who, under similar circumstances, would be all too likely to carry out the impulsive act and murder or mutilate some innocent person without being in any way able to control himself.

Obsessional tendencies may become associated with morbid fears of the kind discussed under the heading of anxiety, and many phobias have an obsessional character. Not only is the fear associated with a certain act or possibility distressing in itself; it is also the subject of painful and incessant preoccupation. Rumination is another aspect of the mental process of obsessional patients. Not only may they ponder ceaselessly and unproductively upon the obscene, threatening, or disagreeable ideas, images, and impulses which may assail them, but they may also spend a great deal of time turning over in their minds all manner of unprofitable speculations of an interminable and quasi-metaphysical kind. 'Why is the world?' was a question to which one patient could find no answer but from which he could find no relief. Another was preoccupied with the nature of the absolute essence of all reality, a preoccupation which was again in no way a search for mystical experience or the apprehension of truth as understood by poets or philosophers, but was rather an intensely tedious and wholly disagreeable examination and re-examination of the words contained in the question.

Obsessional ruminations of this kind, compulsions to descend every flight of stairs a fixed number of times and the inescapable tendency to encounter unpleasant thoughts at all times during one's daily life, are all understandably depressing experiences. Obsessional patients tend therefore to be depressed and to blame themselves for what they are all too ready to recognize is the 'silliness' and 'uselessness' of their preoccupations; but these can drive them to suicide and in some cases can render them helpless to carry out their daily tasks, earn a living or care for a home, and can reduce them to a condition of impotent inaction, bogged down in labyrinthine ruminations or endless and agonizing indecision.

*

Hysteria has been called the most psychogenic of all illnesses, this description implying that the causes which produce it are ultimately entirely emotional while the physical changes which accompany it, when they are present at all, are essentially secondary and completely reversible. The underlying basis of hysteria is always the same: it is the attempt, never fully conscious and frequently completely unconscious on the part of the patient, to obtain some advantage from the representation of symptoms of illness. The advantage may be totally illusory and the symptoms both painful and crippling; but the principle underlying the illness remains the same.

In the most superficial types of hysterical illness, the advantage tends to be comparatively obvious to the dispassionate observer while the symptoms directed towards it may be equally transparent. It may indeed be difficult to draw a hard and fast line between conscious deliberate malingering on the one hand and the more superficial type of hysterical illness on the other hand. Nevertheless true malingering is exceedingly rare if only because of the capacity inherent in every human being to believe what seems to be necessary or desirable to him; hysteria by contrast is comparatively common.

Just as we saw a little earlier that the stylized conventional idea of madness as represented by patients believing themselves to be teapots or hatstands is a popular fiction rather than a real form of mental illness, so an 'attack of hysteria' very rarely takes the form of the wild laughing and crying so frequently represented in the novelette or the cinema. The form taken by hysterical illness will in fact be determined by a combination of factors, of which the most important are the particular stresses to which the patient has been subjected and from which he wishes to escape, and the conception which he has formed of the illness which is to provide this escape. Another important contributory factor is the capacity of the symptom which finally emerges not simply to solve the patient's difficulties or conflict but also to symbolize for him the sort of solution which is emotionally acceptable even though in fact it may be unobtainable.

For example, a young woman who had spent some years looking after a depressed and hypochondriacal aunt for whom she had very little affection developed a severe and alarming illness within a few months of the aunt's death. A striking feature of this illness was the patient's tendency to collapse and lie shaking and gurgling on the ground or the nearest bed, with her legs and arms twitching and her sides heaving with panic-stricken efforts to get her breath. During these attacks she was overwhelmed with a conviction of impending death and a sense of a crushing weight upon her body. In the course of investigating and treating this illness it became apparent that during the long period of her attendance upon her aunt she had from time to time brought a lover into the house, and that upon the night of her aunt's death she had been with him. She had heard her aunt calling to her until this lady was on the point of death, and on reaching her side had felt overwhelmed with guilt and shame at her neglect. The aunt had in fact taken her own life by swallowing an overdose of sedative and this further, although unreasonably, increased the patient's feeling of self-reproach and inadequacy. Shortly after the aunt's death she had been abandoned by her lover and had felt increasingly lonely and afraid.

The illness, for all the unpleasantness of its immediate effects upon her, secured for her interest, attention, and sympathy, provided a partial sense of atonement by suffering for her guilt, and incidentally symbolized the more vivid and spectacular aspects of the death-bed scene and what had immediately preceded it. She had been conscious of none of this at the time when her symptoms brought her under medical care. A further illustration of the way in which hysterical symptoms may symbolize or repeat some aspects of the stress responsible for them is provided by the fact that this patient in the course of treatment in hospital at one time began to develop an addiction to the same type of sedative as her aunt had used; this of course occurred before a detailed knowledge of the background to the illness had been gained; once full understanding of the significance of this symptom was reached it became possible to stop all sedatives without any catastrophic effects.

A form of hysterical illness of particular importance may arise in connexion with accidents for which compensation is claimed and either disputed or not finally settled in amount. There is frequently physical damage as a result of the accident, but long after this has healed symptoms identical with those experienced by the patient during the earlier stages of disability persist and may even become more severe. These are often accompanied by anxiety but in some cases may be regarded by the patient with surprising equanimity. Writing of hysterical symptoms in general Janet referred to their complacent acceptance by the patient as characteristic and gave it the name of *belle indifférence*.

The underlying mechanism in such cases is essentially a sincere conflict in the mind of the patient which he is unable to solve: its basis is the desire to resume work and accept recovery on the one hand, which is opposed by grave misgivings on the other hand as to whether he will really be as fit as he was before the accident and whether, if he resumes work and finds that he is not as fit, he will be able to re-establish a valid claim either to sympathy, consideration, or further financial compensation for his sufferings.

Such cases are exceedingly difficult to treat since so much depends upon the patient's confidence not simply in his physician, or the fairness or generosity of those responsible for compensation, but ultimately in himself; and it is the underlying failure of confidence in himself which all too often produces and maintains the hysterical disability. Nevertheless, the actual position of the patient is often infinitely less satisfactory than if he were able to accept recovery and earn a wage which may be two or three times the compensation he is receiving. The gain derived from the illness is therefore only partial and insubstantial, and the fact that the patient clings desperately to it needs to be accepted as further evidence that he is truly ill, no matter how complete and evident may be his physical recovery.

In general the symptoms of hysteria are as varied and manifold as human concepts of illness in all its forms can be. Every conceivable disorder of sensation or muscular power may be encountered, and there exists a recognized group of hysterical illnesses in which the simulation of insanity, epilepsy, fainting attacks, or prolonged unconsciousness may be the central feature. The problem of recognition of hysterical illness is sometimes baffling and complicated, particularly if the organic illness simulated is one with which the patient has become familiar. Repeated medical examinations may themselves define and further impress the pattern of a specific organic condition upon the patient's symptoms. Treatment also can be exceedingly difficult because the problem is far more than the removal of symptoms which may yield to various methods to be described.

Ideally the aim of treatment must be to gain the patient's acceptance of the nature of the illness and to enable him to acquire not simply recognition of the origin of his symptoms but awareness of the underlying problems and an ability to solve them along less wholly unsatisfactory lines. Unless this is done the patient will not only resist attempts to cure him, since they threaten to deprive him of his last defence against insoluble problems, but may react catastrophically if, despite resistance, symptoms are abolished without further help or understanding being provided.

I have known such a patient, spectacularly cured of a hysterical paralysis, commit suicide the same evening. The paralysis in this case had been the last desperate effort to stave off defeat by an underlying depression which threatened both his capacity to work and his whole conception of his future as a family man and a provider. Hysterical symptoms are not uncommon as the means whereby other more subtle, serious, and insidious illnesses announce themselves. They may be seen in the early stages of schizophrenia or of organic brain disease, such as cerebral tumour, as well as in many other conditions. Often because of their crudity or transparency to all but the patient, they provoke contempt and hostility, but always they are a warning that a human being in distress has found no better solution than a partial surrender. To unmask them is easy. To restore to true health the patient displaying them is often exacting and difficult, but there can be no real dispute about which way the doctor's duty lies.

*

The final group of people of whom an account must be given in any study of abnormal mental life and behaviour, are those whose disturbance is evident not so much in their own minds or feelings but in their conduct and in the adjustment they make between themselves and the rest of the world. Here belong the ne'er-do-wells, the spongers, and that unhappy desperate section of criminal society who offend repeatedly and are as repeatedly punished without the experience affecting their subsequent behaviour in any way except perhaps to make it more hopeless and embittered. These people have been called psychopaths, but the term is widely and sometimes contradictorily defined, and rests as much upon the exclusion of more established forms of mental illness as upon anything else. Two things can, however, usually be said about the disturbance of the psychopathic personality. One is that this disturbance is characteristically life-long and usually begins not later than adolescence, the other is that it appears to rest upon certain physical and emotional factors whose origin we have yet adequately to define or discover.

On the physical side the most striking feature is the high proportion of such people who display a pattern of electrical activity in their brain, recordable by a special instrument, which has come to be recognized as evidence of immature function and resembles that normally seen only in children. Another line of study which recently has led to a striking contribution towards the recognition of the physical characteristics of the psychopath has been the study of the formation of capillary loops in the nail bed. These again show immature forms in a significantly high proportion of cases.

On the mental side the outstanding feature is emotional imma-turity in its broadest and most comprehensive sense. These people are impulsive, feckless, unwilling to accept the results of experi-ence and unable to profit by them, sometimes prodigal of effort but utterly lacking in persistence, plausible but insincere, demanding but indifferent to appeals, dependable only in their constant unreliability, faithful only to infidelity, rootless, unstable, rebellious, and unhappy. A survey of their lives will reveal an endless succession of jobs, few of which have been held for more than six months, many of which have been abandoned after a few days; very little love but often a great number of adventures, very little happiness despite a ruthless and determined pursuit of immediate gratification. Such patients are all too often their own worst enemies and nobody's real friend. If, as sometimes happens, they are distinguished by some outstanding gift or talent they may achieve apparently spectacular success only to throw it away or spoil it at least for themselves by their turbulent and exacting emotional attitude. More frequently, despite a level of intelligence which is as often above average as below, they drift from failure and disappointment through one lost opportunity after another into drug addiction, alcoholism, suicide, or prostitution.

Sexual perversion, which may be acquired in the same way as neurosis, is often found among psychopaths, but by no means all sexually inverted people are psychopathic, nor are all psychopaths sexually abnormal in this sense. What in fact is characteristic of the psychopath's attitude to sexual emotion and experience is this same shallowness and immaturity combined with a frequently disastrous opportunism, which may lead not merely to the prostitution already mentioned but also to deliberate perversions, to wanton repeated and joyless seduction, and many of the more grotesque and outrageous sexual crimes.

Innumerable attempts to classify psychopathic personality have been made. Perhaps the most successful is that which divides all psychopaths into two great overlapping groups, the aggressive and the inadequate. Aggressive psychopaths include the violent, quarrelsome, unstable alcoholics, the bullies, sadists, and most of the recidivists with a consistent record of violent crime; the inadequate group embraces all the minor delinquents, confidence tricksters, and social misfits whose plight constitutes a tremendous problem for society as well as for their families and dependants. Such people in the course of their troubled and catastrophic lives are particularly liable to encounter stresses, frequently of their own contriving, for which they can provide only neurotic solutions; it is by no means uncommon for a psychopath to seek help not for his general disorder of personality and character but for the particular anxiety state or hysterical illness to which his way of life has at this point inevitably brought him. Running through the lives of patients with this fundamental disability seems to be a consistent impulse towards destruction; destruction of their hopes and happiness and ultimately of their health and their lives; a destruction all the more consistently sought because the apparent motives for most of the actions which lead them from one disaster to another are immediate satisfaction or short-term gain.

Sometimes the underlying tendency is wholly unconscious. At others it may emerge with startling clarity, as in these words of an aggressive psychopath in prison: 'I get moods of hating people: I want to kill them . . . I've beaten up women I never saw before in my life – and men. People get on my nerves – I don't trust anybody.

'I beat up my wife and children – and a woman I lived with – nearly killed her. I tell you there are times when I just can't stand people: if they don't leave me alone I'll murder someone. . .'

Insight of this kind is in fact by no means uncommon, and in the inadequate type of psychopath may take the form of an accurate and categorical denunciation of past misfortunes and present tendencies, coupled with vigorous assertions that while they know perfectly well the probable consequences of their disastrous impulses, they are unable at the time to *feel* anything but the urge to which they promptly yield. Indeed they may appear afterwards to be sincerely remorseful and contrite. But like the other manifestations of psychopathic behaviour the feeling behind the gesture is fundamentally egocentric, and the gesture itself where it involves other people is apt to be correspondingly insincere. Despite the somewhat gloomy and discouraging picture created by this description it must be said there exists a strong tendency for the more violent or vulnerable psychopathic traits to improve with the passage of time; this is matched by a similar trend towards stabilization and the emergence of a more normal pattern in the electro-encephalogram, the instrument used for recording electrical activity in the brain and mentioned a little while back. Both the genesis and the treatment of that pattern of behaviour disturbance which we call psychopathic personality or character neurosis will concern us again in later chapters, but in their variety, pathos, and sporadically savage and violent lovelessness, these patients, for patients they really are, constitute one of the most formidable challenges, not simply to medicine but to mankind.

A Consideration of Causes

THE previous chapter has shown how manifold are the ways in which mental life may become abnormal. The causes for this abnormality are at least as varied, but while it is helpful to consider them under a number of apparently separate headings there is no mental illness in which at least some overlapping between a number of causal factors does not occur.

Following the scheme used in Chapter 4, we can consider the two main groups of causes as organic and functional. Included in the organic group, in addition to the factors of physical illness, injury, and intoxication by alcohol, drugs, and poisons already mentioned, are hereditary factors and the constitutional physical endowment of the individual; while the functional group will contain both the vitally important social and environmental factors, and the individual contribution of the patient's own personality, his innate psychological assets and liabilities, and his acquired patterns of response.

Among the members of the first group of causes perhaps the factor most readily accepted by the general public is that of heredity. The unhappy relations of a patient with a severe mental illness may search their own and the patient's family history for evidence of bad stock or of some dreaded characteristic running through the family tree. If their search is sufficiently thorough they will be certain to discover a number of skeletons in the family cupboard, for there is no family cupboard which, carefully inspected, will not reveal some. In discussing a member of their family with a mental illness, and sometimes even in answering the questions of a doctor about their own and the patient's ancestry, they may be tempted to conceal or to forget what seem to them the more discreditable blots on the family escutcheon. Yet just as it is true that such blots occur in all families without exception, although in many they are never revealed to those members of the family who can be kept in ignorance, it is equally true that such studies as have been made upon the effect of heredity in mental illness have provided invaluable information, and are always important and worth while if properly conducted. It is with the nature of this information that we are now concerned.

Accurate statistical data about human inheritance are comparatively rare. Professor D. K. Henderson commenting on this remarks: 'Human families with their long interval between generations and the small number of their members do not lend themselves to studies in heredity. Moreover, it is often necessary to collect data about ancestors on a hearsay basis only. Such terms as nervousness, irritability, and so on, especially as given by lay persons, can have little value. Yet, in spite of the inevitable lack of exactitude, we are certain that the hereditary factor is of great importance.' The first essential in making statistical studies, as we saw in Chapter 3, is to compare the results of any supposedly abnormal group with those of a normal group chosen at random but comparable so far as possible in every way, except that directly under investigation, with the group that is to be studied.

Using this method a comparison of the family histories of 370 patients with psychotic illnesses with those of an equal number of normal people, made by Dr Koller at the end of the last century, revealed a history of psychosis, alcoholism, and abnormal character amounting to personality disorder, in a somewhat higher proportion in the families of the psychotic group. The study was planned to cover not only the type of hereditary involvement already mentioned but also evidence of other illnesses in the family; but these, on analysis of the results, seemed to be less significant since they were virtually equally represented in each group: they included apoplexy, senile dementia, and a number of forms of organic neurological illness. Taking the total figures for hereditary involvement in both groups of family history for all the disorders mentioned, percentages worked out as follows: psychotic group – hereditary involvement in 76·8 per cent of the families; normal group – involvement in 59 per cent of the families. The implication contained in the latter figure, that at least two-thirds of the normal population have a family history including some major nervous or mental illness, is certainly not exaggerated.

Apart from some of the more technical although valid criticisms of this method of study its practical value is less than that of studies devoted to the investigation of particular types of illness, in so far as these can be accurately performed. A more recent study of mental defect in the United States showed that of some 9,500 patients who were in some way or another feeble-minded there was a familial incidence of alcoholism of 32 per cent, of organic nervous diseases of 36 per cent, and of psychotic illness of about 30 per cent. A committee appointed to examine the case for sterilization of the mentally unfit, giving its evidence in a document called the Brock Report, which has since been widely quoted and misquoted, recorded that of 8,841 children whose parents were defective, almost one quarter had died in infancy. Of the remaining children, studies could be made on 3,650, of whom between 40 and 45 per cent were themselves mentally defective.

This type of investigation, despite an obvious weakness of method whereby numbers of different types of mental defect, including some almost undoubtedly due to injury at birth, all tend to be swept up and labelled under one heading, can none the less be accepted as presumptive evidence of hereditary factors in mental deficiency. To obtain a more refined idea of the significance of heredity, and the means whereby mental illness or the predisposition to breakdown of one kind or another may be inherited, the approach to the analysis of hereditary data based upon the Mendelian theory is essential.

The Abbé Mendel was a monk who spent much of his spare time in brilliant researches into plant heredity, crossing and breeding his own plants as a hobby. His discoveries were many and far-reaching and can be mentioned here only in the briefest and most simplified form. A more adequate but still necessarily simplified account will be found in Chapter 5 of *The Physical Basis of Personality*, by Professor V. H. Mottram.[1] Both on

1. Pelican A139, Penguin Books.

account of the intrinsic merit of his exposition of a number of topics relevant to our own study, and also to avoid repeating in one book of a series what has already been more adequately and fully covered in another, I shall be referring the reader to his work more than once in succeeding chapters.

Mendel discovered that hereditary characteristics can be regarded as independent units which are carried in both male and female seed, and which combine to reinforce and modify each other's effects when the union of the seed results in fertilization and the production of a new individual; maintaining all the while their independence and hereditability so that when this individual is in turn sexually mature, his own seed will contain a proportion of the inherited characteristics ready to be passed on to succeeding generations.

The production of male or female seed, the sperm cells in the male and the ova in the female, occurs by a process of splitting of the normal mature bodily cells of the individual. This splitting takes place in such a way that each individual sperm or ovum contains half the total number of minute rod-like bodies in the nucleus of the mature cell, called chromosomes, from their capacity to stain particularly deeply with cellular dyes used in microscopic examination. Each chromosome carries its own quota of unit characteristics which are called genes, and each gene in turn transmits the particular hereditary factors destined to shape the nature of the future individual.

After a division of the parent cell into two sperms or two ova as the case may be, each one of the two sex cells will be complementary to the other, in the sense that each will contain half, and a different half, of the total number of hereditary factors carried in the chromosomes of the parent individual. The offspring formed by the union of one of these sex cells with that of another individual will, of course, start off with a full number of chromosomes and therefore of hereditary factors, of which exactly half have been contributed by each parent in the union of the sex cells.

One simple example is called for at this point. The hereditary factor for eye colour which gives a person blue eyes can be contributed naturally by one or both parents. If two blue-eyed people marry their children will all be blue-eyed, and understandably these children will possess two hereditary factors for blue eyes in their chromosomes. But if a blue-eyed person marries someone with brown eyes the children will have in their chromosomes one factor for blue eyes and one for brown; the normal effect of this will be that all the children of the first generation will have brown eyes, but their chromosomes will carry one blue-and one brown-eyed factor. This is expressed in the terminology of the theory by saying that a brown-eyed factor is dominant and the blue-eyed factor recessive. If any one of these children, brown-eyed but with one blue- and one brown-eyed factor in their cells, marries another person of identical hereditary make-up so far as eyes are concerned, the colour of their children's eyes will be distributed throughout the family in a special way which is mathematically predictable along very simple lines. Roughly one quarter of the children will have brown eyes, one quarter pure blue, and a half hazel or brown flecked with blue.

What has happened has been that the normal chance mixing of the parents' sex cells has resulted in an assortment of offspring in which similar and dissimilar colour factors have come together over a succession of matings in a way that could be predicted on the basis of chance alone.

When both parents carry a characteristic which is dominant and carry this characteristic on both sides of their ancestries, then all their children will tend to show it and to transmit it. Similarly, if both carry a characteristic which is recessive, that is one which will appear in the individual only if it is contributed from both sides and unopposed by any other dominant feature, then all children will carry it but not all will pass it on. Increasing understanding of the way in which recessive characteristics can lie dormant sometimes for several generations before being reinforced by a particular union to produce children displaying the characteristic, enables us to come nearer to understanding something of the inheritance of all kinds of normal and abnormal human attributes, of which mental deficiency or the predisposition to particular kinds of mental illness is simply one example.

The two most common forms of mental illness which offer hopeful fields for study along these lines are schizophrenia and the affective disorders, particularly manic depressive illnesses or recurrent depressions. Neither of them, however, can be explained along purely Mendelian lines or indeed on a purely hereditary basis: but this after all is only to be expected since numerous other causes and contributory factors remain to be considered, and the stresses of existence, both in the environment and in the development of the personality, are at least as important in the production of mental illness as they are in the production of other forms of illness such as cancer or tuberculosis.

The percentage incidence of affective illness in the children of manic depressive parents is higher than can be accounted for by supposing the hereditary factor to be recessive. On the other hand it is not as high as would be demanded by a wholly dominant single factor reinforced from both sides. The probable explanation is that the tendency to develop this illness may be split among more than one hereditary factor or gene and that these may have to be combined; also that before the illness can appear in its developed form in an individual a sufficiently severe degree of external stress may be required. Recent figures for the liability to develop this illness among relatives of patients displaying it have been given as follows:

	Per cent.
Parents	11·5
Brothers and sisters	9·1
Children	9·5
Nephews and nieces	2·3
Uncles and aunts	5·0
First cousins	2·5

By comparison, the incidence of this form of illness in the general population is 0·4 per cent.

Among various forms of schizophrenia, liability to develop the disease on a hereditary basis may vary considerably, but again along Mendelian lines it looks as though the factor concerned is recessive, and the frequency of its appearance is less than would be expected were reinforcement from both sides of the family alone sufficient to ensure it. With one parent schizophrenic, just over 10 per cent of the children of the union are liable to develop schizophrenia. When both parents are schizophrenic, just over half the children face this risk. The significance of these percentages will fall into its proper place when it is remembered that in calculations of this kind no special allowance can be made for stillbirths, miscarriages, or the suppressive effect on fertility of contraceptive techniques.

That the hereditary factor is none the less sufficiently important when strongly present to determine a great deal of the outcome of a susceptible individual's life, is illustrated by a notable study by Professor Kallmann on the development of schizophrenia in similar twins. Similar twins are those who spring from a single union of sex cells, the fertilized cell splitting into two identical individuals after fertilization has been completed. They therefore carry exactly the same hereditary characteristics as each other, and differ in this respect from dissimilar twins, who are simply two individuals conceived at the same time by the separate union of two distinct pairs of sex cells. Kallmann studied similar twins born to schizophrenic parents. He found that where one twin developed schizophrenia not only did the other also develop the illness in four out of every five cases, but also, despite the fact that in some instances the children had been separated by force of circumstances since birth and had been brought up under widely different conditions, the second twin developed the illness within a year or so of its onset in the first, without knowledge of this event or any comparable environmental contribution.

The gradations of intellectual ability and disability from genius to mental deficiency in the population show, as we have already seen, a normal curve of distribution in the main. This can be accounted for along hereditary lines by supposing that a number of different genes are involved in the production of mental defect in most cases, and this is borne out by the wide variety and comparatively non-specific nature of such defect as normally seen. It is of some interest that in the case of Mongolism, which as we saw in Chapter 3 is a peculiarly characteristic and specific form of congenital defect and therefore particularly suited to genetic study, there is evidence that hereditary transmission plays only a very small part. Mongols themselves do not achieve sexual maturity nor is their incidence related to a particular strain of human stock. A parental factor which may have some possible significance in this respect is the age of one or both parents at the time of conception: but even so it is common for the parents of a Mongol to produce subsequent children who are entirely normal.

In addition there are, of course, some forms of defect wholly attributable to birth injury or to damage to the developing embryo in the womb by maternal disease or infection, in no way related to hereditary factors; while on the other hand there are also certain specific types of mental deficiency which are inherited on a purely recessive basis and some rare forms which are wholly dominant. These latter forms, far from spreading in the way in which a dominant characteristic might be expected or feared to multiply, are prevented from so doing by the very low fertility rate of the individuals who display them. Many in fact fail to achieve sexual maturity, many more never mate at all, and of those who do few are fertile. In fact their recurrent appearance in the population is due more to spontaneous appearance of the faulty gene in normal stock than to its inheritance in successive generations. By contrast the fertility rate of people of low intelligence who are not idiots or imbeciles tends to be comparatively high.

There is no evidence for direct inheritance of particular kinds of neurotic illness at all, although predisposition to breakdown in this way in the face of the stresses of existence is almost certainly bound up with hereditary factors and distributed throughout the normal population on much the same basis and probably in the same kind of way as the factors responsible for lower or defective intelligence, although there is no correlation between the two.

Whether there is an innate constitutional element in the production of psychopathic personalities is still undecided. If there is, it must almost certainly be bound up with the rate and extent of physical and psychological maturation. Whether this factor, if it exists, is subject to the laws of inheritance is even more uncertain. The most recent work upon genes, and the study of their distribution throughout inheritance, known as genetics, does suppose, however, that what are being transmitted, and becoming available for study only in their finally emergent form, are not so much characteristics as rates of development and tendencies towards these developments' crystallization at certain stages, which will eventually combine to make the individual what he is. There is therefore nothing about this conclusion which excludes the possibility that the complicated pattern of the psychopathic personality may be due in part to hereditary factors, although their contribution is almost certainly no more important than that of early parental relationships in the formation of the patient's character.

The implications of all this upon marriage, and the practical concern of the individual for his own or his partner's family background in their effect upon the children of the marriage, can be stated simply in this way. There is virtually no such thing as a flawless family tree. To demand one from one's partner or believe that one possesses one oneself is to court deception. There is an alcoholic or someone who has had a mental illness among the parents, grandparents, aunts, uncles, and first cousins of at least 60 per cent of the normal population; moreover this is nothing whatever to worry about because it *is* normal. A similar state of affairs prevails among a rather higher proportion of people who are themselves mentally ill, and the inheritance in their cases is more likely to be direct.

The chances of someone with an established mental illness, such as schizophrenia or recurrent endogenous depression, producing children who are liable to mental illness, are substantially but not overwhelmingly greater than those of a healthy person. On the other hand, union between neurotic or temperamentally unstable individuals and normal partners may well produce potentially normal or above average children, whose subsequent development will be more significantly affected by the atmosphere of the home and the attitude of the parents than by their constitutional endowment.

As a general rule the normal partner in a marriage will contribute favourable and dominant characteristics which will outweigh the unfavourable contributions of the less healthy partner. But among some neurotic and unstable people are the seeds of genius as well as of frailty, and these may sometimes emerge with a dazzling brightness from most unpromising soil.

Whatever the constitutional and hereditary endowment of the individual, the effects of external environment are of supreme importance in determining development, and in the maintenance of health or the decline into illness. Before turning to the effects of the general stresses and strains of existence there are one or two specific factors which we would do well to consider at this stage. These are the effects of physical illness and injury, of drugs, of alcohol, and of other rarer poisons.

The possible damage to the brain during intra-uterine life or in the actual processes of birth has already been mentioned in connexion with mental deficiency. We now know that various congenital defects including some forms of mental deficiency can, for example, be caused by damage to the developing child induced by an attack of german measles in the mother during the first three months of pregnancy. A small proportion of children also suffer damage to the brain, which may be permanent, as a result of prolonged shortage of oxygen or the effects of physical pressure and stress involved in a difficult birth. Brain injury and damage at all subsequent stages of life may produce changes not only in intelligence but in the personality as a whole.

A potent and specific form of cerebral damage due to involvement of the brain in the spread of organic disease is exemplified by general paralysis of the insane, which, as we have seen, is due to syphilis and is only one of the many manifestations of this remarkable disease. There remain the whole range of physical ills to which human beings are subject: for it cannot be too often stressed that the body is part of the environment of the mind, wherein it dwells, by which it is affected and which it also affects. Any bodily injury or illness cannot but produce repercussions upon the mind of the person who suffers it, and the patient stricken with a broken leg or with some more alarming insidious and progressive affliction such as tuberculosis or cancer, is not precisely the same person as he was in health. Of particular importance in this connexion are the functions and balanced relationship of the endocrine glands, and we shall have more to say of their relationship to mental illness in a later chapter; but this interdependence of body and mind is so powerful a condition of our mortal existence, and so completely taken for granted as to be almost overlooked, that I make no apology for reintroducing it here.

Alcohol raises a fascinating problem of the relationship between cause and effect to which no wholly satisfactory answer can be made. On the one hand we know that the solace of alcohol as an escape is sought by many people whose desire for escape springs from an already established mental illness; on the other hand continued addiction to alcohol will produce physical and mental changes and be accompanied by a progressive deterioration in the entire personality, chiefly evidenced by a loss of self-respect, by jealousy, suspiciousness, and often a maudlin camaraderie with comparative strangers, in contrast to a savage and brutal indifference to family and friends, which are so characteristic in the presence of the habit and so rare without it as to be accepted as a response to the effect of the drug upon the tissues.

In considering the role of alcohol in the production of mental illness we are concerned both with its direct effects upon those who take it and its indirect effect upon their children. We saw in the section on heredity that mentally defective children at least appear to be more likely than many others to have alcoholic parents or a strong family history of alcoholism; alcoholism is also represented in rather more than 25 per cent of the ancestors of patients with epilepsy, but once again it may be the possession of transmissible epileptic tendencies which leads to the taking of alcohol rather than the reverse.

When we come to consider the direct production of mental illness by alcohol in those who take it, we find a remarkable variation in the figures produced by research into this problem. In the early part of the twentieth century between 15 and 25 per cent of all admissions to mental hospitals were apt to be ascribed to alcohol, but it seems likely that in the majority of these alcohol was a symptom rather than a cause. Professor Mott was able to claim only six cases of alcoholic dementia in over two thousand patients dying in mental hospitals whose brains he wished to examine. He also drew attention to the fact that cirrhosis of the liver, a condition at one time believed to be highly correlated with alcoholic excess but now recognized as having many other causes, was far less frequent among patients dying in mental hospitals than among those examined after death in general hospitals throughout the country.

It is probably true to say that something under 5 per cent of major mental disorder is directly and solely due to alcohol, but it is equally likely that alcoholism is one of the most potent single causes of unhappiness among families, of broken homes, of minor and major crime, and particularly of violence and homicidal attacks, and that not a few of the behaviour disturbances seen in children and the character disorders which may cripple the lives of adults owe a great deal to alcoholic addiction, not primarily on the part of the patient but on the part of one or both of the parents.

As a cause of mental disorder drug addiction is almost negligible. In itself it is exceedingly rare in England although more common in America. While the fear that continued resort to narcotics or sedatives, even under direct medical supervision, is likely to lead to dependence on them, is widespread among the general public, this danger tends to be exaggerated. It is probably true that except in the most unusual circumstances, such as indefinitely prolonged painful illness or persistent insomnia for which no more adequate treatment is prescribed, addition to drugs does not occur in people not predisposed to this kind of dependence by an already immature or psychopathic personality. The most striking type of deterioration produced by drug addiction is in the sphere of moral and social responsibility. Its role in producing certifiable insanity is infinitesimally small.

Certain forms of industrial solvent can produce transient or, rarely, permanent mental change, just as they may produce physical illness or even death. Carbon monoxide, the most dangerous constituent of coal gas as commercially supplied, can lead to mental and neurological changes on an organic basis which may be lifelong. Very rarely a suicidal attempt by coal gas poisoning, which is not successful in leading to death, may leave the patient with a severe and irreversible mental and physical illness. Carbon monoxide poisoning can in this way appear both as a symptom and a cause of mental illness.

But in general the effects of poisons, of drugs, and even of alcohol and physical disease and injury, are important in the production of mental illness not solely by virtue of their physical impact upon the brain or body of the individual, but also in taking their place along with the innumerable forms of environmental stress in their effect upon the patient's mind. There are, for example, many more people worrying themselves to distraction about the possibility of suffering from syphilis or tuberculosis or cancer, than there are patients whose mental life is impaired by the physical effect of these conditions upon the cells in their brains.

Illness and disease of all kinds are undeniably important in the production of suffering, anxiety, and unhappiness, and it is chiefly in this way that they make their contribution to much of the functional mental illness which exists in the world. In general terms it is not so much the particular nature of the stress, whether it be external disaster or internal damage or disease, which is of supreme importance, but rather how a person faced by this stress feels about it himself. Ultimately mental illness is an extremely personal form of suffering: and unless this is understood and taken to heart further study of it will profit little.

* * *

All that we have examined so far in this chapter about the discoverable causes of mental illness has been related to constitutional or hereditary factors, or to the effects of specific physical injuries, illnesses, or intoxications; from the start it was necessary to stress that any categorical method of surveying such causes must guard against the error of supposing that any particular mental illness is likely to be due solely to any one separate cause. When we have reviewed all the different kinds of stress or natural endowment which seem to be associated with the development of such illness, we must be prepared to find an intricate combination of them at work in any particular patient whose case we study. None the less, in pursuit of our aim in classifying these causes for the sake of clarity, in much the same way and for the same reason as we classified the main types of mental illness themselves, we have come now to a point where we need some sort of a bridge between the somewhat concrete or organic type of cause with which we have already dealt, and the infinitely complicated, intricate, and subtle collection of causes which are summed up under the headings of social and psychological factors, including the structure and development of the personality itself. We are provided with a link between these two main sets of causes from a somewhat surprising quarter: that is, the realm of head injury.

Head injury of the kind in which structural damage to the brain leaves behind it discoverable physical signs of abnormal function has long been understood, and comes recognizably into the type of physical cause of mental disturbance which we have already discussed. Head injury accompanied by no apparent physical damage to the brain, and without signs of impaired neurological function on subsequent physical examination, has none the less been known for some time to be followed in many cases by an increased tendency on the part of the patient to develop neurotic symptoms, characteristically hysterical in nature but sometimes associated with depression or anxiety.

This tendency towards a functional type of illness following physical injury is of course by no means confined to head injury, as we have seen in the section on the so-called compensation neuroses in Chapter 4; but what excited the interest of neuropsychiatrists in this instance was the significantly higher proportion of cases in which such reactions followed head injury, when compared with injuries to other parts of the body. It was as though something had happened to the patient as the result of head injury which made him more liable to display a neurotic pattern of reaction; a lowering of his threshold to stress which did not seem to accompany other injuries even when their outward and physical effects were more severe.

It was not until a more subtle means of studying the functions of the brain in relation to mental life, and of testing these functions objectively, became available, that the answer to this problem was provided. Even now it is an answer whose final acceptance must await further experimental work. To understand it we have to return temporarily to a consideration of normal mental life in an aspect which was not mentioned in Chapter 3. This is the study of perception in rather more detail than was necessary for the general development of that chapter.

Originally perception was believed to be simply a process whereby the incoming sensory impressions, relayed through the nervous system, were assembled item by item like parts of a jigsaw puzzle and the final picture was recognized only when the assembly was complete. This so-called atomic view of the nature of perception is best illustrated in the field of vision. Looking at an orange the normal person was supposed to be receiving a number of separate sensory impressions; of yellowness, of dimpled smoothness, of shininess, of solidity, of opacity, and of size and shape. Only when all these had been put together in the mind, so to speak, and furthermore only when the assembled total of impressions had been extracted from the rest of the visual background, could the person be supposed to be *seeing* the orange he was looking at.

There were a number of objections to this theory of perception. We need not concern ourselves with them in detail, but in essence they are concerned with the impossibility of explaining just how all these different types of visual sensation are separately conveyed along the limited number of nervous pathways available, in the enormous complexity in which they might be supposed to occur; there is furthermore a perfectly valid scientific objection that it is uneconomical to suppose that there have to be as many separate pathways for receiving visual impressions, as there are separate ways of describing them in words.

Further experimental work has shown these objections to be well founded at least to this extent: there is now ample evidence to suggest that our brains are so constructed that we do not have to reconstruct complicated visual images from the constituent, separate, and unrelated impressions of all parts of our visual field, but rather that we tend to see certain patterns and shapes readily and naturally, and in fact to pick these patterns and shapes out of whatever background may contain them. This all sounds very complicated and difficult, but what it really means is that certain configurations, such as triangles and circles, and certain combinations of colour, shape, and solidity, and perspective, are in some way inherent in our way of seeing things, and there is very good evidence to suppose that we all see them in much the same way in any given setting.

Furthermore, we tend to see them, given the slightest opportunity, whether they are really there or not; for example, people who have suffered the misfortune of losing a part of the sensitive screen at the back of their eyes, called the retina, on which visual images are reflected through the lens of the eye, are unable to see the whole of what is before them. None the less they are not aware of the gaps in their field of vision and it may require very careful testing to discover that these gaps exist. Such a patient confronted by a diagram of a circle or a triangle will tend to see that diagram complete even though certain portions of it are in fact being reflected upon the missing areas of retina. Similarly all normal people who get a momentary glimpse of a similar diagram on a piece of paper, which is either illuminated so briefly or taken away so quickly that they are barely able to see what is there at all, will report faithfully having seen circles or triangles even when the actual diagram contains only a part of such a figure. It is this tendency to complete the picture along certain defined lines, to accept this completion as real, and to identify it so far as possible with what is familiar, that enables us, among other things, to enjoy the cinema, for the moving picture does not in fact move at all. What we see is simply a rapid succession of pictures each one a little different from the last. Their simultaneous recognition and identification with each other and the merging of the completed whole into a familiar sequence of movement, is one of the many remarkable functions of the living brain.

This innate tendency to perceive 'wholes' and to abstract them from an indefinite or apparently chaotic background is more than a capacity of normal mental function; it is in one sense an inescapable necessity. To put it in the most simple form, it is what both enables and compels man to understand and make some sort of sense of his environment. The theory of mental function which has been evolved from this conception is known as the Gestalt theory, the German word gestalt meaning 'whole' or 'configuration', and is of fundamental importance in modern psychology. One development of it of considerable clinical importance has been the evolution of tests of mental function along perceptual lines by various workers, including Goldstein, Halstead, and Scheerer. Here again we cannot concern ourselves with the details of the tests but must be content with the general statement that they are bound up with the capacity of the subject to make full use of his gestalt capacities, and in the words of Goldstein himself: 'To hold in mind simultaneously various aspects and compare them; to associate common properties reflectively; to plan ahead; to assume an attitude towards the merely possible, to pretend something; to think and perform symbolically; to detach himself from the outer world or from inner experiences.'

Application of these tests to subjects with quite trivial head injuries has in some cases shown their capacities to be markedly reduced; and these are in many cases the patients whose neurotic reactions following the head injury have been noted but always before regarded as inexplicable upon any physical basis. It seems now possible that what has really happened has been that these patients have found themselves handicapped after the head injury in ways far too subtle and elusive for their own understanding or explanation, and have been driven to neurotic patterns of behaviour as a defence against a comparative inadequacy which neither they nor anybody else has been able adequately to explain.

Here then is the link which we promised ourselves. A subtle but important disturbance of mental function is connected on the one hand with physical damage, in no other way detectable, which causes it; and on the other hand with the emergence of patterns of functional mental illness for which it is responsible, but which are in no other way referable to physical damage.

Hysterical reactions can result from disappointment or frustration on a purely emotional basis when that disappointment can neither be acknowledged nor accepted. In the special instance we have considered, the reaction seems to result from frustration and disappointment based upon diminution in the complex and almost indefinable capacities which we normally take for granted, a disappointment which in this case the patient can neither accept nor acknowledge because its physical basis, although real, has only recently begun to be understood by the medical profession themselves.

As our knowledge increases we may well find that this example of the intricate interrelationship between mind and body is only the beginning of a whole new chapter of knowledge in psychophysical relationships, which may ultimately lead us far away from the distinction between organic and functional mental illness on the one hand, while on the other hand the even wider and more arbitrary distinction between bodily and mental illness as a whole may come at last to be recognized as the illusion it has always been.

*   *   *

We can now turn our attention to a number of other factors influencing the incidence of mental illness, which are not primarily or essentially material in origin although they are necessarily bound up in some of their aspects with physical effects. The sex, age, race, cultural background, and social position may all have some importance in influencing the type of illness displayed by a particular individual. For example, women are not only differently constituted from men, different in physical structure and glandular function; they also face different emotional stresses and tend to react to them in different ways, just as they face different physical stresses in menstruation, pregnancy, childbirth, and the change of life.

Similarly, the age of a patient is significant not only because of the physical effects of youth or senility, or the glandular stresses of adolescence or the involutional period; but also on account of the widely differing personal emotions, problems, and responsibilities of the seven ages of man.

In the sphere of social factors the influence of race and the comparative complexity and culture of a society have been studied by sociologists and anthropologists. Some of their findings, expressed statistically, do suggest that certain types of mental illness tend to be associated with certain racial and cultural groups; yet again, inferences of this kind must be accepted with considerable reservation because so many other environmental factors may be influencing the type of mental illness shown.

In the United States of America, where a number of communities of different racial and cultural background have grown up together, intermingling in varying degree, but often preserving at their core characteristic features of their country of origin, studies of the incidence of mental illness should have a particular validity, since the general environmental background of all these communities living in the one continent are more nearly the same than they are in Europe. Results of some of these studies, dealing with mental illnesses sufficiently severe to demand admission to hospital, show that while alcoholic psychoses are twice as common among the Irish as in any other race, the proportional incidence of general paralysis of the insane among them is the lowest of all racial groups. Alcoholic psychoses are extremely rare in the Jewish population of the United States of America, and Jews also display a very low incidence of mental deficiency; on the other hand, they provide more than their share of patients with drug addiction, and are well represented among that section of the population with neurotic illness sufficiently severe to require in-patient treatment.

Cultural differences seem to influence the nature of some of the symptoms of mental illness as well as the incidence of such illness in general. The suggestion has been made, but by no means proved, that psychotic illnesses are less common in primitive societies, and that when they occur they contain a higher proportion of states of exaltation and mania than are seen in modern civilizations where anxiety and depression tend to be prominent. Kraepelin and Jung have both studied primitive peoples in Africa and Asia, and their general conclusions agree that psychoses encountered in such communities are of the same general type as those seen in European and Western communities. A more recent investigation among the Trobriand islanders, conducted by the anthropologist Malinowski, suggests that psychoneuroses are rare among these happy people; and this the investigator attributes to their conception of family structure whereby no connexion is recognized between sexual intercourse and paternity, so that fathers are unknown, and the masculine influence in the upbringing of the child is provided by male relatives, usually the brothers of the mother. The possible significance of this separation of the sexual from the parental role will become apparent when we turn to a consideration of individual psychopathology.

In all communities the structure of the family and the relationship of the child with the parents, as well as their relationship with each other and with the society of which they form a part, is almost certainly the most important single influence upon the development of the personality and the liability to mental health or mental illness. The size of the family, its stability, and the security which the child can feel within its protection, the certainty of whole-hearted acceptance and love, and the provision of consistent, tolerant, and responsible standards of behaviour, by example at least as much as by precept, all form a vital part of that essential shaping of an individual's character and possibilities which must take place during the first two decades of life. Most important of all is the emotional background of family life; loss or separation of parents, for example, are among the most serious environmental threats to a childhood's security which can occur; but even more important than the actual loss or deprivation are the circumstances and emotional accompaniment to the experience, and what follows.

For example, a fatherless child or an orphan can still gain an underlying confidence, hope, and inner stability, with the capacity to make personal adjustment to this loss and to subsequent experiences in life, if the disaster has been handled by the remaining parent or by those responsible for the child's subsequent upbringing with calmness, fortitude, and an abiding love. But where the separation has been the result of parental friction or accompanied by bitterness, hatred, and disillusionment, these feelings in their turn will influence not simply the child's immediate response but a great deal of his expectations and subsequent attitude to life and people as a whole.

We have mentioned briefly the devastating effect on the personality of a growing child of persistent drunkenness, violence, and brutality on the part of one of the parents. There are other more subtle but no less damaging ways of undermining the faith and happiness of such a child, and thereby compromising and threatening the emotional stability of the adult whom he will one day become. Sustained envy or bitterness on the part of the parents, jealousy or persecution within the family circle, or the deliberate distortion and betrayal of family life and ties often forming so obnoxious and degrading a feature of totalitarian systems, can all make their mark upon the inner life of the individual and upon his attitude to himself and his fellow men.

Later in life social factors of course continue to operate, but, as we saw in Chapter 3, by the time that adult existence has been reached most of the innate patterns of response and feeling have already been laid down. None the less the material upon which they have to operate continues to be important. Frustration in social or personal existence, or at work, is a most important form of stress in producing unhappiness and in some people actual neurosis. The more severe or long endured the disappointment a man feels with his place in life or the job he has to do, the more this disappointment reflects earlier setbacks and real or imagined failures of childhood days, the more intolerable will it seem to him and therefore the more likely to be thrust from the forefront of his mind where it can no longer be borne, to take its place in the less accessible but even more powerful reservoir of feelings and ideas which prey upon his mental peace, and lie in wait to produce symptoms of illness, to disrupt judgement, and to interfere, perhaps catastrophically, with his capacity to face reality and live with himself and others in hope and happiness.

*

We must now begin to translate this appreciation of the importance of emotional factors, whether derived from the social or the physical environment of the individual, into a concrete understanding of the way in which an individual's personality reacts to these emotions and is affected by them. This in turn will involve a study of the actual mechanisms which are believed to be responsible for all the varied kinds of physical and mental reaction to emotional stress: this is the study of psychodynamics, and when the outcome of psychodynamic processes are morbid, or the processes themselves become unfavourable to the happiness or survival of the individual, then the name given to the study is that of psychopathology.

We began our study of psychodynamics in Chapter 3 when we saw something of the development of human personality through childhood and adolescence. From early on in this study it became necessary to hint at a mental mechanism which at that time we were not in a position to amplify. This was the mechanism of repression, and to understand what it means it is necessary to examine a little more critically the general concept of mind and consciousness.

There are innumerable ways of defining consciousness, but a serviceable one for our purpose is to say that consciousness is the experience of being aware, while the content of consciousness is the sum of everything of which a person is aware at a given instant in time. This should immediately suggest that there must be a great deal more in anyone's mind than can be present in consciousness at any particular time.

You are at present reading this book. You have, I hope, your attention fixed upon what I am trying to convey; at the same time you are perhaps aware, although less acutely, of the position in which you are sitting or standing, and of a number of other immediate mental and physical factors in your present existence. All these are to some extent present in consciousness. Think now for a moment of the date of your birthday, or of a few words of a foreign language which you may know, or of any of the innumerable facts or fancies in your life which were not present in consciousness when you began to read this sentence. Thus summoned, they are immediately present. They have entered consciousness from another part of your mind where they were held immediately available but quite unobtrusive. We can call this much larger area of your mind, wherein much of what you remember is stored available for immediate recall when wanted, the pre-conscious area.

Now imagine that you are taking an examination and have just been asked a question to which you know the answer perfectly well, though at this precise moment it completely eludes you. This is a most irritating but all too familiar experience for most of us. The position now is that you know perfectly well that an idea is present somewhere in your mind but you cannot get hold of it for the moment; unlike other more accessible pre-conscious material, it won't come when it is called. But still, you know that it is there. If you try to think of it directly you are liable to experience a mounting sense of frustration and, if the occasion is sufficiently important to you, a most unpleasant feeling of tension and alarm. But this does not help you to remember it. A more effective method is deliberately to allow your conscious preoccupations to range around the missing area, whereupon if the emotions connected with it are not too powerful, a series of associated ideas will tend to follow one another and to lead quite often to the one which has been lost.

This method of recall is effective because it utilizes a whole network of associations which, like the network of nervous filaments and electrical circuits within the brain to which they are related, provides innumerable links between one idea and another. Ideas tend to become associated in many different ways, but the rules governing these associations are now fairly well understood and seem to depend upon fairly simple principles which form the basis for the whole process of learning and remembering. The general lines along which this took place had been successfully studied for many years before Freud pointed out the vitally important role played by emotion in determining whether or not a chain of associations could be readily followed and lead automatically to a particular idea or constellation of ideas appearing in consciousness.

He wrote an entire book devoted to the part played by emotional factors in everyday remembering, forgetting, understanding, and misunderstanding, of the kind with which we are all familiar. This book is a classic, and worth the time and money of anyone interested in this subject: it is called *The Psychopathology of Everyday Life*. We must now inquire whether, in addition to our conscious and pre-conscious knowledge, the recognition that there are areas of experience present in the mind, but not available to recall, should lead us to suspect the existence of a more remote area of mental life. We shall find not only that such an area does seem to exist, but that this area is the most important of all from the standpoint of psychopathology.

How much can anyone remember of his childhood? Very little indeed, if by remembering we mean recalling at will even a reasonable part of the emotions and ideas of those vital and vivid years. Indeed in a general sense, when we begin to think about it we realize that we must have forgotten not only the unimportant things but a great many things which at the time must have appeared tremendously important to us and been accompanied by feelings of the utmost intensity.

By evolving a most skilful method of making use of people's capacity to retrace ideas by means of their associations, Freud was able to demonstrate conclusively that much of this forgotten material, while still present in the minds of adults, had passed not simply beyond their capacity to recall it at will, but even beyond their capacity to remember that it had ever existed at all. The area of mind wherein this material lay buried, but, as we shall see, far from inactive, Freud called the unconscious. Those glib references to 'the sub-conscious mind' which we encounter on all sides in modern conversation, mean, when they mean anything at all, essentially the same thing.

We are now faced with at least three main areas of mental life which may contain ideas and feelings of importance in determining behaviour: consciousness, which is an immediate, constantly changing reflexion of a part of all we know and feel; pre-consciousness, which is the reservoir of all that is accessible to voluntary recall; and finally the unconscious area of mental life, which contains both the more primitive drives and impulses which may influence our actions without our ever becoming fully aware of them, together with a number of extremely important constellations of ideas with a strong emotional quality, which have at one time been present in consciousness but which are no longer available to it.

This is one of the fundamental hypotheses on which Freud built up his epochal conception of psychodynamics and psychopathology, and upon which a very great part of modern theory rests. His next concern was with the reason why certain constellations of ideas associated with powerful feelings should be forgotten in this particularly dramatic and far-reaching way, and with the means whereby such a process could be brought about. To clarify his thought and writing about this fascinating problem he employed two words whose meaning I hope in due course to make absolutely clear, but whose use has been just about as prostituted as has the employment of any other words in any language, even including the words liberty and democracy. These words are 'complex' and 'repression'; the first was coined by one of Freud's earliest and most original followers, Jung, while the second was Freud's own idea. In psycho-analytic usage, the term 'complex' means a constellation of ideas with a strong emotional overtone; and the process whereby a complex becomes buried in the unconscious part of the mind is called repression.

Any constellation of ideas which are associated with strong feelings in a person's mind can legitimately be called a complex, without the usual somewhat woolly implication that all complexes are vaguely ominous or disgusting; in point of fact they are usually memories of real or imaginary experiences, together with the conclusions which the subject has reached about them, and the intense feelings which they have produced. They may be helpful or harmful to his subsequent emotional adjustment, and they may on occasion emerge partly or wholly into the pre-conscious area of the mind, although for reasons which will become clear in one moment many of them remain buried in the unconscious area. Similarly, repression means a particular, compulsive kind of forgetting, which results in forgotten material being neither available to direct recall nor even represented in consciousness or pre-consciousness by the vaguest awareness that it ever existed.

The ideas inherent in this theory are of course at once highly stimulating and decidedly controversial. But for the burning genius of Freud they were only a beginning. Why should repression take place at all? Freud suggested that when the emotion connected with a particular complex reached an unbearable degree of intensity, the automatic defence of the individual's mind called for one or both of two processes: the first was suppression, the deliberate refusal to think about something intensely painful any longer; if this was not enough to secure temporary respite, if the painful emotions were too insistent and threatened the patient's mental integrity, then repression took place.

Most of us are aware of suppression as a voluntary process; Scarlett O'Hara, the heroine of *Gone with the Wind*, used it constantly: 'I won't think about that any more to-day ... I'll think about it to-morrow ...' We are, however, quite unaware of the more serious and involuntary process of repression which is none the less part of the normal mental functioning of every one of us.

Freud came to the conclusion that once repression had taken place there was a further mental process responsible for the prevention of the return of the repressed material into consciousness; this he called the 'censorship', and to anyone familiar with some of the more facile jargon which inevitably comes to surround and compromise successful ideas, the 'invisible censor' becomes either an old friend, or an intolerable nuisance, whichever way you care to look at it. In its original usage the term censorship was an allegorical one, although unfortunately it is dangerously easy to think of such an allegorical conception as though it were an actual physical reality interposing some kind of barrier between repressed complexes and their host's awareness of them.

Once embarked upon a study of unconscious mental life, Freud, by a series of brilliantly intuitive but logically developed hypotheses, proceeded to the examination of both the waking life and dreams of his patients, by studying the free associations which they could provide. His approach to dreams was to take the bare remembered material of each dream item by item, and to examine with the patient every association to every item which the dreamer could produce. This led Freud to postulate that virtually the entire structure of thought and imagery in dreams, their bizarre quality, symbolization, independence of considerations of time and space, and their frequently intense but incongruous emotional flavour, were due to a combination of the primitive drives and mental processes of the unconscious area of the mind striving for release and expression, and to the distorting effect upon them of the process of censorship, which even in the absence of conscious control consistently interfered with progress of unconscious material towards awareness and recognition.

His studies convinced him that certain complexes were virtually universal, and so constantly of importance in the psychopathology of many forms of mental illness that their general description and understanding comprised an essential part of the elaboration of this theory. They form, as it were, the cornerstones of any comprehensive appreciation of the effect of unconcious mental processes upon the development of human personality and behaviour.

Complexes and Complications

THE complex which Freud considered one of the most fundamental in the psychopathology of the normal individual was what
he called the Oedipus complex, which we encountered for the
first time in Chapter 3. We saw there that this is essentially a
blend of rivalry and jealousy, leading to aggressive wishes and
feelings directed against the father, when the father's influence
and claims upon the mother come into conflict with the child's
desire for her exclusive attention and concern. These powerful
hostile feelings are not only forbidden in the child's mind, but are
also opposed by the love, respect, and trust which he normally feels
for his father as a person. Furthermore, his natural desire, if a
boy, is to model himself upon his father and to be like him; he is
therefore faced with a conflict between hating and loving the
same person, between holding that person up as a wonderful and
admired model for his own emulation on the one hand, and yet
at times wishing for his overthrow or disappearance so that the
child himself can take his place.

The conflict occasioned by loving your rival, and by feeling
your happiness and security threatened by jealousy of your best
friend, is a theme whose poignancy endures throughout adult life
and is a favoured motif in literature and drama; this reflexion of
the earliest and most acute emotional problems of childhood
upon the wider screen of adult experience is but one example of
the way in which the powerful feelings associated with complexes
influence all our later interests, hopes, and fears. But the child
first experiences the Oedipus situation in the very earliest years of
life, at a time when there is no possible solution of it which can
prove finally or decisively satisfactory to him one way or the
other. A constellation of ideas connected with the father's role

and the child's feelings about it, and about his own position in the whole situation, provide a vivid example of the sort of complex for which some degree of repression provides at the time the only solution.

We have seen that the Oedipus complex is virtually universal; it may at least be presumed to exist wherever there is a father in the family, yet while it plays a part in the genesis of most forms of neurotic illness, the reader may reasonably inquire why in so many people its presence seems to cause no trouble at all. The answer to this question must be bound up partly with the innate resilience and capacity for tolerating stress which the particular person happens to possess, and partly with the presence or absence of experiences in early life which intensify the Oedipus situation, to a point where the emotion connected with it becomes even more powerful than would normally be the case.

One way in which intolerable intensity may be given to the emotional conflict concerned is by the child's involvement in the actual sexual relationship of the parents. The most crude and obvious example of this is where children live so much on top of their parents that they are likely to see sexual intercourse taking place; but even a far less drastic acquaintance with adult sexuality is apt to prove extremely disturbing to children and to cause them uncontrollable anxiety. When this happens the subsequent repression may carry with it into the unconscious area of the mind feelings so strongly charged, and so widely connected with the vague and as yet far from completely understood or accepted implications of sexuality, that the subsequent development of the individual through adolescence, and his attitude to his own sexual maturity, may be extremely disturbed.

Another complex which may be widespread, if not universal, but whose emotional intensity may be heightened by misguided although probably rarely intentionally evil parental interference, has been called the castration complex. This begins as a fear which a child may develop, that the parents may intend to punish him for wicked thoughts or deeds by cutting off a part of his body. The classical example of this is the helpless fear of the small boy who may actually be threatened with the snipping off of his penis as a punishment for what his parents regard as his deliberate masturbation. 'If I catch you fiddling with yourself again Johnnie, I'll cut it off, I will really.' Of course, the mother or the father do not really intend anything of the kind; but while for them the threat is pure fantasy, regarded perhaps as a salutary deterrent, they remain totally unaware that its origin in their own minds owes a good deal to the buried fears of their own childhood. To the child himself it is indeed a powerful and an appalling possibility; for there is no hard and fast division between fact and fantasy, between what is possible and what is probable, in the mind of a child. Such a threat, even if not openly expressed by a parent, may already be present in some nebulous form in the child's own mind as the possible retaliation which he fears for the forbidden aggressive feelings involved in the Oedipus complex.

Once an association has been formed between the idea of loving and hurting, between physical pleasure and the possibility of mutilation, then what we have called the castration complex will inevitably be intolerable in consciousness and will suffer repression, to emerge perhaps many years later in an anxiety neurosis with impotence as one of its most distressing symptoms.

The rivalry which a little girl may feel for her mother, and which may include a desire for exclusive possession of her father, has been called the Electra complex; it is in many ways strictly comparable to the Oedipus complex, and when its influence persists and cannot be resolved spontaneously in the normal emancipation of adolescence, it may lead to the type of emotional immaturity characterized by a failure to develop beyond the stage where the father remains in fantasy the only possible object of admiration among men, the ideal but essentially forbidden mate. This idea remains at least partly repressed although the emotional attitude to which it gives rise may be evident. The word 'fixation', ugly, slipshod, and avoidable as it is, is often used to describe this emotional attachment to a parent. In this sense a father fixation can be expected to involve an immature attitude towards the normal feminine role, and to lead in many cases to a neurosis in which hysterical frigidity is a prominent feature.

We also saw in Chapter 3 something of the way in which patterns of thought and feeling, once established in the first two decades of life, tend to be repeated for better or worse time and time again in subsequent years. A patient whose sexual adjustment has been compromised in the sort of way we have just been considering will be found to repeat the unsuccessful pattern of behaviour in his life without perceiving its basis, and often the more disastrous the consequences the more persistent will be the repetition. In this way a series of unhappy frustrated love affairs may be followed by a disastrous marriage with recurrent breakdown of health and happiness on the part of the patient; while all too often both the other partner of the marriage, and the children, may suffer stresses which in turn seek out the flaws in their own emotional structure. In this way neuroses breed at least as much by direct repercussions on existing lives as by any elements of heredity.

In the intensive investigation of human emotional development which followed Freud's original approach, and the technique which he discovered, many other actual or potential complexes were described. A further two will serve as illustrations. Rivalry in children is not always confined to feelings about parents. While the only child has to suffer a much more lonely and more intense battle in the Oedipus situation than the fortunate possessor of brothers and sisters, who are so to speak in the same boat, rivalry among children can occasionally be severe, particularly if intensified by persecution of one ugly duckling, or isolation from the group for any other reason. The word sibling is a convenient one for describing children of the same parents whether they are brothers or sisters; sibling rivalry, once again a compound of natural affection and equally natural jealousy and aggression, will sometimes emerge as a complex which has influenced an individual's whole attitude to his own life and his relationship with others.

While the fear of castration is understandably likely to be greater among little boys, whose potential loss is all too obvious, some investigators have encountered a deep sense of insecurity and inferiorty among girls which they believe can be traced to the child's fantasy that girls have somehow lost a part of their bodies which would have made them like boys. A certain amount of envy blended with natural interest can be seen in the uninhibited sexual curiosity of children about each other, and there can be no doubt that in some women a profound sense of dissatisfaction and deprivation does seem to derive its psychopathological roots from a deeply repressed envy of this kind.

The whole question of the effect upon personality of a natural striving for success and superiority was raised by Adler, another of Freud's earliest followers, and subsequently elevated by him into a separate school to which he gave the name of individual psychology. The central thesis of this school is that the drive for power is at least as important as the search for sexual gratification and must be separately considered.

Linked to this was the concept of a feeling of inferiority which both prompts the drive for power and is naturally intensified by failure in the struggle; hence arose the immortal phrase 'inferiority complex' which we are now in a position to see does not mean simply a conscious feeling of inferiority, but rather an unconscious constellation of ideas characterized by a sense of insecurity and inadequacy which is intolerable and of which the subject is largely unaware. The effect of such a complex upon behaviour is by contrast to produce a somewhat authoritative attitude, and to drive the individual into situations wherein he must prove the deeper misgivings to be false.

Adler was particularly gifted in the art of evolving apt and memorable descriptive terms; to that compensatory drive which some women display in the pursuit or achievement of executive position he gave the name 'masculine protest'. Some, but by no means all, of the disciples of Freud would maintain that masculine protest is simply the superficial description of the outward and visible manifestations of a repressed penis envy.

To Professor Carl Jung we owe another wide and far-reaching sweep of ideas in psychopathology which have been developed once again out of the original system of thought produced by Freud. Jung studied the mental life of patients with schizophrenia, using the theory and technique which Freud had evolved, and made a number of discoveries which carried further the pioneer work of Bleuler on this subject, but like Adler, although for different reasons, Jung parted company with Freud, largely over the question of the nature of that prime source and origin of emotional energy to which Freud had given the name libido.

Freud believed, as we saw in Chapter 3, that libido was derived essentially from the impulse to love and to obtain gratification through loving; to Adler the supreme incentive was the urge to achieve power: Jung preferred to be less specific than either his teacher or his erstwhile fellow disciple, and maintained that while libido could be canalized either in the direction of loving and hating or of achieving power and success, it was in essence a fundamental force, mysterious and indefinable but virtually limitless in its possibilities.

Jung never denied the importance of the Oedipus complex, or of the deep-laid sense of guilt and shame which might dwell at the heart of the inferiority complex postulated by Adler; but he regarded these phenomena simply as aspects of a wider whole whose breadth and sweep he has spent a lifetime in studying and describing. As might be expected with so vast and cosmic a psychology, the easiest and most immediate criticism which has been levelled at the Jungian school is that it is mystical, contradictory, obscure, and so all-embracing as to be in effect meaningless. While these criticisms are themselves frequently unjust and superficial, and moreover· owe a great deal to the emotional attitude of the critics, the study of Jungian analytical psychology is one which requires considerable application and critical interest on the part of the reader, although approached in this way it is extremely rewarding and remarkably stimulating.

Some of Jung's central conceptions demand particular mention here although they form only a part of the complicated structure of the original. These include his theory of the structure of human personality, his concern with the idea of the death and rebirth cycle in life and its significance in human psychology, and his conception of the universal unconscious.

*

His conception of the structure of human personality is based upon the essential antithesis of thinking and feeling, and of sensation and intuition, in their contributions to personal experience. He begins by dividing the basic attitude of man to his existence into two opposite tendencies, introversion and extraversion. Introversion consists in concern with subjective experience, with the person's own mental processes and the world of his own thoughts and fantasies; extraversion implies by contrast a predominant interest in objective experience, in the external world of appearances and outside reality. Introversion has been compared to introspection, but it means very much more than that. The introvert is not simply withdrawn or self-absorbed, not merely preoccupied with himself; on the contrary he is concerned with the meaning below the surface of all things, with the nature of reality rather than with its visible and possibly superficial appearance.

Jung believes that both tendencies exist in all men and women: but where the conscious attitude is one of introversion the unconscious tendency will be towards the more uncritical acceptance implicit in extraversion, and vice versa. Similarly where thinking dominates the conscious approach, feeling will reign in unconscious attitudes; and where sensation, or the objective perception of experience, supplies the basis for conscious shaping of opinion, intuitive judgement will hold sway beneath the surface of the mind.

The detached, seemingly aloof scholar with critical and contemplative intellect who may fall hopelessly and helplessly in love with a mercenary trollop, forms one admittedly stylized example of the antithesis whose contradiction is in Jung's view only apparent: a paradox whose deeper explanation belies the superficial inconsistency. Another example is the impulsive man of action who, apparently without conscious deliberation, chooses for a mate a woman who will subordinate her life to his, and for lieutenants men whose subtlety is matched only by their loyalty and devotion. In the first instance an individual characterized at the conscious level by introverted thinking and behaviour, displays extraverted feeling responses in the release of unconscious emotion; in the second, an extraverted character with a direct approach based on sensation is guided at a deeper level by an unconscious but shrewdly introverted intuition. Jung called the outward appearance of the personality, its conscious manifestation, the persona. Its unconscious and opposite counterpart he named the anima, in men; the animus, in women. These names, borrowed from classical drama, stand respectively for the mask assumed by a character and the spirit investing his role. By their nature and interrelationship, the persona and anima of an individual determine not only his character and personality but also his emotional stability and resilience, together with the kind of disorder he will display if he becomes mentally ill. This is but an indication of one aspect of Jung's views on human personality, to which he has devoted a great deal of writing and many years of study. We shall be compelled to deal even more summarily with the remaining two concepts which we selected for attention.

In the course of his life and work Jung has travelled widely and studied the psychology of primitive tribes in many parts of the world as well as most of the more complicated communities of Europe and America.

One of the themes which he found recurring constantly in tribal myths and fairy tales, and in those hitherto unconscious areas of the mind of individuals whom he examined, revealed often symbolically in their dreams and in the products of their associations although they themselves were often at first unaware of its significance, was that of the striving of man for a rebirth from which he could emerge changed and made anew. An example is the primitive belief that the sun is a god who daily rides the sky, to return at night into the womb of his mother, the sea, whence he is reborn the following day. The contained idea of a re-entry into the mother's womb is to be found at the core of many other myths. This theme of rebirth is indeed universal. It appears in the rites of springtime celebrated in every part of the world, in the myth of the phoenix, in the hopes of every mother about her newborn child, and it forms an essential aspect of all the great religions of mankind.

Jung accepted the significance of this fact and recognized that something so universally acknowledged must ultimately have an integral relationship with the whole of life itself. Nor was he surprised to discover that this same idea recurred repeatedly in the symbolized fantasies of patients with mental illness whose contact with external reality had changed, but whose preoccupations became explicable along the lines of this great central channel of human emotion and experience. From its contemplation he was led also to discover that innumerable other elaborations of his theme were to be found occurring apparently spontaneously in human minds all over the world.

His studies were anthropological as well as psychological, and he became particularly interested in certain widespread myths which formed a part of the background of every culture and civilization which he studied. These included, for example, the story of the great flood or disaster which almost eclipsed all life and was followed by a new generation with a new opportunity. From his studies he evolved the remarkable conception that beneath the individual area of unconscious mental experience, there existed a wider reservoir shared in the first instance by all members of any self-contained community. To this he gave the name of the Racial Unconscious.

Deeper still, and in some way in the depths of the unconscious mind of every human being, there lay a common pool of all human mental life, extending both in time and in space to embrace the background to the whole of human existence. This Jung has called the universal unconscious.

The easiest and most diagrammatic way to imagine what this conception means, is to think of all human experience and mental life as one vast plateau rising above the surface of the unknown, and separating into a number of mountain ranges, which in turn give rise to innumerable separate peaks. A line drawn just below the level of the tops of the peaks will disclose only a vast number of separate islands projecting above the surface. These are the separate minds and consciousness of living individuals, and the area immediately below the surface in each one of them is that area of unconscious mental life of which we have essayed so necessarily brief a glimpse in the earlier part of this chapter, and with which the detailed study of Freudian psychopathology is essentially concerned. But further down the shoulders of the peaks spread and merge until whole joined ranges occur, from which each separate pinnacle has taken origin and to which it owes its solid foundation. This can be compared to the racial unconscious, the shared but totally unconscious mental life of a self-contained community, their common fears and hopes, myths and dreams, of which each may be aware only at times and only in part. Still deeper stands the central plateau, the universal unconscious common to all humanity, upon which rests the whole mental life of mankind.

This of course can be but the merest indication of the trend of Jungian theory. Its practical applications in treatment and research will concern us for a while in later chapters, but its detailed study can in no way be attempted here. For the student of psychopathology and psychodynamics it is an indispensable field for exploration. In our relatively superficial approach we can do no more than skirt its borders and stand for a moment pondering at its mass and complexity.

*

Wherever lies the final truth approached along these different paths in the study of psychopathology, there remain a number of relatively concrete and established mental mechanisms whose understanding can help us appreciate the processes at work in certain kinds of mental illness.

Broadly speaking, it is evident that the effect which will be produced when a repressed complex is stirred by some event in the conscious experience of the individual, which has similar associations, will be the production of emotions appropriate to the complex and therefore probably highly unpleasant or unbearable. The two most common reasons why repression has originally taken place are that the material repressed has been charged with feelings either of intense guilt or intense fear and anxiety. These then are the feelings which are most likely to be aroused when such a complex is activated. But we have already seen that a powerful mental mechanism, whose precise nature is as yet entirely unknown, but which has been given the convenient name of 'the censorship', exists to prevent the spontaneous reappearance of repressed material in consciousness. What happens therefore is that the unpleasant feelings are aroused but the person concerned remains completely unaware of their source. Immediately other compensatory mechanisms come into play; the two most common are called 'rationalization' and 'projection'.

Most of us are familiar with the somewhat impressive statement that 'nature abhors a vacuum.' This is certainly nowhere more true than in the realm of conscious mental life. Confronted by powerful feelings with no apparent explanation, the immediate tendency is either to attach to them the first explanation available, or to attribute them to some source which seems likely and appropriate. We do precisely the same thing with physical symptoms if their origin is similarly obscure. The first of these processes, whereby some simple, convenient, and ready-to-hand explanation is produced and accepted in our own minds, we can call rationalization; the second, whereby the disagreeable experience is attributed to some acceptable scapegoat, is known as projection. Both rationalization and projection can be entirely conscious or entirely unconscious; they can also be obvious to other people, or the deception which is being practised can be as convincing to others as it can be to ourselves.

Suppose you are in the company of someone who disturbs and embarrasses you but whom you do not wish to offend. You seize the first opportunity of taking your leave and you make what you hope is a reasonable excuse. That is the simplest form of rationalization and is usually entirely conscious. When we make excuses to ourselves about feelings whose real nature we are unable to acknowledge, the rationalization is one which includes our own critical faculty, if it is successful. This sort of rationalization is of course unconscious.

Similarly if things go badly for us we may blame ourselves, or we may project the blame on to somebody else. The bad workman who blames his tools is projecting his criticism of his own incompetence, which he cannot bear to acknowledge, on to the instruments which he is using. In Chapter 4 we saw how paranoid ideas involve the blame for misfortune being attached to other people: 'It's all their fault. "They" won't give me a fair chance.' It is the mechanism of projection which is responsible for 'them' rather than 'me' being the object of blame.

Projection is one kind of displacement of feelings from their true and appropriate basis to a more convenient one; but displacement itself can take place in other ways, and again it can be deliberate or unconscious. The legendary office boy who kicks the office cat because he has been ticked off by the boss is displacing his resentment and thirst for vengeance. His motives are reasonably obvious; they may or may not be conscious. He may even rationalize them: 'That damned cat is always getting under my feet.'

In dreams, where the normal control exercised over mental life in consciousness is completely abrogated, symbolization, displacement, and projection all play a large part in that distortion of events so characteristic of the dream world. When we awake after a particularly vivid dream, our recollection of it, and particularly our account of it to somebody else, will be bound to contain a further element of elaboration to make it seem just a little less chaotic. If its general emotional flavour was disturbing or alarming, our explanation of it is far more likely to be a rationalization than a true interpretation, which can only be reached with the skill and responsible help of somebody else trained to evaluate and interpret our own associations to the material of the dream itself.

*

We can now begin to see that on a psychodynamic basis a great deal of mental illness is beginning to become intelligible. The effect of certain painful and powerful complexes can be to produce apparently causeless anxiety or depression, which may be allied to constitutional or hereditary factors in the personality or body of the patient concerned, and may further initiate and maintain changes in the mental and physical function of the patient so that a developed illness results.

In other patients the same complexes may be dealt with by the production of hysterical symptoms rather than the direct experience of the painful emotion, which is prevented from reaching consciousness at the price of the emergence of the hysterical symptom in its place. Again in other patients whose constitution predisposes them to yet another pattern of response, the defence against painful and unbearable emotion originally derived from repressed complexes may take an obsessional form, whereby the ritualistic performance is called out to protect the patient from awareness of the forbidden wish or the intolerable dread.

It is perhaps in the realm of schizophrenia, where the normal control of mental life is more completely disintegrated than in any other form of mental illness apart from profound dementia, that the aberration of mental mechanisms we have been studying is most vividly seen. The key which Bleuler proposed to the bewildering confusion of schizophrenic thought and behaviour was the conception of a general loosening and failure of all the connecting processes, which normally bind and relate ideas and their expression, emotions and the behaviour to which they would normally give rise. Intra-psychic ataxia was the name given to this postulated internal dissolution. The term was coined by Stransky, and can be loosely translated as a giddiness within the mind. Bleuler saw as the reason why so much schizophrenic behaviour is contradictory, bizarre, and incongruous, and why the thought of these patients is scattered, jumbled, chaotic, and inconsequential, that both the normal framework of the mind, and the very bonds which held it together and gave it shape, had disappeared.

This is a vivid but not a complete explanation, since it leaves us uninformed as to why this dissolution should have taken place. A possible explanation is that, whatever the inherent flaws in the pre-schizophrenic personality, whatever the inherited or innate constitutional handicaps such as a lack of resilience and capacity for adjustment, the basic psychopathological disturbance is one of withdrawal from reality; a withdrawal which occurs because the mere experience of the stresses of outside existence threatens the personality with the activation of too much unbearable emotion, imperfectly assimilated and hitherto repressed.

The effect of such withdrawal would then be not simply to remove the patient's mental life from the same basis of participation in reality as that shared by others, but, at the price of admittedly terrible illness, to render unnecessary on the one hand further repression, or on the other, any attempt at conscious control of such treacherous mechanisms as projection and displacement. Repressed material does in fact frequently appear in consciousness in patients with schizophrenia; they may, for example, maintain and believe that they have murdered their father, slept with their mother, and been castrated; or their more bizarre ideas may be essentially symbolized and distorted references to such experiences. Furthermore they may project not simply their emotions, in the form of ideas of reference or paranoid delusions, but also their sensations, which then take on for them the semblance of external physical reality and become hallucinations. In this way they feel tingling as electricity or rays played upon them, they hear their own thoughts as spoken voices, and may even see the images of their erupting fantasy in the form of indescribable visions.

*

If withdrawal of interest from external reality, and the surrender of a feeling of responsibility for conforming to its demands, are at the root of the disintegration of thought, emotion, and behaviour which occurs in schizophrenia, we are led to inquire what is the normal mechanism which controls and directs thought, action, and emotion, to bring these three manifestations of mental life into a consistent relationship with the individual's own personal standards. We want to know in fact how we acquire our standards, and how we maintain a capacity to judge whether or not we are conforming to them.

This introduces the last of the important psychodynamic concepts with which we have to deal; that of the conscience, or, in psycho-analytic terms, the super-ego. The theory of the formation and organization of this part of mental activity is generally agreed among all the principal schools of dynamic psychology, even though it was first devised by Freud himself.

The developing awareness of the difference between 'me' and 'not me' in the child's mind, with which we are now familiar, becomes elaborated early in life to a point at which the conception of 'me' is again divided into two. There is 'I as I am and feel' and 'I as I believe I ought to be.' This latter 'I' embodies the standards which for 'me' exemplify both personal aims and ambitions, and the rules and customs which my surroundings and upbringing lead me to accept. The prime source of these standards, both for personal ambition and for the day-to-day regulation of existence, is of course parental attitude and example. Furthermore, the child's own emotional experience comes to be identified with these attitudes on the part of the parents so that in the normal course of events the ideal concept of self is felt to be both loving and, at least potentially, punishing; to be in fact both as kind and indulgent on the one hand, and as severe and just on the other hand, as are the parents on whom this concept is modelled. In this way, so Freud believed, arises the conscience; he preferred to call it the super-ego or the ego ideal.

As life goes on we tend to incorporate into our ego ideal at both conscious and unconscious levels the further accumulations of our experience of law and order, of justice or injustice, and of faith or doubt and disillusion. We tend to acquire the pattern of mercy or severity in our conscience which we have observed and been able to accept in our parents, and later in our teachers and those of our fellow men whom we admire or respect.

It will be observed that this view of conscience makes no provision for any inherent or absolute appreciation of right or wrong, and is in this sense completely independent of fundamental religious or moral significance. For Freud this conclusion carried considerable force. Indeed he went on to treat the idea of God and the fact of religious belief as simply projections of the child's relationship to his father, made in response to the wider stresses and threats of human existence against which no human father could be expected to protect his son. In this respect his philosophy might be compared to that of Voltaire: 'If God did not exist it would be necessary to invent Him.'

Freud assumed as the result of his own subjective experience that God did not exist, and that mankind had unconsciously followed Voltaire's maxim and invented Him for its own comfort and security. We shall have more to say about this remarkable conclusion in a later chapter. But for the moment it is perhaps reasonable to point out that Freud's authority for his conclusion was no more and no less than that of the subjective speculation of anybody else; his ability to explain how the idea of God and the idea of fatherhood might be linked in the human mind, and how both these ideas could be expected to become involved in the developing conscience of the individual, is in no sense an answer to the very much wider and infinitely more complex question of why both the concept of fatherhood and the existence of God should be a part of human mental existence at all, if they are based upon an illusion. Nor can any conclusions, no matter how valid or convincing, about the way in which beliefs occur, affect the essential validity of these beliefs themselves; unless such conclusions are based upon the substance of these beliefs as well as upon their mechanism and propagation.

In point of fact Freud himself had strong emotional reasons for his attitude towards religion, and his own feelings about his father were sufficiently conflicting and intensely charged with emotion to colour his attitude to this part of his own work. Moreover, unlike his numerous disciples, he himself did not undergo the experience of a personal psycho-analysis from somebody else; and whatever may be the claims to relatively complete self-knowledge and objectivity, advanced by some of those who have completed this process, Freud himself was never so naive as to deny that he was subject to at least the same general prejudices, and the distorting effects of personal feeling upon attempts at abstract thought, which he was constantly detecting in the minds of his patients.

Without therefore becoming further embroiled in considerations of Freudian philosophy or metaphysics at this stage, we can apply the concept of the super-ego to our knowledge of psychodynamics and psychopathological processes, to complete the picture which we have of mental mechanisms in health and sickness.

The super-ego is conceived as being partly conscious and partly unconscious both in its content and in its method of operation. We can put this another way by saying that while we are certainly aware of a number of our personal standards and moral values, and the way in which they influence our own behaviour and our attitude to the behaviour and views of other people, we are equally certainly quite unaware of many of the reasons *why* we have adopted these attitudes or accepted these beliefs, just as we are unaware of why some things seem naturally good to us and other things unquestionably bad.

The part which the operations of the super-ego must play in mental conflict and its resolution is obvious. Whenever in fact our desires or impulses clash with the promptings of our conscience, conflict ensues. At the unconscious level it is the super-ego which both prevents the expression, and ultimately even the awareness, of forbidden emotion, and is thereby subsequently responsible for its repression. Similarly the censorship can be thought of as the unconscious manifestation of the judicial role of the super-ego: what has been repressed must never again be acknowledged.

It is part of the theory of psychodynamics that the formation and subsequent activity of the super-ego, including repression and the operations of the censorship, are all part of normal unconscious mental life. Their special involvement in mental illness must therefore represent a relatively abnormal state of affairs. This will differ according to the nature of the mental illness concerned.

In neurosis it is largely the effect of conflict which can neither be successfully resolved nor wholly repressed, which is responsible for the development of symptoms. The psychodynamic element in depressive illnesses can be conceived as the operation of a very powerful and very punitive super-ego, which leads the patient's mood to be one not simply of misery and despair but often of bitter although apparently causeless self-reproach and recrimination. The patient has turned against himself to such a degree that suicide may in this instance represent final execution of the death sentence of the man upon himself.

In states of pathological exaltation and excitement such as mania or hypomania, the punitive and critical element in the super-ego is postulated as having been overthrown, and the patient enjoys a wild and irresponsible elation at the price of a loss of self-criticism and ability to regulate his conduct in conformity with his normal standards. We have already seen that in schizophrenia the psychodynamic picture is explicable along lines of a total withdrawal of interest and emotional investment from reality, so that the need for super-ego control is abrogated, and the whole mechanism is evaded and may even participate in the general disintegration of the personality which occurs when such control is finally lost or surrendered.

In Chapter 4 we noted that the distinguishing feature of the behaviour displayed by people with what we called psychopathic personality was a failure to adjust themselves to the demands of society, to moderate their own conduct in the light of experience, or to adopt any but a short-term and impulsive solution to their difficulties. In psychodynamic terms this can be recognized as a failure of the normal super-ego development; and it is not surprising therefore that the parental relationships of these patients are so frequently chaotic, unhappy, or incomplete.

Whether the psychological immaturity implicit in this explanation is secondary to the physiological immaturity so frequently encountered in such people, and mentioned in the previous chapter, or whether it is itself causal, is not finally known. But the correlation between the two factors is striking and their joint contribution can be accepted as significant.

One of the most powerful destructive impulses with which human beings have to deal is that of hatred or aggression. If it is turned against the subject himself we have already seen that depression is the expected outcome. Sometimes a hypercritical attitude, with obsessional behaviour in conscious existence, is a reflexion of the reinforcement of unconscious defences erected by the super-ego against aggressive impulses. The link between obsessional and depressive illnesses suggested by this psychodynamic view is reflected in clinical experience, where it is not at all uncommon to see patients with obsessional tendencies seeking help for the first time because they have developed a severe depression. Similarly an inevitable stage in the treatment by psychodynamic means of many cases of obsessional neurosis is the development of profound depression, which had hitherto been avoided at the price of the obsessional mechanisms.

* * *

At the beginning of Chapter 5 we prepared ourselves for the discovery that while the causes of mental illness would prove to be extremely varied, there would in the end be found to be no mental illness in which at least some overlapping between a number of different causal factors did not occur. The obvious importance of psychopathology in mental illness must never be allowed to obscure this fundamental fact. Intimately related to the emotional disturbance implicit in neurotic illness, and contributing in no small measure to the nature of the symptoms displayed, are the disturbances of physical, nervous, and glandular function which are always associated with emotion, and which are mediated by the autonomic nervous system and the complicated balance of the endocrine glands.

Autonomic and endocrine disturbance are at least as important in the course and progress of affective disorders, and indeed recent work in America and Britain suggests that one of the methods which has proved most effective in the relief and cure of depressive illnesses owes a great deal to its effect upon glandular function. In Chapter 4 we mentioned some of the more striking physical accompaniments of schizophrenic illness. The profound underlying physiological changes in schizophrenia have long engaged the attention of doctors and biochemists. At the present time there is a renewed search for some internal poison, produced through metabolic error in the actual biochemistry in the brain, as the answer to the riddle of schizophrenia. The hypothesis is that the patient who becomes afflicted with the disease has been born into the world with a biochemically determined predisposition, possibly because of an abnormality in his or her genes which may remain latent or may flower into clinical symptoms later in life. The basic postulated flaw is in the most highly developed nerve cells in the brain, called the cortical neurones. These are known to produce, and to be affected by, minute quantities of highly active chemical substances called enzymes. If these brain cells do produce, under stress, chemical substances poisonous or antagonistic to normal enzyme action, then communication in the brain will be disturbed, and the patient's brain is literally stewing in its own juice. If this hypothesis is correct, transference of bodily fluids from healthy to sick, or sick to healthy, should produce striking results. Instances are on record where this has been proved true. Exchange transfusions between healthy individuals and schizophrenic patients, in adult life and in childhood, have produced marked although transient benefits. In the reverse direction, citrated plasma from schizophrenic patients has produced temporary schizophrenic syndromes in volunteers. Animal studies, using albino rats, have suggested a specific factor in schizophrenic blood affecting behaviour in measurable and predictable ways. Fascinating and hopeful as this stimulating research hypothesis has seemed to be, it remains unfortunately true that we have yet finally to prove its truth, while all attempts to isolate the toxic substance, if it exists, have so far proved blind alleys.

Nevertheless, the evidence that there may be nothing more fundamental than a difference in the degree of stress, and the kind of biochemical reaction which it excites within the brain, between the normally tired and frightened person and the patient with schizophrenia, is steadily gaining ground. We have already learned that the experience of anxiety in a normal human being is accompanied by an increase in concentration of adrenalin, not only in the circulating blood, but in the brain itself. This has been shown experimentally to affect pathways of conduction in the brain, and may well account for the tendency in anxious and apprehensive people to misinterpret or marginally to misidentify external experience.

The worried sentry, crouching in his foxhole, tends in his accumulated fear and tension to mistake a tree for an approaching enemy, a creaking bough for the sound of a crawling man. During the Second World War, I can remember cold and lonely rear gunners firing streams of tracer ammunition at the shadow of their own aircraft cast by the moon upon the clouds below. This misinterpretation, which could have been fatally dangerous, by giving away the position of the aircraft itself, may have been caused by nothing more toxic or abnormal than a high adrenalin concentration combined with exhaustion and hunger.

If exhaustion, depletion, and fear together last long enough, they may be followed by actual hallucinations and disorder of thought. This has been proved by observations of volunteers who have taken part in sleep-deprivation experiments and subsequent tests. At a still further degree of stress, states of delirium are seen in sick people whose exhaustion and depletion have been further heightened and complicated by fever or failure of the normal metabolic processes. It is but a short step from these to the manifestations of schizophrenia itself.

It remains important to remember that in studying brain function we cannot afford to allow our relative technical proficiency in measuring biochemical changes to blind us to the fact that these are of ultimate importance only in their effect upon patterns of electrical activity, conduction, communication, and control in the functioning of the brain; and as doctors first and foremost, practising psychiatrists have always to remember that communication remains the ultimate key to the treatment of schizophrenia, or indeed of any other kind of illness. Part of the essence of successful treatment is always the gaining of contact and confidence in the relationship with the patient; once this has been achieved and a human and personal understanding created, the foundations have been secured for building the bridge over which such patients may cross back into normal harmony and contact with everyone else. This is a constant need, whatever the actual nature of the gulf which must be bridged.

Abnormality of glandular function has been postulated as a possible important factor in some forms of sexual inversion, although again the evidence for this tends to be not only complicated but sometimes contradictory. Often the most obvious basis of disturbed or abnormal sexual behaviour seems to lie in the emotional development of the person concerned. By no means all sexually inverted people regard themselves as ill or seek treatment, but for those who do the combined possibilities of physiology and psychopathology are available to help them.

There is another and most important side to this recognition of the contribution of many related causal factors to human illness. This is the rapidly developing body of knowledge which we possess about the significance of emotional factors and psychopathological processes in the development of what have hitherto been regarded as essentially physical or organic disorders. If a single patient reader takes away one idea from all those pursued in this book, the one I would most wish to convey is the essential interdependence of mind and body in health and sickness. This is, of course, no new idea; we encountered it from the outset of our preliminary historical study. But even now it is apt to be contested at the most untimely moments in the pursuit of truth in medicine, and always when this occurs the patient is ultimately the sufferer.

At present we are in the midst of a wave of enthusiastic study of the relationship between physical and psychological factors in disease. To those organic illnesses in which psychological stress appears to play a prominent and perhaps predominant part, the name of psychosomatic disorders has been given. Some of them will concern us in a later chapter, but in a wider and less rigid sense all illness is essentially psychosomatic, in as much as all illness forms part of the experience of the sick person, and both affects and is affected by that person's mind as well as his body. The emotional impact of a broken bone upon a patient's happiness and personal adjustment may be just as important as the effect upon his stomach or bowels of prolonged anxiety or resentment: and in both cases such effects may be considerable and far-reaching, and may demand a full and careful appreciation of the whole living person for their cure.

When, in retrospect, we survey the raw material with which anyone who intends to treat and therefore to try to understand human sickness must be concerned, whether such sickness be predominantly of mind or body, we see that its province extends from genetics to philosophy. It must include contributions from anatomy and physiology, embracing the field of normal physical structure and function, and in turn leading into biochemistry, and that delicate co-ordination of nervous and glandular activity which combine to shape the physical basis of personality. It must range further and concern itself with normal psychology and with the related studies of sociology and anthropology, at least in so far as they deal with the problems of the individual, and it must rest upon an appreciation of the fundamentals of psychodynamics and psychopathology.

No one of these fields of study is irrelevant or superfluous to that humble approach to the mystery of human existence which should characterize psychiatry; and while no one man can be proficient throughout the whole of so vast a field, and each student in it must be aware of the limits which his own capacity must inevitably impose upon his pretensions, it remains all the more necessary sometimes to stand back and open our eyes to the dimensions of a subject whose foundations are so inescapably wide.

In this as in any other appropriate study, the more learning, the more humility; the more humility, the more wisdom; and the more wisdom the greater the chance that among all who search and strive, one or two may stumble a little further towards the truth.

A Consideration of Treatment

WIDE indeed as are the implications of psychological medicine when regarded as a field of human knowledge, one aspect which is of supreme importance to patients and to practising doctors, and probably of greatest interest to the general public, is the question of treatment. This will form the subject of the next two chapters. In general the same kind of divisions can be made in a consideration of treatment as we have already found helpful in considering both the clinical manifestations and the causes of mental illness in general. But the method of treatment which is most closely associated in the public mind with psychiatry, the method in which psychiatry has at present the most original record and the most important contribution to make to the essence of the problem, is that of psychotherapy. Psychotherapy means literally the treatment of the mind. It therefore could logically be applied to all methods of treatment for mental illness. But its use is in practice restricted to those methods which rely for their effect upon an exchange of ideas between patient and doctor, directed towards relief of the patient's symptoms and distress.

The general aim of psychotherapy is therefore to improve the patient's capacity to deal with his own problems, to adjust himself to the conditions of his existence, and to make the best possible use of his own emotional and intellectual resources. Broadly speaking there are two kinds of psychotherapy, both having the same aim in common, and both capable of further subdivision, but differing essentially in that one kind seeks to alter the patient's circumstances or his immediate feelings about them so that they will become more bearable for him, and his subsequent adjustment therefore easier, while the other kind devotes itself principally to the task of so altering the patient that his innate capacities for dealing with any circumstances are improved.

Another way of indicating the difference between these two types of psychotherapy is to say that while the first type aims to deal primarily with those symptoms or problems which the patient at least recognizes as existing, even if he does not fully understand them, the second and necessarily deeper approach has the more fundamental goal of making him aware of faulty patterns of thought and feeling underlying his whole attitude to life, but neither present in consciousness nor immediately available to deliberate introspection.

Among the group of techniques coming under the first heading are those forms of reassurance, support, understanding, and guidance, which can be said to include general counselling of the Dutch uncle variety at the most simple end of the scale; while the more complicated applications of this technique, based upon a deeper understanding of the patient's problems gained through the knowledge we have encountered in earlier chapters, form part of the armoury of the general psychiatrist.

Also included in this group of psychotherapeutic techniques, but capable of auxiliary employment in any form of therapy, are those measures designed to provide meaningful occupations for patients in hospital or at home who are unable to carry on with the normal work of their daily lives. This type of activity is called occupational therapy, and its purpose lies in quickening the patient's interest and improving his morale by leading him to discover that there are useful things which he can still do successfully. A variety of constructive tasks are provided and their techniques taught by skilled professional occupational therapists. These are people who have been trained in a number of crafts of varying degrees of difficulty and complexity, and who have also received some personal training in dealing with the sick or disturbed individuals.

Occupational therapy provides contacts and interests which, although allied to the general purpose and direction of medical treatment, are separated from the immediate supervision and administration of doctors and nurses. In addition to the satisfaction and enjoyment which the acquisition and use of new skills can give to a patient, participation in occupational therapy can also provide a salutary change in personal and emotional environment for a patient who is finding his relationship with the nurses or his doctor difficult or distressing because of his illness.

Occupational therapy is not therefore simply a means of passing the time. It is an active method of treatment with a profound psychological justification. It is often a means whereby a depressed patient will take the first conscious step towards regaining hope and confidence in himself, or a schizophrenic will find a way of expressing his feelings which strengthens instead of weakening his contact with reality. In the quiet and constructive use of the hands to make things, even the most unhappy can often find a strange peace. And this in turn can make them better able to accept and benefit from other forms of treatment.

Under the general heading of psychotherapy may also be included social measures which seek to alter the patient's environment without necessarily involving the patient himself at all. These include recommendations about conditions of work, provision of alternative employment or housing, general advice to employers or members of the family, all aimed at eliminating some of the major difficulties with which the patient has found himself unable to contend. These are the province of the trained psychiatric social worker acting under the general supervision of the doctor, and will be more fully discussed in the next chapter.

The second kind of psychotherapy consists essentially in an individual approach undertaken with the particular patient, whereby a definite and permanent change in his personality is sought. The key to this type of procedure lies in increasing the patient's awareness of the real nature of his problems and his own methods of dealing with them, and is less concerned with reassurance or support of his existing capacities.

Both types of psychotherapy, which we shall presently consider in some detail, can be administered over long or short periods of time, either individually or, in some circumstances, to groups of suitable patients who come together for this purpose. In so far as any attempt to improve the happiness and well-being of an individual by dealing with his feelings and ideas can be called a form of psychotherapy, just as any attempt to improve his bodily health no matter how amateur or inexpert can be called a form of treatment, it is arguable that encouragement at a purely social level by friends or relatives might be included under this heading. In point of fact the majority of patients who come for treatment to a psychiatrist have had a great deal of this kind of gratuitous advice and therapy before any more serious attention has been given to their problem.

Both kinds of psychotherapy rely for success upon the establishment of a working relationship between doctor and patient; and this in turn implies a capacity on the doctor's part to manage this relationship with tact, honesty, integrity, and detachment. This last is an indispensable component of the relationship on the doctor's side; far from implying that the therapist does not care what happens to his patient, it must enable him to make the best possible use of his concern for his patient's health and happiness by preserving intact the judgement and clear-sightedness about the patient and his problems which can only come if the therapist is not himself emotionally involved. This is why it is absolutely impossible for a psychiatrist to treat successfully or even competently intimate friends or members of his own family. Moreover as we shall see later on, it is eminently desirable that he should have as little social contact with his patients outside the treatment relationship as possible.

That type of psychotherapy which, either because of the patient's limitations in time, mental or physical adaptability, or willingness to contemplate the risk and effort involved in more radical treatment, confines itself to an acceptance of the patient as he is, and to reinforcement of his existing assets without attempting to change or widen his self-awareness in any way, may still require considerable skill, experience, and training if it is to accomplish more than the usual advice and encouragement which is apt to be so freely proffered on all sides. Normally it takes the form of a series of interviews, which resemble superficially most other kinds of interview that the patient may already be used to having with doctors or lawyers or potential employers, except that here there must be ample time for the patient to describe his difficulties, and the doctor must be disposed to listen to them with unwavering patience and attention. The form of the first two or three interviews will in fact be dictated by the doctor's need to gain a complete life history of the patient, both from what he himself can tell, and from what any reliable informant in the family can add. A history of this kind is noted by the doctor, within the framework and under the headings which he has been trained to hold in his mind and to make the focus of his initial inquiries.

Such a history will in fact cover all the ascertainable circumstances of the patient's birth, early life, and development, physical and emotional growth and maturity through schooldays, adolescence, and subsequent career. It will embrace the history of previous mental and physical health in the patient and his family, the pattern of family life and personal relationships, and what can be deduced about the previous personality of the patient himself. Within the first few interviews it should be possible for the doctor to gain an understanding of his patient in some ways more comprehensive and detailed than perhaps has ever been gained by any other single person, including of course the patient himself.

Bearing in mind what we have seen of the significance of physical and emotional factors in the growth and development of all human beings, in the special importance of their early life and the patterns of behaviour which they have acquired during this time, it is evident that the picture which the doctor should be able to acquire of the patient, and the general direction and significance of the tendencies which he sees revealed in that patient's life, should enable him even at this early stage to form a reasonably sound idea of the genesis of the patient's symptoms, and the ways in which the stresses which he has encountered may be lightened or relieved.

Thereafter such advice or explanation as the doctor has to offer will be based not upon his own personal feelings about the desirability of any particular solution, still less upon a projection on his part of what he would do if he were in the patient's shoes – these being the two shortcomings from which so much well-intentioned advice so often suffers – but will rest upon his objective assessment of the patient's particular needs and possibilities, gained from the knowledge of the patient which he has carefully acquired and accepted without prejudice. At the same time he may feel that the social circumstances of the patient, and the emotional complications of his family life or employment, may well be modified successfully with the aid of further investigation and personal work with the family or employer by a trained psychiatric social worker.

He may also consider that the patient will require periodic advice and supervision over some time in order that the readjustment which is desirable may be followed up and consolidated. From the standpoint of the patient the knowledge that there exists somebody who not only understands him and his symptoms, but who is able to accept him without hostility or distress, to explain to him the nature of his difficulties and their connexion with the symptoms which he has developed, and to help and support him through the stresses which underlie those symptoms, is in itself often of very great help and comfort. It may enable such a patient to resume work and domestic responsibility which hitherto had proved impossible, and to take his place once again as an active member of the community.

Achievement of this kind, based essentially upon a comprehensive and detailed study of the patient's life, family background, and personal development, which is then subjected to careful and dispassionate analysis in the light of the doctor's knowledge of general medicine, normal psychology, genetics, and psychopathology, represents as it were the first line of defence against mental illness which the medical profession has to offer; and much of the avoidable unhappiness caused by fear, anxiety, and guilt in daily life can be successfully relieved or prevented in this way. Often it is quite unnecessary to confront the patient with more than a fraction of the underlying implications which such a study of his life has revealed. Indeed, by definition we are devoting this section of our description to the treatment of those patients for whom deeper insight is either impossible, unacceptable, or perhaps dangerous. But as a basis for any kind of professional advice, explanation, or reassurance, insight on the part of the doctor, and insight as accurate and complete as his skill and training can provide, is indispensable.

It is not too much to hope perhaps that one day psychotherapy of this limited but invaluable kind may be available to everyone who needs it. This could be achieved if only one-tenth of the total time spent in training doctors were devoted to the teaching of this technique, and to practice and experience in its use.

The more ambitious type of psychotherapy is that aimed at providing the patient with a varying degree of insight into his own conscious and unconscious life, into the deeper relationship of symptoms to emotional conflict, and thereby enabling him to achieve an awareness of himself which will not only help to arm him against his present difficulties, but will make it easier for him to control at least a part of his fate in the future. The aim here is not to make decisions for the patient, nor to offer him advice. It is so to increase his own awareness, that the decisions he makes himself will be based upon a fuller understanding of the motives which are prompting them.

It is easy to see that, at any rate to begin with, this is a far less comfortable and acceptable sort of treatment for the patient than the former kind, whereby at least a proportion of his burdens can be laid on the shoulders of his doctor. It is in fact a more difficult form of treatment for both the doctor and the patient, since it imposes a considerable strain upon both, and does not permit the doctor to relieve his anxiety about the patient by taking the patient's fears out of his own control.

Of all the forms of treatment which share this aim of increasing awareness and thereby liberating the patient from the bondage of unconscious conflict and emotion, the outstanding and pioneer contribution was that of Freud, who built up the system of investigation and therapy known as psycho-analysis. It is around the technique of psycho-analysis that almost all the popular conceptions of psychiatry have been built up. There belong the couch, the recumbent patient, the wise, silent, and in the popular eye faintly ludicrous figure of the psychiatrist, industriously writing down the random and remarkable statements uttered in the secrecy of the consulting room. All this of course is a heaven-sent gift to the robust opponents of psychological medicine in any form, as well as to the lively satirists and cartoonists whose admirable task it is to reflect our pompous foibles and to invite our mirth. The psychiatrist who resents this barrage of ridicule, by no means all of it malicious, is partly at the mercy of his own inner insecurity. In this he is of course only human. But lurking behind this confusing blend of popular interest and suspicion, which is responsible both for the recent avalanche of films and books with a psychiatric theme on the one hand, and the cartoons of parrots reclining on couches unburdening their souls to solemn bearded men on the other, there is the familiar and perfectly sincere conflict of feeling which we have seen characterizing the public attitude to mental illness from time immemorial. What really goes on in the course of psycho-analysis of an individual patient? For those who have borne with me thus far it should not prove too difficult to discover and understand the answer to this question.

The initial interviews are likely to follow the same general pattern as those of any other psychotherapeutic procedure. So far as possible the history must be obtained and noted in an orderly and comprehensible way in the analyst's records. Thereafter it is the task of the patient to produce, out loud and absolutely without suppression or selection of any kind, all his thoughts and feelings about whatever is uppermost in his mind. This may sound difficult, but in practice it is far more difficult even than it sounds, at least in the early stages of treatment.

Offered the hitherto inconceivable opportunity of acknowledgement and expression, many of the ideas which rise into the patient's mind are thrust down almost before he has had time to become aware of them; and this of course is preconscious rather than truly unconscious material. How much more difficult still is that acknowledgement of the underlying source of such ideas, which can only be achieved with time, practice, and above all, a confidence which at the outset no patient can possibly have.

The nature of the immediate practical difficulties of conforming to this one essential rule of procedure, namely that nothing shall be suppressed and nothing selected, demands that every possible measure which will help the patient to do his part of the work be adopted. It is for this reason, and this alone, that patients are encouraged to lie down, to relax completely, to look at nothing more exciting than the ceiling, and to talk without the visible presence of another person to distract them. The analyst sits out of their range of vision, and while they are able to continue their part of the job, may have no cause for intervention of any kind. But all the time the analyst is recording, sorting, and studying the material produced, bearing in mind its possible interpretations and its correlation with what has gone before, so that as the analysis proceeds he accumulates a deeper source of understanding of the patient which he does not obtrude into the process, but uses only when, without his help, the patient cannot go further.

Inevitably and repeatedly any patient conscientiously doing his best in this way encounters resistance in his own mind, violent feelings which he cannot or dare not pursue further, and often finds, when approaching the outer defences of some long-buried painful memory or feeling, that he cannot go on. We know from our brief survey of normal psychology and psychopathology that much of what must inevitably cause him difficulty and distress will date from the earlier personal relationships which have been connected with intense and conflicting emotion. The release of such emotion in the course of treatment, before its source has reached awareness or been understood and accepted, is in itself intensely disturbing, and the patient instinctively seeks to rationalize or project the emotion which he feels. Under the conditions of treatment the person who is inevitably selected for this rationalization or projection is the analyst.

In this way during the course of treatment the patient comes to feel the love and hatred, the dependence and the rebellion, rivalry or rejection towards the analyst, that he has felt but never fully acknowledged for other people in his life; people whose impact has been earlier and inescapably close, people such as his parents, his first love, or the friends and enemies, heroes and villains, of his childhood. This uncritical and barely understood investment of emotion in the person conducting the treatment is called the transference. Normally it begins by being positive, in the sense that the natural gratitude and respect which the patient feels for someone who is prepared to take a considerable amount of trouble in helping him, is uppermost. No transference ever remains wholly positive throughout the course of treatment; and if it did, nothing of fundamental importance could be achieved, for no unbearably hostile emotions would be uncovered.

Sometimes a transference may become almost entirely negative, and then the course of treatment, perhaps the patient, and sometimes even the analyst, will be in danger; but the control of the transference, the regulation of its depth and intensity, are to a great extent in the hands of the analyst, since he has the underlying interpretation available for use as the occasion demands. To interpret or interfere with the transference too early is to deprive it of the strength necessary to enable the patient to carry on with his already difficult contribution to the treatment. It is also, at a deeper level, to imply a tendency on the part of the analyst to escape from the obligation of his part in treatment, and may even spring from his own anxiety or insecurity if this has not been adequately dealt with in the course of his training. But to interpret inadequately or too late, or to fail to deal with the transference situation at all, is to risk the development of a total dependence on the part of the patient which may be a more serious complication than the illness with which he presented himself.

The handling of the transference situation is thus of vital importance in the course of psycho-analysis, as indeed in the course of all forms of psychotherapy. It is the existence of the transference which both enables the patient to discover the nature of his underlying feelings and then to acknowledge them. Once this has been done he often finds himself able to regard them in a far more tolerant and dispassionate light, and so be liberated not simply from their effect upon his past but from their influence upon his future.

The task of the analyst is at first to establish a working relationship and to gain an overall appreciation of the nature and probable trends of the patient's personal problems and ways of dealing with them, and then, working within the influence accorded him by the transference relationship, to help the patient acquire insight into his own personality and to acknowledge the implications of his own emotions, as they emerge in the course of treatment. He does not give advice nor impose restrictions upon the patient's life outside the treatment; nor, in the course of orthodox analysis, does he attempt in any way to direct the sequence or the course of the patient's own self-examination. This naturally means that an analysis is apt to be a very lengthy and time-consuming procedure. The patient may spend many interviews working through or around a single conflict in all its ramifications in his personal life; moreover he may evade or shelve problems as long as his own emotional tension permits him to do so. The analyst may interpret such resistance if he feels that the patient cannot otherwise surmount it, but he does not make such interpretations simply to speed up the procedure.

The advantage claimed for this method of treatment is that when completed it is radical and exhaustive. What has been spent in time has been repaid in depth and degree of awareness and consequent stability. In practice a full analysis demands not less than three to five interviews a week for anything from two to four years, excluding only the inevitable breaks caused by holidays and absence of doctor or patient. Any procedure which demands so much expenditure of skilled time is inevitably costly. Moreover it is suitable only for patients whose intelligence, determination, and resources of time and money, are sufficient to enable them to go through with it and to profit from it.

It is thus a highly selective and self-limiting form of treatment, and moreover it can be practised safely and successfully only by those whose training has fulfilled certain rigorous conditions which we shall be examining in a later chapter. But despite these limitations it is a procedure of great importance. This importance derives not simply from the results which it can produce in individually suitable patients, but from the body of knowledge which the method has contributed to psychopathology, and most of all from the application of both the knowledge and the method in modified form to the evolution of various techniques of briefer psychotherapy devoted to the attainment of insight, but aimed at providing this at least in its immediate essentials within a matter of weeks or months, and by means less expensive in time and money.

*

All brief methods of analytical psychotherapy depend for their brevity upon the reduction of two main elements which normally comprise a considerable part of psycho-analytic procedure, and absorb much of the time involved. These two elements are the repetition involved in working through problems against resistance, while relying solely upon the patient's free associations to bring these problems back into the field of exploration every time they are evaded or shelved, and also the time and effort consumed in dealing with comparatively irrelevant material, and in coming to the point in material which is unquestionably important but too emotionally charged to be readily handled by the patient.

The essence of all methods of brief psychotherapy is therefore in some way to select those areas of the patient's life which are most relevant to the problems he faces and the symptoms he displays, and having selected them to focus the entire procedure upon them until they have been dealt with, and the necessary changes thereby effected in the mental life of the patient. Techniques of this kind are on the whole harder to acquire and to practise successfully even than the methods of full-scale analysis; there are a number in existence, but only a few have proved their worth. The need for them, provided that they are consistent and dependable in competent hands, is unquestionable.

The earliest technique of this kind was that used by Freud himself when he was working originally with Joseph Breuer. In fact it preceded the development of the standard procedure of analysis, produced by free associations on the part of the patient, and was abandoned by Freud in favour of free association because he found the latter method more comprehensive and therefore more effective for full analysis. This early method rested upon the use of hypnosis.

Hypnosis, as we have seen, was widely used at the Salpêtrière, when Freud was a pupil there, to produce and remove states of altered consciousness by suggestion. Freud discovered that under its influence patients were sometimes able to remember and disclose emotions and experiences of which they had no knowledge in consciousness. Moreover, after such revelation, they usually lost many of their symptoms, and might even become well, if the emotionally charged material were retained in consciousness after hypnosis had been terminated.

It is one of the indications of Freud's vision and genius that he perceived what nobody else had realized before, namely that the important thing about the success of this treatment was the patient's ability to recover lost memories and feelings, and to accept them afterwards, rather than the particular procedure whereby this was achieved. This was all the more a considerable feat since the obvious drama and spectacular nature of hypnotic states had hitherto obsessed the attention of everyone at the Salpêtrière.

When Freud discovered that by no means all patients could co-operate in hypnosis, and that certain others were unable to accept or integrate the material uncovered during sessions once those sessions were concluded, he abandoned hypnosis completely and went to work with free association. The technique of orthodox analysis is still built exclusively upon this latter method. However, in recent years the increasingly recognized need for some short cut in analytical procedure has led to a resumption of hypnotic methods by some workers in this field. The disadvantages, that only about one person in four or five is a suitable subject for this method of treatment, and that the degree of conscious participation, acceptance, responsibility, and full awareness of the emotional implications of the material produced, are all liable to be diminished, remain. It is as yet too early in the renaissance of this method to say whether it has much future in routine practice. Its value in particular types of research is more likely to become established.

Another method of brief psychotherapy which utilizes a similar technique for the rapid production and subsequent handling of difficult material, relies upon the use of physical methods, such as partial anaesthesia with ether, or the intravenous injection of solutions of soluble barbiturate preparations, to reduce the patient's difficulties in producing material, or in living again in imagination situations which are painful to remember. We shall have occasion to mention the physical aspect of these techniques later in this chapter, but their principle does not differ essentially from that of hypnotherapy.

It remains at this point to add that there is some dispute about the degree to which emotional resistance can be overcome by such methods. Certainly in clinical practice, where the well-being of the patient must always take precedence over any and every short cut in treatment, there is little to suggest that patients will disclose under the influence of drugs or anaesthetics, or even under hypnosis, anything which they have consciously determined not to disclose before treatment has begun. They may indeed encounter and express memories and ideas of which they were previously *unaware* in consciousness, and which unaided they may be entirely unable to accept or face. But there is no parallel whatever between the use of methods of this kind in the treatment of sick and disturbed people, and those naive misconceptions of their use implied by the terms 'truth drug' or 'truth serum' when applied to them. Information extorted by force or subterfuge against the will of the informant has no place in medicine. Moreover such information is in fact notoriously unreliable, being coloured by the effect of the procedure upon the morale and judgement of the informer, and inevitably influenced in one direction or another by his conception of what his inquisitor wants him to say.

All other techniques of brief psychotherapy are based upon direct interviews between patient and doctor in which, after the initial life study had been made, the doctor selects and in one way or another focusses the work of treatment upon those areas in the patient's life which his experience and judgement lead him to consider the most important in the production of the patient's difficulties. Mention, but only mention, can be made of the importance of the method of distributive analysis, in conformity with the original principles of Adolf Meyer and described by Diethelm, Muncie, and others in America; of the brief analysis of Alexander and French; of Stekel's shortened analytical technique; of the method of Karen Horney; of the applied psycho-analysis of Felix Deutsch; and of the method of insight therapy taught by Professor Finesinger in the University of Maryland.

Distributive analysis entails a reasonably wide selection of areas for exploration and leaves the degree of detail, the extent of active participation by the doctor, and the general method to the discretion of the individual therapist. It is preceded by an exhaustive life study which includes a full consideration of physical and hereditary factors, in the tradition established by Professor Adolf Meyer.

The method propounded by Alexander and French differs little in technique from that of orthodox analysis, except that the patient's attention is directed towards immediate constellations of emotion and experience which seem most closely connected with symptoms, interviews are held at lengthening intervals once relief has begun, and cessation of symptoms is accepted as the limited goal of treatment, no matter how much or how little material has actually been worked through.

The Stekelian technique embraces the enterprising innovation of announcing beforehand that the treatment is to be limited in time to a certain fixed period, usually three or four months, no matter what the outcome. Thereafter, whenever resistance is encountered, interpretation of that resistance is made at once, and in this way the patient is constantly thrown back upon the necessity for facing reasons for evading the issues involved, or dreading the feelings which they arouse.

Doctor Felix Deutsch employs a technique similar to that first described by Professor Korzybsky. He focusses attention from the outset upon the actual complaint of the patient in the very words which the patient employs, claiming with some success that the physician can rapidly relate particular descriptions of pain and suffering, whether of mind or body, to those aspects of the patient's emotional existence with which they are most closely if unconsciously connected. He keeps the process of treatment concentrated as far as possible upon the substance of these presenting complaints, by saying little or nothing in reply to questions or demands from the patient, except to pick up and repeat to him the particular words which the patient himself has used in telling his story; particularly those parts of it which seem to the doctor to be linked most directly with the underlying psychopathology.

Examples of such links, which occur repeatedly in practice, are found in the association of repressed disgust with the subjective complaint of nausea; hostility and aggressive feelings with the symptoms of stabbing or gnawing pain in the abdomen or head; and anxiety with palpitations, breathlessness, or muscular tension, felt as cramp or aching in the limbs. Superficial as these few examples necessarily are, they reflect a fundamental relationship between emotions and bodily symptoms which finds expression in such everyday terms as a 'sick or aching heart', 'cold feet', or 'a pain in the neck'. Deutsch believes that patients can often be led directly from their account of such symptoms to a release and awareness of underlying emotional problems, which once encountered will prove endurable, while the complaints which overlay them cease.

Professor Finesinger has evolved a technique which bears some resemblance to the one just described, but differs in that, as in the method of distributive analysis, the areas on which attention is to be focussed are selected by the therapist, in the light of the general picture of the patient's life which emerges in the early interviews. Thereafter the technique of contributing to the discussion as little as possible, and then only by echoing words or phrases actually used by the patient, to encourage him to elaborate them, forms the basis of the method in its early stages. Later on in treatment, interpretations, of a depth and complexity appropriate only to the scale demanded by the level at which the therapist has chosen to work, are given; but such interpretations are never made primarily on a theoretical basis, or out of the resources of the therapist's knowledge and experience in general, but are related entirely to the actual material about the patient's own life and his own feelings provided by the patient himself in his own words.

All these methods therefore have in common the paring down of the analytical procedure to deal exclusively with the immediate or essentially alterable sources of complaint. The criticism sometimes offered by orthodox analysts of such methods, is that they tend to patch rather than to re-create the personality of the patient. The answer to this criticism is that the resources of medicine as a whole must in practice often be content to do just that and no more, for as many people as possible. Moreover the perfectionist attitude implicit in this criticism cannot claim to be supported by the results of full-scale analysis, in any but a minute proportion even of those for whom it is practicable.

Apart from psycho-analysis, and the many techniques which

are derived from and based upon it, there remain the schools of Jungian and Adlerian analytical psychotherapy to be included under the general heading of those psychotherapeutic techniques which aim at insight and awareness as the basis of change. The way in which they differ in their underlying content and philosophy from psycho-analysis has already been indicated in outline in the preceding chapter. The technique of their administration to an individual patient in terms of interviews, time, and money, does not differ essentially from those already described, although they are not usually as prolonged as a full-scale analysis along Freudian lines.

There remains the somewhat contested school of eclectic individual therapy, which has been vigorously assaulted in its time but continues to command the respect and practical attention of many well-trained psychiatrists, to whom exclusive submission to one particular line of orthodox dogma in their subject makes no appeal. In their methods, technique, and the proportions in which they draw upon the various schools already outlined, they display in their treatment of patients as much diversity as artists or technicians in any other craft, such as surgery or painting. As to the merit of their method, they would perhaps choose to be judged by results. On this basis they will stand comparison with practitioners of any other school.

*

Every one of the methods just described is used primarily on an individual basis, whereby a single patient is treated by a single doctor in a number of interviews. But while the wider and more competent use of supportive and re-educative forms of psychotherapy, mentioned at the beginning of the chapter, can help to bring treatment and relief to many patients who stand in need of it, and the further evolution and practice of brief methods of insight therapy will progressively enlarge the possibilities for treating patients with more complex disorder, there must remain a great many patients whose need of treatment based upon an understanding and concern for the emotional element in their illness, can find little or no relief from the resources of the medical profession at present available. This is the more understandable when we remind ourselves that about a third of all human sickness contains an emotional element at least severe enough to require recognition and inclusion in treatment, whatever else is done. The most economical, and therefore in many ways the most practical way of extending psychotherapy to patients of this kind may be by the method of group treatment.

This is a way of treating people which has received professional recognition and development only during the last twenty-five years; but the principles which underlie it are as old as man himself, and were used by Mark Antony when he roused the people of Rome to avenge the death of Caesar, and by Mesmer when he grouped his patients together round the magnetic cauldron. Feelings which people develop in a group can be studied and used to amplify and intensify their natural urge towards recovery and understanding. Furthermore their presence as members of a group can increase the sense of support and the readiness to accept and to be accepted, which form an important part of the process of treatment.

Groups of various sizes have been treated, but probably the best size is somewhere around eight to a dozen people. Such people meet together with a doctor as a member but not as the leader of the group, to talk about their feelings and their problems, and as their confidence increases to attempt to offer and and to accept among themselves awareness, courage, and compassion, and to contribute to their experience as well as to gain from it. The doctor's role in the group must be largely that of observer and occasionally interpreter; his interpretations must confine themselves to the meaning of the emotional interaction which is taking place and the ways in which everyone concerned can accept and learn from it. He neither seeks nor assumes formal leadership, because this would interfere with his capacity to reflect an awareness of the struggle for power which, even in a small community, is one of the powerful emotional factors which will inevitably appear. Group therapy is still comparatively in its infancy, but already it has begun to achieve interest and stimulate results.

One vivid and spectacular outgrowth has been the method of what is called psychodrama, whereby members of the group produce and act scenes from the daily life or past experience of one of them which have a particular significance for him, and wherein he plays his own role while they play the parts of others in his life or in the world about him, which in real existence he finds threatening or provocative. After the performance the players and spectators discuss what has happened, what it has meant to the protagonist, and what emerges from his attitude and experiences in this situation. By taking it in turn to accord to each member who desires it the central role in such a drama, the group achieve a collective interest, sympathy, awareness, and sense of union, which are not the least valuable results of this kind of treatment. The contrast between the role of the doctor in modern group therapy, and that assumed by Mark Antony or Mesmer, is not unimportant, nor is it accidental. The role of the orator or of the charlatan is more often to make men blind than to make them aware.

At the beginning of this chapter we defined psychotherapy as a method of treatment relying for its effect upon an exchange of ideas between patient and doctor, directed towards relief of the patient's symptoms and distress. It is time now to add that by far the most important factor in effective relief or cure, or indeed change of any kind, is the emotional quality and reality of the ideas exchanged.

A competent psychiatrist can often see in essence the core of a patient's problems by the time he has completed the preliminary study of the patient's life. Sometimes patients, sensing something of the purpose of this study, will demand an exposition of what is in the doctor's mind, in the belief or hope that this will offer them an immediate key to recovery. But in this sense unfortunately no one can learn from another's experience of his life, no matter how expert or accurate the impression formed by the doctor may prove to be.

We build up our patterns of thought and feeling slowly and often painfully, and the emotional experiences which have gone into them have to be relived rather than retold before we are liberated from their influence upon us. There is all the difference in the world between the intellectual formulation of a man's problems and personality, and that change of heart which alone can bring him release from the chains in which they may have bound him. Whether we call the link which the doctor can establish between the one and the other the transference situation or the patient–doctor relationship, we are really dealing with an emotional bond which acts as a catalyst for all the chaotic feeling and experience of the sick or unhappy person.

On the patient's side much of this emotional bond springs, as we have seen, from the reservoirs of stifled and forgotten passions; on the doctor's side from the detached but absolutely sincere and dedicated concern to help, however humbly, another human being. Behind them both there must be that greatest gift of all, the capacity to love; and for all the wisdom, skill, and technical accomplishment which ought to go into it, psychotherapy is fundamentally but another way of using the creative power of love towards the restoration of human happiness and peace of mind.

*

Seen in this way, there is clearly a place for psychotherapy in the treatment of all forms of illness, in so far as, in its widest sense, psychotherapy forms the basis of much that is most valuable in the relationship between doctor and patient. Its principles are employed, sometimes almost unwittingly, even in what is known as a good bedside manner. It is in the handling of human relationships in medicine that psychiatry has still something to teach, which extends far beyond its own technical province. But in the sphere of mental and emotional illnesses the degree to which psychotherapy will be employed alone, or will be combined with other forms of treatment, will depend a great deal upon the nature of the particular illness under consideration.

Generally speaking it is in those disturbances of mind and personality whose physical basis is as yet undetermined that psychotherapy alone has the greatest part to play. It is of particular value in states of anxiety, where physical methods may also be employed but are usually subsidiary; in hysteria; in obsessional compulsive states of certain kinds; and in general for those neuroses in which the patient both needs and can co-operate in a personal relationship of this particular kind.

Psycho-analysis is most effective in the treatment of long-standing neuroses in general, of certain types of sexual inversion, and of personality disorder. It has been used experimentally as the sole treatment for depression and for schizophrenic forms of illness, but here physical methods have a greater part to play in the opinion of most psychiatrists, although the value of psychotherapy in the course of such treatment must never be overlooked.

*   *   *

Like psychotherapy in its widest sense, physical treatment for mental illness has been employed as far back as medical history can take us. In Chapter 1 we encountered very early the shamans, or medicine men of primitive communities, who bored holes in patients' skulls to release the imprisoned devils. That blend of hostility, and faith in the magical power of some dramatic action, which we have also seen characterizing the human attitude to mental illness, has produced a succession of physical forms of treatment which, in the degree of violence or shock which they involved, have seemed to survive at least in part in certain modern forms of what is called 'shock therapy'.

In psychiatry today we hope and believe that these comparisons are based upon a similarity more apparent than real. Neither in motive nor result need we equate the sudden fall into the icy dungeon, the twirling stool, or Reil's non-injurious torture, or even the cupping, blistering, and purging which psychiatry of an earlier day shared with general medicine, with modern electrical methods of treatment, with insulin therapy, or with those operations of neuro-surgery expressly concerned with the relief of mental suffering.

Before considering in detail those specific modern techniques which psychiatry has evolved and learnt to use in the treatment of particular forms of illness, we must take account of the general principles of physical treatment derived from the whole art and science of medicine, whose application is at least as important in the practice of psychiatry as elsewhere.

The treatment of intercurrent disease or injury in patients with mental illness is of course an obvious necessity. Even before the full implications of the relationship between body and mind in medicine were consciously accepted, this principle was indisputable on the grounds of humanity alone. Nowadays, whether the connexion between the mental state of the patient and any physical illness from which he may be suffering is understood or not, all the necessary measures to restore him to physical health are undertaken as a matter of course. Moreover there is increasing evidence to show that there is no single aspect of physical well-being which is not immediately relevant to and affected by the psychological condition of the patient. Of particular importance in the general assessment and subsequent treatment of all forms of mental illness are the level of the patient's general nutrition, the state of his blood, and the functioning of his endocrine glands. Vitamin therapy, blood transfusion, and in certain cases the administration of appropriate extracts of glandular secretions all have their place in the general physical therapy of mental illness.

In Chapter 4 we saw that a substantial proportion of mental illnesses arise in the course of physical diseases or defects, and could be accepted as being due to them. The treatment of such diseases or defects is a task which may be carried out by the general physician or surgeon, or by the psychiatrist whose background is sufficiently comprehensive; or such treatment may be shared between them. Examples include the treatment of acute toxic confusional states, of which delirium tremens is only a special example, by correcting underlying infection or physical disturbance, and the treatment of general paralysis of the insane by the modern anti-syphilitic methods, such as penicillin, designed to destroy the disease parasites in the brain.

Such methods of treatment, like those used in all other branches of medicine, are constantly being improved or replaced, and psychiatry makes use of those best suited to its purpose at the time. Until quite recently the method of choice in the treatment of syphilis involved the use of organic arsenical preparations, and, where the brain was the organ chiefly affected, treatment by increasing body temperature to 105° F. or more, which was achieved by deliberately infecting the patient with a particular strain of malaria and then controlling the fevers with the appropriate drugs. This latter form of treatment is used in conjunction with penicillin in a number of clinics today, although there are indications that it may well be supplanted by penicillin alone in the near future.

A field of general medical treatment in which psychiatry is naturally concerned is in the use of sedatives of all kinds, from the most mild to those which can produce and maintain an unconsciousness of varying degrees of depth for hours or days at a time. The most common general use of sedatives in psychiatry is as an adjunct to treatment of other kinds, whereby the level of emotional tension may be reduced and the patient thereby enabled to deal more effectively with his environment and to co-operate more readily in psychotherapy or whatever forms of treatment are necessary. Modern sedative drugs, taken under supervision, are so varied and graded in their effect and the rapidity with which they are broken down in the body and excreted, that the fear which many people have of making use of them, even as a temporary measure, can be safely discarded. They form an invaluable auxiliary tool in the hands of the qualified doctor, and used in this way will often restore sleep at night and something approaching relaxation and well-being by day, at an early stage in the treatment of people suffering from tension, anxiety, and distress.

A particular application of the use of sedatives or partial anaesthesia in the release of suppressed or repressed emotion, has already been mentioned. This technique has been called abreaction, and is apt to be particularly valuable when the buried material is comparatively recent and compact, as in the experiences of war or natural catastrophes such as fire, earthquake, avalanche, or other accident in which the patient may have been involved. Often after such experiences memory for the event, which has been partly or completely lost, can be restored in one or two periods of treatment in which much of the unbearable emotion returns, but is on this occasion accepted and integrated in consciousness.

Abreaction can be secured with ether, when an explosive emotional outburst is anticipated and can be controlled; less explosive or more protracted work of this kind can be done with the aid of intravenous barbiturate preparations. As well as states of amnesia, recent and severe attacks of acute anxiety will sometimes respond to treatment of this kind. It is obvious that the selection of cases suitable for this type of treatment must be made with great care, and must depend to a considerable extent upon the capacity of the patient to deal with the material released in this heroic fashion. The use of abreactive techniques in patients on the edge of schizophrenic illness, for example, can prove utterly disastrous.

Another valuable method of employing sedatives, this time for a specifically quietening effect, is in the production of continuous sleep for up to twenty out of the twenty-four hours, for periods of from five to ten days. This is a method of treatment which requires considerable skill and experience in its management, particularly from the nursing standpoint, since the essentials of the patient's intake of food and output of waste products, and the general physiological balance of his system, have to be maintained by attention during the brief periods of wakefulness. Properly handled it has a place in the treatment of states of agitation or hypomania, as a temporary measure which sometimes succeeds in ending or mitigating an attack, and in some conditions where acute anxiety is related either to conscious and unbearable stress, or to factors with which the patient is as yet simply unable to deal.

During the past ten years there has been a remarkable advance in the number and diversity of particular groups of medicines, usually marketed in tablet form, which have been proved to produce changes in mood and subjective emotional tension far more specific than either general sedation or stimulation. Four groups merit brief mention, although an adequate understanding of their chemical nature and mode of action is essentially the responsibility of the doctor rather than the layman. These four groups are respectively:

1 the tranquillizers
2 the more powerful anti-excitement and anti-confusional preparations
3 the symptomatic anti-depressant medicines
4 the more basic anti-depressants.

The tranquillizers, although represented by a large number of medicines, are not the enormous group which the public are apt to imagine, nor are they in any way the most important. But they have one essential characteristic in common, which can be very valuable in psychiatric treatment. This is their power to produce comparative calmness and tranquillity without making the patient sleepy. The most successful are derivatives of the chemical compound called meprobamate, and although they appear to be completely safe, like all drugs with an active effect on the central nervous system they should never be taken except under medical supervision.

The second group listed above are all derivatives of another newly-discovered chemical compound, chlorpromazine. They appear to affect the brain by diminishing the vicious circle of exhaustion, apprehension, and misinterpretation which we saw was potentially important in the genesis of delusions and hallucinations. They are therefore of extreme value in controlling states of delirium, states of toxic excitement or confusion which may follow the sudden withdrawal of alcohol or narcotics in people who are addicted to them, and above all, in the treatment of schizophrenia itself. In this field, in combination with electrical treatment they have virtually replaced the pioneer method of deep insulin treatment, discovered by Sakel, which was for many years the only active hope for patients with this disease.

The symptomatic anti-depressant preparations have been known to psychiatry for a longer time, although even they have only come to the fore in the last twenty years. Most of them are derived from a chemical known as amphetamine, and its derivatives, and like the other drugs which we have been considering, are marketed under various trade names such as dexedrine, methidine, benzedrine, ritalin, methedrine. These are all highly reliable preparations made by very reputable firms, but their unsupervised use is not without danger. Their subjective effect is to increase mental alertness and to diminish the awareness of fatigue. Their exact method of action is not fully known, but they appear to affect the biochemistry of the body, and particularly of the brain, in such a way that the accumulation of the normal waste products of activity is delayed, at least in the brain itself. Taken at night they may interfere with sleep, and in large doses over a period of time may actually disturb judgement and consciousness. This is particularly liable to happen when their use is combined with that of alcohol in sensitive people.

None the less they have a real contribution to make to the treatment of minor states of depression, retardation, and that irritable fatigue which we have seen associated with certain neuroses and with the aftermath of some kinds of injury or damage to the brain. They are also useful as a temporary method of warding off mental and physical fatigue when this is particularly essential.

They were used in this way during World War II, particularly in certain special units; but their general use among, for example, members of air crew was discouraged since errors of judgement sometimes occurred in fatigued pilots using these preparations experimentally, errors of which the subject was not even aware. This may be the basis of the widely circulated story of the student who entered for an examination after priming himself with a massive dose of one of these preparations, proceeding, as he thought, to excel himself, only to discover some days later that his paper contained nothing more informative than his own name written repeatedly several thousand times. But this particular story is almost certainly fiction from start to finish.

The effect of some of these preparations upon children is of particular interest. We shall be considering some of the broad principles which underlie the treatment of disturbed or sick children in the next chapter; but in the management of such cases the part played by drugs is small. In practice they tend to be limited to specific anti-convulsant and anti-epileptic preparations for children suffering from epilepsy in any form; and the administration of benzedrine compounds in the treatment of excessively aggressive, destructive, or over-active children.

A combination of benzedrine with ephedrine is often effective in the treatment of certain cases of bed-wetting in children who are particularly heavy sleepers. The value of ephedrine in these cases probably lies in its direct effect upon the autonomic nervous system: by raising the general level of alertness of the system and increasing the tone of the muscles closing the valvular opening of the bladder, it helps to diminish the tendency for the bladder to empty itself automatically during sleep. Automatic emptying of this kind, which occurs without waking the child, is normal in infants, but it has to be superseded by a capacity to wake when the bladder becomes distended, before the child will become dry at night.

This is an important step towards maturity in the child's development, and takes place normally sometime about the end of the first or second year. It represents an increasing involvement of the higher centres of the brain in controlling primitive functions even during sleep, but anything which disturbs the child's general emotional state may delay its completion, or cause it to disappear after it has already become established. In this way a previously clean and dry child may revert to bed-wetting if it is upset or disturbed, for example by being separated from its parents.

It seems probable that the contribution of benzedrine to the treatment of bed-wetting lies more in its effect upon the controlling function just mentioned than in any increase in wakefulness. Indeed in children the stimulant effect of benzedrine sometimes appears to be reversed. Over-active, excitable children may become placid and equable, and a dose which, in comparable proportion to body weight, might send a father leaping about the house, will sometimes put a frenzied child to sleep. This effect, however, is generally confined to children who are suffering from aggressive and over-active behaviour as their chief complaint.

The fourth group in our list, the basic anti-depressant medicines, are in some ways the most interesting of all recent innovations in the psychiatric pharmacopoeia. They consist of one large group of drugs, called the mono-amine-oxidase inhibitors, and one much smaller group derived from a compound called imipramine. The M.O.A. inhibitors seem to work by preventing or delaying the destruction in the brain of adrenalin and its precursors or potentiators, such as sympathin and serotonin. This is necessarily an over-simplification of what must happen, but it enables an account of the second or imipramine type of drug to be fitted into a comparable plan of action, in that imipramine compounds themselves potentiate sympathin, serotonin, and adrenalin. The hypothesis has therefore been raised that it is an exhaustion or an incapacity of the brain to use adrenalin, sympathin, and serotonin normally, which is one of the factors responsible for depression.

Whether this hypothesis is true or false, the important clinical fact is that by the proper use of the anti-depressant preparations, the illness itself can, in about a quarter of all cases, promptly and correctly be diagnosed by the doctor, and respond to medicinal treatment alone, without even the necessity for admission to hospital. It is not too much to say that this is yet one more way in which recent advances in treatment have revolutionized the general outlook in mental illness.

A striking and somewhat disturbing reflection which is bound to occur to the thoughtful reader, a reflection which will be further endorsed and emphasized when we go on to consider the discovery and development of modern methods of physical treatment in this subject, is the fact that so much of this discovery has been based upon empirical findings; that is, upon finding that things work long before we knew how they worked or why they worked. Many of our most valuable medicinal preparations, and several of our most important techniques in physical treatment, have been developed from ideas which, however fruitful, were often wide of their original target, and sometimes actually completely wrong. But the combination of patience, open-mindedness, and readiness to change the direction of experiment and enquiry, has enabled many of these achievements to be brought to a very high level of reliability in the actual relief of suffering, within the past two or three decades.

While in the realm of tablets there remains one other important preparation to be mentioned. This is the drug called 'antabuse' (tetraethyl-thiuram-disulphide), which has been evolved as a useful weapon in the treatment of chronic alcoholism. Its action upon the body and brain appears to be comparable to that of the amphetamine derivatives, but it produces its effects in precisely the opposite way. That is to say, it prevents the *breakdown* of certain toxic products formed at one stage in the digestion of alcohol, so that these products which are called aldehydes accumulate in the circulation instead of being swept away. The result of this is that when a person who has a sufficient concentration of antabuse in his circulation takes alcohol in any form, and even in quite minute doses, he experiences within a few minutes a number of highly unpleasant symptoms which combine the more disastrous features of a bad hangover with certain other horrible sensations and bodily changes peculiar to the antabuse reaction itself.

Antabuse thus provides a method of insuring oneself against the sudden impulsive relief which a quick drink promises, particularly to those who depend upon it. For the alcoholic for whom, in the words of a famous organization, one drink is too much but a thousand drinks are not enough, insurance of this kind can be of great value. It means that for a period of some eight to twelve hours after taking this twice-daily dose of antabuse, he knows that it will be useless, certainly unpleasant, and possibly extremely dangerous to take a drink. Therefore, while he may very well decide to omit the treatment and, after waiting for a suitable period, resume drinking, this will be a comparatively deliberate decision; while he still wishes to remain a total abstainer he can use antabuse to strengthen his resistance to the fatal impulse which otherwise might prove his undoing.

In practice antabuse is never used alone. It is combined with physical treatment along general lines designed to improve physical health and morale, with psychotherapy to deal with the sources of tension and conflict which underlie the impulse to seek relief in alcohol, and with other measures to improve the individual and social adjustment of the patient, which we shall encounter in the next chapter. Used in this way antabuse can be invaluable, and can certainly stand comparison with various other methods of rendering alcohol nauseous or disagreeable to the patient, either with or without his consent. It is a cardinal principle with antabuse treatment, that it is never attempted without the full co-operation and understanding of the patient; to pop a tablet or two surreptitiously into the patient's food or drink, apart from being obviously unwise on psychological grounds, and understandably an indefensible breach of faith, might conceivably prove fatal. One or two cases have been reported in which death followed quite moderate quantities of alcohol in patients who had taken antabuse and whose subsequent reaction occurred away from medical supervision.

*

In the past twenty-five years there have grown up, largely on an empirical basis, three groups of special techniques which have radically altered the whole outlook for certain types of mental illness by providing methods of physical treatment which in many cases can relieve or cure conditions which were previously beyond the power of psychological medicine to control. These three techniques have culminated in what are known respectively as electro-convulsive therapy, or electroplexy, deep and modified insulin treatment, and those operations of neuro-surgery which are primarily concerned with the relief of mental illness, and of which the best known is the operation of leucotomy or pre-frontal lobotomy.

The origin of the method of convulsive therapy was due largely to a Hungarian physician, Dr von Meduna. It proceeded from the belief of a colleague, Dr Nyiro, also a Hungarian, that epilepsy occurred very much less frequently in conjunction with schizophrenia than could be accounted for by chance alone. From this he concluded that there might be some mutually antagonistic effect between epileptic fits and the development of schizophrenic illness; this is not a theory which has stood the test of time, but Meduna proceeded to test its practical implications by producing epileptic fits in schizophrenic patients.

His original method was to administer camphor in oil, intra-muscularly, which would produce an epileptic convulsion. Even after camphor was replaced by substances which could be given intravenously, and produce their effect far more rapidly and certainly, this remained a most disagreeable procedure for the patients; but in a number of cases, notably those who were showing symptoms of depression or who were so withdrawn as to be virtually stuporose, the treatment appeared to lead to improvement. It was taken up and employed sufficiently widely for the further observation to be made that it was far more effective in the treatment of depressive illnesses than in the majority of cases of schizophrenia for whom it had originally been tried. Its greatest value of all seemed to be in the treatment of states of involutional melancholia which had previously proved particularly intractable, and which now began to respond within a matter of days or weeks in the most dramatic and gratifying way.

The subsequent history of this treatment is essentially one of refinement of the method until the past few years, during which additional sources of understanding of the way in which the treatment works have been discovered. The refinement of method led to the almost total abandonment of convulsive drugs in favour of the production of the epileptic fit by means of a carefully graded electric current, passed for a fraction of a second across the frontal area of the brain. This important innovation was first proposed by Professor Cerletti of Rome. Further steps towards improving the technique and minimizing its risks and disadvantages were the administration of the convulsive dose under a short-acting anaesthetic, and finally the elimination of the actual convulsion by giving curare or a similar synthetic preparation intravenously.

The effect of curare or allied synthetic compounds is to paralyse temporarily the major groups of voluntary muscle, by interrupting communication between the nerve ending and the muscle itself. This effect wears off fairly rapidly and can be reversed at will by a suitable antidote. The result of these measures in combination in modern treatment is that the patient receives a small dose of anaesthetic by injection, which acts within a few seconds and absolutely without causing the patient distress of any kind. Immediately afterwards the temporary paralysis of voluntary muscle is achieved, oxygen is administered, and the dose of electricity is given.

Apart from a temporary alteration in breathing, and a flickering in certain muscles which give evidence of the adequacy of the dose, there is very little visible accompaniment to the patient's response. As soon as the current has passed and the response has been achieved, the antidote to curare, if curare has been used, is given, and oxygen administration continued. Most of the synthetic preparations with a similar effect to curare require no antidote under normal circumstances, since their influence is short-lived, but of course such antidote is always at hand in case of need.

Within a short while the patient recovers consciousness with no knowledge whatever of the details of the procedure and no memory of anything more unpleasant than the administration of the anaesthetic. The temporary relaxation of voluntary muscle has by this time completely vanished, its purpose being to spare both the violence of muscular contraction, and the possible risk of fracture, which at one time attended this treatment. From the point of view of the patient's experience there is no more to the whole thing than the anaesthetic, and the knowledge that a procedure of about comparable status to the removal of a wisdom tooth has been undertaken.

Treatment is usually given once or twice a week, and the average number of treatments necessary to relieve completely a severe depressive illness is somewhere between six and twelve. Treatment can under special circumstances be given on an outpatient basis, but it is obviously preferable that it should be given in hospital.

The results of such treatment, and of other treatments described in this chapter, we shall consider later in the book; its general effect is progressively to relieve depression until the patient is restored to full normal health and happiness. This effect is quite remarkable, and the nature of the relief accorded can be spectacular when a tormented, agitated, weeping, suicidal patient is transformed into a calm, vigorous, active, and happy person. Needless to say, psychotherapy both before, during, and after the course of electrical treatment is part of the whole process. In the early stages its most effective form is essentially that of encouragement and reassurance, based upon an appreciation of the patient's grief and fears. At a later stage, when improvement has begun, the degree to which personal problems may remain to be dealt with will vary among individual patients and will affect the nature of the psychotherapy required.

We have as yet only a partial idea of the way in which this remarkable treatment works, but some research into the biochemical changes which accompany it in patients who respond, much of it undertaken by Dr Pincus and his colleagues at the Worcester State Hospital in Massachusetts, and by Dr Altschule at the McClean Hospital in Waverley, Massachusetts, suggests that an important element is the glandular output of the endocrine system, which is controlled mainly from the pituitary gland in the skull beneath the brain. It is at least possible that the effects of treatment are secured not primarily by the convulsive response of the brain to stimulation, but by the effects of that stimulation upon the biochemistry of the brain, and upon the connexions between the brain and the pituitary gland. Altschule found that certain glandular secretions increased after successful electrical treatment. He was subsequently able to show that administration of these glandular secretions to the patients considered suitable for electrical treatment would in some cases produce a favourable response without the use of electrical stimulation at all. However, these results were neither as consistent nor as completely effective in the treatment of depression as those obtained by electrical treatment itself. In a later chapter we shall consider again some of the recent trends in research in this subject, but for the time being the practical value of electroplexy in the treatment of depression is established and unsurpassed.

*

The history of the discovery of the second great advance in physical treatment, that of insulin therapy, is no less interesting. Most of this was owed to Dr Sakel of Vienna, and once again a method which has proved of great value for a particular type of mental illness, in this case schizophrenia, was evolved through the study of an apparently unrelated problem. Sakel was interested in the control of the physical and mental distress undergone by drug addicts when their drugs were restricted or withheld in the course of treatment. He found that small doses of insulin, a secretion of the pancreatic gland in the abdomen, responsible for the metabolism of carbohydrate in the body, and widely used in the treatment of diabetes, were peculiarly effective not only in increasing the appetite and mitigating the physical suffering of his patients, but also in reducing their tension and emotional distress. Its physical effect is to remove sugar from the blood stream and enable it to be stored in reserve in the tissues. In the quantities in which insulin is normally produced by the pancreas this process goes on smoothly, always leaving enough sugar in the blood to act as a fuel and maintain ordinary energy. When larger doses are given artificially, so much sugar may be removed from the circulation that faintness and lassitude occur.

Sakel began to try insulin in the treatment of other types of mental disturbance. In the form of treatment known as modified insulin therapy, wherein doses no larger than those needed to produce faintness, sweating, drowsiness, and confusion were given, a very great improvement could be produced in patients suffering from states of anxiety. Such patients not only regained appetite and put on weight, but became calmer and were better able to accept and profit by the psychotherapy which remains the staple element in treatment.

But in a form of illness far more malignant and formidable than anxiety, whose treatment seemed baffling, and all too often wholly unsatisfactory by any known method, heroic doses of insulin proved extremely promising. Sakel founded the method of treatment for selected cases of schizophrenia whereby insulin in progressively increasing doses was administered daily, five or six days a week, until quantities of the order of five or six times that previously believed possible if the patient were to survive, were being given. Patients receiving these very large doses of insulin passed through a stage of confusion, drowsiness, and sweating, into a deep sleep and thence into a profound coma. If the process is not halted this coma will go on to death, but in the practice of the treatment coma was allowed to last only for a limited period, usually half to three-quarters of an hour, before it was interrupted by the administration of glucose solution either by a tube into the stomach, or into a vein.

Deep insulin treatment is now, however, essentially of historical interest only. The full course of treatment, as originated by Sakel in 1927, was undoubtedly in its day a milestone in the advance of psychiatry. Such a course would comprise thirty to sixty comas, was not without risk, and demanded a high degree of skill and teamwork from doctors and nurses. Even in the best hands mortality from irreversible coma was a danger, although in practice its incidence could be kept down to 0·5 per cent. The best results quoted for it occurred when it was begun within six months of the onset of illness, when something like 75 per cent of all cases treated were claimed to be recoverable, with a further 18 per cent responding by marked improvement.

Treatment undertaken after six months but within two years of onset showed a drop in the recovery rate to 20 per cent, with a rise in the rate of improvement for the remainder treated to 50 per cent.

While insulin still has its champions, the weight of modern clinical evidence suggests that the results of alternative treatment, combining electroplexy with administration of chlorpromazine in suitable forms, are at least as good, and considerably easier and safer to achieve. For this reason insulin has been virtually abandoned in most clinics.

Nevertheless, it had deservedly a revolutionary impact upon the whole trend of psychiatric thought in the therapy of psychotic illness in the early thirties and thereafter lasted on its merits for about twenty-five years, before being superseded; and it is not too much to say that deep insulin treatment, together with electrical treatment, played a historic and epochal part in totally transforming the outlook for two groups of mental illnesses, schizophrenia and depression, which hitherto could be offered at best only protracted treatment in a mental hospital; and, at worst, inflicted a living death, with suicide as a stark alternative, upon no less than one-fifth of all who suffered from them.

The role of neurosurgery in the treatment of mental illness is the most recently developed of all the established techniques for physical treatment. Like the rest it has its roots far back in history, but the basis of its present development began with the speculations and experimental work of a brilliant Portuguese neurologist, Dr Egaz Moniz. Dr Moniz has an international tradition of clinical observation and brilliant hypotheses in neurophysiology on which to build. The observations of the great Hughlings Jackson upon function and localization in the brain, the pioneer work of Harvey Cushing in brain surgery and its effect upon brain function, and the theories of the German neurologist, Kleist, upon the role of the frontal lobes of the brain in consciousness, were all familiar to him. He had also the famous medical history of a patient in whom that part of the brain had been destroyed by an accident in which a crowbar had penetrated his skull without killing him, and who had subsequently lived for a number of years, to stimulate his imagination.

The conclusions to which the experiences of others and the fruits of his own observations led him were that the thoughts and feelings of disturbed and deluded people might be altered by altering the physical structure of the brain. He hoped particularly that incorrigible delusions might be abolished in this way. He chose the frontal lobes as the site of attack because all the available evidence showed that these at least did not appear indispensable to continued life, and because they were at that time regarded as the seat of intellectual activity.

Dr C. F. Jacobsen had designed a series of surgical experiments whereby in trained and intelligent apes the frontal lobes were removed or severed from the rest of the brain. He noted and described the apparent placidity and indifference to previously irritating stimuli which these animals displayed after the operation. But it was Moniz who was first ready to take the extremely bold step of transferring the operation to man, when confronted by patients with apparently incurable mental illness, in some of whom emotional tension and distress were wholly crippling.

Isolation of the frontal lobes from connexion with the rest of the brain was originally secured by the injection of alcohol into the pre-frontal areas: later the surgical interruption of the fibres traversing these areas was substituted for this procedure. This was the operation of pre-frontal leucotomy, so-called because it depended for its effect upon severance of the connecting nerve fibres between the frontal lobes and the rest of the brain. These fibres run beneath the surface of the grey matter and are themselves white; leucotomy is derived from two Greek words and means the cutting of white matter.

There can be no doubt that both in conception and in performance the operation was and still is a remarkable combination of brilliance and crudity. Judged by later results it is outstandingly successful in certain carefully selected types of cases, truly disastrous in certain others in which it has been employed. But the success of Moniz's first series of cases demonstrated that while the operation undoubtedly produced changes in the minds of the patients, these were far less evident in the content of their delusions than in the attitude they displayed towards these delusions and towards life in general: like Jacobsen's chimpanzees they had become far more placid, tranquil, and phlegmatic.

Clinical observation and research were stimulated and proved more enduring than the volume of psychiatric opposition which the procedure had provoked. The thesis which eventually emerged, largely owing to the industry and brilliant exploitation of the surgical technique by Drs Freeman and Watts of America, was that a great deal of emotional tension, and the conscious control and preoccupation with behaviour which might lead to such tension, are in some way connected with the function of nervous pathways connecting the frontal lobes with the rest of the brain, and particularly with the thalamus, a ganglion of nervous tissue, about half the size of a golf ball, situated in the brain stem. The role of the thalamus appears to be that of central reception station for incoming messages of all kinds, and it has special connexions with the frontal lobes which appear to be concerned with the elaboration of conscious appreciation and emotional response to these stimuli. In this sense it would seem to play a fundamental part in shaping the patient's conscious emotional relationship with reality and experience; or, to put it in its simplest terms, the way he feels about things.

This is the basis for the recent extension of the use of the operation in certain cases of intractable physical pain, not otherwise accessible to surgery, as well as to patients whose suffering is predominantly mental. In both instances the relief appears to depend on the patient's altered mental attitude to the symptoms, rather than upon their total disappearance.

The enormous task of studying in detail the methods, results, and indications for the treatment is going on at this moment in a large number of centres throughout the world. The first international conference to exchange and correlate research data and information was held in Lisbon, the university centre and home of Dr Egaz Moniz, in 1948. At that time Great Britain could supply the largest detailed and studied series of cases on which this operation could be performed – a thousand cases selected from mental hospitals up and down the country. Apart from this, the work of the two American pioneers in the field, Drs Freeman and Watts, and more recently the vast research project of the University of Columbia in conjunction with the Greystone Hospital, N.J., working on the results of a modified operation, and the publication of a series of three hundred cases of leucotomy studied in detail and followed up for one and a half to three years after operation by Dr Maurice Partridge of London, are contributions towards a wider understanding of the implications of brain surgery in mental illness. They are selected from among hundreds for their attempt at comprehensiveness in a subject in which certain knowledge is still to be achieved. There are at present a number of variations and modifications of operative technique which appear to be established; undercutting the surface of the brain, as in the C. U. Greystone project, being one, and direct electrical cauterization of certain deeper brain centres being another; they have in common the severance of nervous pathways in the brain between the frontal lobes and other centres, and they all demand the highest degree of surgical experience and skill for their successful performance.

Over the last ten years one particular operation has been developed whereby the tracts concerned are cut under direct vision only in their upper and inner segment. This has enormously reduced both the risk of haemorrhage, and the subsequent incidence of personality changes involving severe blunting and diminution of emotional and intellectual flexibility.

The general indication for such operations as a whole would seem to be otherwise intractable mental illness in which tension and emotional distress are paramount, while apathy and withdrawal are not. Such states of mental illness would normally need to have existed either continuously or intermittently for at least one or two years, but ideally for not much more than two, and preferably for no more than five, and to have been treated by other appropriate physical methods, either without success or with only temporary relief, before such operation is justified. There can be no doubt that this operation, whatever the particular form or technique adopted, is essentially a destructive procedure; moreover its effects, in so far as they are under the control of the operator, are irreversible in most cases; so that while the undeniable and sometimes seemingly miraculous benefits which may accrue from it in suitable cases can never be excluded in weighing the indications for its use, the utmost care and deliberation is justifiable before advising it, and the decision as to whether or not it is the right procedure is often one of the most anxious and difficult which the psychiatrist and neuro-surgeon in consultation together may have to make.

The price which may have to be paid for the very great gain in peace of mind and capacity to adjust to reality, which leucotomy confers in selected cases, is a change of emphasis in the general balance of intellectual and emotional life by comparison with that which prevailed before the patient was ill at all. An increased complacency and self-satisfaction with diminished interest in, or awareness of the feelings of others, can be one effect. Tactless and inconsiderate behaviour, usually the result of an attitude which is self-centred rather than deliberately offensive, are not uncommon. Together with the relief from acute self-criticism or despair there may be a corresponding loss in imagination, sensitivity, and intuition, so that judgement suffers, and while day-to-day intellectual capacity remains unimpaired, the fullest and highest ranges of mental life may no longer be scaled.

Professor Golla has said that the basic change is an impairment in the power of ethical judgement; the patient's conscience, his views about right and wrong in both abstract and concrete situations, tend to become conventional rather than personally important. Sincerity takes second place to expedience. All this may lead to subtle changes in personality far more apparent to relatives than to the outside world. Despite these disadvantages, the human brain appears to possess remarkable powers of recovery and reintegration of function. Improvement in all the residual disabilities just described may continue to take place for one to two years after the operation, and in this way the personality of the patient may be progressively restored. Meanwhile his capacity to live outside mental hospital, and often return to work with a large measure of success and confidence, may far outweigh the disadvantages inseparable from the operation, which themselves vary considerably from one case to another.

*

These then are the main established types of physical treatment, applicable in the practice of psychiatry to a very great number of patients for whom, without such treatment, the future would be dark indeed. Research into methods and results of treatment in psychiatry goes on continually. Sometimes it leads to development of techniques with an immediate practical application; sometimes it opens up further possibilities for investigation rather than hopes for immediate cure; sometimes the particular path chosen appears to end blindly and the hypothesis on which it was based fails to stand the test of time and patiently repeated experiment. But always the research continues, and the gains, whether great or small, are sifted and stored against further discoveries which may make possible further advances.

One such method of research and investigation whose full implications have yet to be grasped, but whose immediate therapeutic gain is definite though not widely applicable, is exemplified in the work of Professor Gjessing of Sweden, on periodic catatonia, an illness which we have seen is normally described under the general heading of schizophrenia. He found that careful and detailed studies of the body chemistry of patients suffering from this complaint revealed changes in protein intake and output which fluctuated in time with the alterations in their mental state. Professor Gjessing then discovered that protein metabolism in these patients could be controlled by the administration of extract of thyroid gland, and that when such control was established the periodic mental changes could themselves be modified or abolished. The group of patients to whom this form of treatment is particularly applicable is not large. But the method whereby their biochemistry was studied, and the possible lines of future research suggested by Gjessing's observations on the role of nitrogen in protein metabolism and its control by thyroid, are contributions whose full value may far exceed the use which has as yet been made of them.

*

We have seen in this chapter something of the armament of modern psychiatry in the battle against established illness in individual patients. At least as important, and perhaps a greater challenge still, is the forging of weapons for use in prevention of such illness before it becomes established and wreaks its damage both upon those who suffer from it and upon their dependants and relatives. Preventive treatment in all branches of medicine is a subject which has caught the attention and imagination of doctors to the full only in the last hundred years, and the origin of mental hygiene and the whole field of work with children has a still more recent origin. This, and a general survey of the results of treatment as they stand today, will be the subject of the next chapter.

Means of Prevention and Chances of Cure

THE term mental hygiene, first used in Europe in the early part of of the nineteenth century and a few years later in America, has a general meaning embracing the principles of care and prevention of mental illness and the preservation of mental health. The methods by which these principles can be achieved demand the attention not only of doctors, but also of sociologists and some of the more enlightened politicians, and the techniques which seem to promise fulfilment along these lines are among the more important goals of psychiatric research. The names most readily associated with the foundation of this movement under its present name, in America in the early part of the twentieth century, are those of Clifford Beers and Professor Adolf Meyer. However, the movement in its earliest form was chiefly concerned with the improvement and reform of the hitherto monstrous and appalling conditions in mental hospitals, and this, as we saw in Chapter 2, had inspired courageous reformers like Conolly, Daniel Hack Tuke, and Lord Shaftesbury in England, Pinel, Esquirol, and Ferrus in France, and Dorothea Lynde Dix in America and later in Europe.

Following the great work of Lord Shaftesbury in persuading Parliament to pass a bill regulating the conditions in private madhouses, an effort which cost him many years of single-minded struggle against official apathy and prejudice, a Society for Improving the Condition of the Insane was founded in 1842 at the instigation of Dr Daniel Hack Tuke, with Lord Shaftesbury as its first President.

We have seen enough of the horrors and abuses prevalent in the care of mentally ill patients to realize how desperate was the need for such a movement. It is perhaps a significant reflexion that as recently as 1900 a patient in a mental hospital could be knocked down, spat upon, kicked, and then strapped into a strait waistcoat for twenty-one days on end by attendants resentful of the symptoms of his illness. This was one of the experiences recounted by Clifford Beers, who was himself a patient in mental hospitals in America between 1900 and 1903. At the end of this time, when he emerged recovered in spite rather than because of the treatment he had received, he was determined to found a world-wide movement for the protection of patients in mental hospitals and the prevention of illness wherever and whenever this could be achieved. After careful deliberation he chose the method of authorship to awaken interest and attract powerful and enlightened support for his ideas.

In this he is said to have been influenced by the example of *Uncle Tom's Cabin*, the book which did so much to arouse and focus opposition to slavery in the United States of America. In 1907 he abandoned the business career which he had resumed after his illness, to write the book and to circulate it privately among eminent psychiatrists, psychologists, and public men for comment and criticism before securing its publication. The book was finally published in 1908 just before the author's thirty-second birthday. It was called *A Mind that Found Itself*. It has since gone through over twenty-five editions and been translated into many languages.

Other books by ex-patients from mental hospitals had been published before, and not a few have been published since. All too often they display, alongside authentic and horrifying detail, evidence of incoherence, distorted thought, and even of delusions or an outlook sufficiently warped to enable their readers, after savouring the sensational aspect of such accounts, to dismiss them as the mere ravings of contentious and truculent madmen. But here, at least in the form in which it finally emerged, was a comparatively sober, sincere indictment, written with passionate conviction but in no way unbalanced or confused, with a foreword by William James and the authority of Professor Adolf Meyer to support its claims and its proposals. Coming at a time when preventive medicine in other fields had already proved its worth, the book struck the blow for which its author had designed it. It remained to be seen whether the practical implication of his programme would achieve all that Beers so fervently hoped.

The first society for Mental Hygiene in America, established by Beers following the success of his book, was in New Haven, Connecticut, where Beers was made the Executive Secretary. Within a year a National Committee had been formed with Beers in the same position. Its programme as outlined in one of its first publications was as follows:

To work for the protection of the mental health of the public; to help raise the standard of care for those in danger of developing mental disorder or actually insane; to promote the study of mental disorders in all their forms and relations and to disseminate knowledge concerning their causes, treatment and prevention; to obtain from every source reliable data regarding conditions and methods of dealing with mental disorders; to enlist the aid of the Federal Government so far as may seem desirable; to co-ordinate existing agencies and help organize in each State in the Union an allied but independent Society for Mental Hygiene similar to the existing Connecticut Society for Mental Hygiene.

From the outset therefore mental hygiene opposed with uncompromising courage two concepts previously entrenched in much of the public and professional attitude to mental illness: that such illness was neither preventable nor curable, and that it was not only incurable but also disgraceful.

Money and active support came more slowly than popular goodwill; but in 1912 Henry Phipps, founder of the famous psychiatric clinic at the Johns Hopkins Hospital in Baltimore, gave 50,000 dollars to the National Committee, and Dr Thomas W. Salmon of the United States Public Health Service was engaged as its first Director of Special Studies. He initiated a far-reaching survey of existing facilities in America and later, after the entrance of the United States of America into the First World War in 1917, the National Committee for Mental Hygiene was entrusted with the task of organizing a Division of Neurology and Psychiatry within the American Army. Dr Salmon was made Senior Surgeon in Neuropsychiatry to the American Expeditionary Force.

It is an oft-remarked irony of war that only under stress of its carnage, misery, and brutality is that all-out national attention given to medical progress which will enable it to make some of its most significant advances and contributions. The First World War and the period which immediately followed it saw mental hygiene given its first practical opportunity to prove itself. The reluctance both of the public and many of the medical profession to acknowledge and understand the nature of emotional stress and its effect upon health had led to a number of naive and costly mistakes in the diagnosis and treatment of those neuroses which occur in response to the stresses of combat and wartime existence. 'Shell shock', conceived as a specific response of the body to the physical impact of explosion, but in fact a straightforward example of emotional illness, with symptoms characteristic of anxiety or hysteria, cost its sufferers months or years of invalidism and the governments of the combatant countries untold expenditure in pensions, until its nature and its capacity to respond to psychiatric treatment was belatedly recognized. The same is generally true of many other forms of neurosis, in no way specific to war, but occurring among the general casualties on a scale believed unprecedented only because it had never before been recognized.

One of the legacies of war was that the size and shape of the social problem of mental illness in peace time began to be recognized. Such figures as we need to indicate this will be forthcoming in Chapter 10. Their eventual recognition involved as one of its results the extension of the scope of mental hygiene to include such varied fields as the care and health of children, public health, general and medical education, industry, social work, and the problems of criminology and the law. In each of these active work has been going ahead for the last three decades. The first International Congress on Mental Hygiene was held in Washington, D.C., in 1930 and attended by more than three thousand people, representing fifty countries besides the United States of America. Among its major purposes were:

(1) To bring together from all countries workers in mental hygiene and related fields, for . . . exchange of information and experience and for mutual consideration of individual and social problems arising out of nervous and mental disease, mental defect, and mental and emotional

maladjustments of the individual to his personal and social environment.

(2) To consider ways and means of world co-operation and of more effective promotion of mental hygiene in the various countries.

At this Congress a permanent National Committee for Mental Hygiene was founded. A second International Mental Hygiene Congress was held in Paris in 1937, under the shadow of the approaching war. The third, and the most hopeful as yet, was held in London in August 1948, sponsored by the International Committee for Mental Hygiene which had grown out of the first two congresses. At this third Congress the World Federation for Mental Health was founded in conjunction with the World Health Organization of the United Nations, and the United Nations Economic, Social and Cultural Organization. Dr John R. Rees of Great Britain, who during the war had been in charge of Psychiatric Services in the British Army, was elected first President.

Clifford Beers himself did not live to see full achievement of his aims: they are indeed still far from final attainment. He died on 9 July, 1943; but the work which he had started and the organization which he had created had already proved itself at least a powerful source of hope, not simply for the mentally ill for whom it was first designed, but for all those people whose lives were clouded by the threat and the shadow of mental illness in all its repercussions. The idea of guilt and the idea of hopelessness, which for so long were combined in the public attitude to mental illness, die hard. Against them we must set the concepts of early treatment, of acceptance of mental illness in all its forms as an aspect of the larger problem of illness and unhappiness as a whole, and the aim of psychiatry today and in the future to understand and to alleviate as far as possible every form of suffering in which its contribution can in any way be of value.

*

Every approach to the preventive aspect of psychiatry tends logically and inevitably to focus attention upon the health and happiness of children. We have seen in preceding chapters how the patterns of behaviour acquired by the adult are laid down in childhood, and how his whole personality and constitution are an intimate blend of hereditary factors and the effects upon him of his environment from the very earliest years of his life. There can be few doctors with experience of psychiatric disorder in adult patients who have not felt a deep compassion for the child whom they have never known, but who now stands before them, physically grown but emotionally starved or stunted, outwardly mature but inwardly anxious, unhappy, and a prey to that insecurity which is the enemy of calmness and fortitude.

Not simply in mental and physical health, but in his whole attitude to life and to those who share it with him, is the child father to the man. Recognition and treatment of emotional disturbance in childhood is therefore one of the foundations upon which the concept of mental hygiene has come to stand.

In Chapter 3 we studied the way in which the early development of the child's personality takes place. We saw that it occurred at first almost entirely within the wider area of the mother's personality and emotional state. This provides us with an important clue as to how young children are likely to be affected by emotional stress, how they will respond, and how they may be treated. One thing is clear already. The most powerful kind of stress to which the young child is likely to be subjected is some disturbance in his relationship with his mother, or later perhaps with his father and other members of the family. The ways in which he will show evidence of this disturbance are almost always by some alteration of behaviour, rather than by any outspoken complaint on his part. Children very rarely complain in words about their health or happiness, and when they do, the complaint they make is as likely to be symbolic, or to have private meaning which they cannot explain, as it is to throw objective light on the real cause of the trouble.

Moreover the abnormal states which are most damaging to the child's happiness and peace of mind, such as long continued anxiety, insecurity, fear, jealousy, or disappointment, are those which children are least able to express in words or even fully to recognize themselves. They affect the child fundamentally by holding up his development and usually by throwing him back upon an earlier and less mature pattern of behaviour.

An example of this is the recurrence of bed-wetting, which is a normal process in infancy, in children of any age up to about adolescence, in response to emotional stress and particularly to anxiety and insecurity. Another is the appearance of temper tantrums, in which once again the expression of rage and frustration by violent uncoordinated movement is reminiscent of infancy, but which may be seen in considerably older children whose emotional balance has been disturbed by stresses with which they cannot deal. Children in fact tell us that there is something wrong by what they do rather than by what they say, and very often this behaviour is quite plainly not under their control.

Therefore, while it is sensible and even essential for a child's own happiness that he should be trained to behave in certain ways, and to recognize certain wide but reasonable limits upon his freedom of action, it is neither reasonable, just, nor incidentally of the slightest use, to punish him for disturbances of behaviour which are really symptoms of illness, and which he himself may not be able to control at all.

This raises the oft-disputed and seemingly difficult question of the difference between naughtiness on the one hand, and behaviour disorder, which is a medical problem, on the other. The question is not, however, as difficult as it is sometimes made to seem. Children do not enjoy being consistently in opposition to their parents or those in authority; nor do they enjoy being unhappy or in disgrace. But like everybody else they want their own way and they are often prepared to risk displeasure and defiance in order to get it. Sporadic natural naughtiness, as an occasional enlivenment to family life, is something that parents as a whole have little difficulty in recognizing. A chronic and continued state of strife between parents and children on the other hand is quite a different matter, and bespeaks something wrong either with the child or with the parents or more frequently with both. It is no part of the child psychiatrist's job to interfere with the normal relationships between children and their parents within the wide limits through which such relationships tend to fluctuate, nor is it any part of his job to issue blanket warnings against occasional moderate and appropriate punishment or control. Rewards and punishments are part of the background to human existence, and so long as they are just, and free from caprice or vindictiveness, they form an essential part of the training of the normal child. The child psychiatrist's job in fact begins when the normal relationship has broken down, when resentment, distrust, and mutual unhappiness have taken the place of affection and understanding between the child and his parents.

Then it is time, with that care, patience, attention to detail, and experience of many other such problems which we have seen must characterize psychiatry in all its approaches, to examine the whole background to the child-parent relationship which has become unhappy and unsuccessful, and in the light of this examination to prescribe treatment.

Young children with behaviour disorders, whether they be of habit, such as bed-wetting, nail-biting, temper tantrums, breath holding, or screaming fits, or of appetite, or even of more obvious emotional quality, need to be treated through their relationship with their mother. For it is she whose feelings and attitude most influence her child, she who can begin to understand and accept the doctor's help, gaining thereby a confidence which can reach the child only through her: and she who often needs, at least as much as the child, the wisdom and support which a good doctor with adequate training and experience can give her.

The principles of the psychiatry of childhood, for which the term 'child guidance' is not altogether a fortunate one, rest therefore upon two fundamental considerations, both of which are derived from the study of normal children, outlined in Chapter 3. These, as we have seen, are the primitive and some-what unmanageable nature of emotion in childhood and its tendency to appear in behaviour rather than in words; and the essential bond between the child and its mother which make any attempt to treat or help him unrealistic if his mother is not included in the general situation, and her understanding and co-operation are not completely secured.

As children grow older their ways of showing distress and unhappiness begin to resemble more nearly those of adult life, but even up to and including the time of adolescence, disordered behaviour is at least as likely to be met as an indication of distress as is any complaint which the patient may be able to make. At the same time the relationship between the individual and his parents remains of vital importance, and the attitude of the parents to his problems and life as well as to his symptoms can never be ignored.

If one vital aspect of child psychiatry, therefore, consists in understanding the parents' side of the problem and helping them to deal with it, what in fact can be done directly with the children? The first step is of course to get and remain on good terms with the child himself. Contrary to popular belief, this rarely means indulging his slightest whim. What it really implies is treating the child as a lovable individual whom one is prepared to like and to respect, accepting him and his behaviour without comment or criticism, and getting to know him on a basis of mutual interest and sincerity. Thereafter he can be helped to express the problem as it affects him, and for him it will almost always be a problem of relationship with those nearest to him. He may express it indirectly in his play, or in his drawings or paintings, or through the medium of puppets or fairy stories which will often reveal a wealth of emotion which can find release in no other way.

Sometimes the problem will centre around anxiety, rigidity, and too much restriction on the part of the parent, often based on the parent's own personal problems and attitudes derived from the earlier days of that parent's own life. But often too it may be concerned with precisely the opposite situation; that of excessive indulgence or concern for every impulse which the child may display, whereby at one time he can sense no limit to what he can do, while at another some particularly outrageous excess is suddenly and, as far as he can see, unreasonably punished. Parental anxiety can lead to the permitted and half-accepted limits of a child's behaviour being too wide and undefined, as well as being too confined and narrow. In either case the result as far as the child is concerned is likely to be insecurity, and a need to discover where he stands by testing out parental responses often at the cost of his own happiness and the limits of parental forbearance.

If then we try to sum up the essence of much of the practical work which is done with children and their parents in child psychiatry, we can say that the first task is to recognize the nature and area of the trouble through detailed attention to the child's behaviour and an exhaustive study of his life, background, and relationship with his parents; then to get to work both with the parents and with the child so that the parents become aware of the problem and its implications, while the child feels able both to accept and to be accepted by the doctor and by the parents themselves; and then to follow up this stage by such detailed work with the child and such further help to the parents that confidence and understanding replace the stresses of the presenting situation, and the doctor can step back out of the picture, leaving the vital union of the parent and child as intact and secure as it must be if both are to be well and happy.

In practice this is not a job for one person. It is a job for a team. The normal and ideal composition of the team is a doctor who is a psychiatrist with special experience with children, a psychologist who is not medically trained but who is expert in assessing the child's intellectual possibilities and personality structure, and a trained psychiatric social worker who will form a link between the team and the home, and who will be able to work with the parents while the doctor is working with the child, after the initial interviews and examination have decided the lines along which the problem shall be tackled.

A team of this sort is needed for the proper elucidation and management of behaviour disorders in children; and these constitute a great majority of problems in the realm of child psychiatry. They are in fact the corresponding manifestations to the whole field of neuroses in adult life. They differ from adult neuroses not only in their form but also in the readiness with which they usually recover, given a modicum of understanding, tolerance, and co-operation on the part of all concerned. Residential schools, placements away from home, even the intervention of the court, where blind and stupid cruelty or disharmony among parents threatens the whole future of the child, are sometimes necessary in the management of such cases. But ideally the team works through the home, with the parents, and for the child.

The results of the practice of child psychiatry are encouraging in as much as problems which seem beyond the resources of parents when they come for help and advice will very often prove within their power to solve once help has been provided. Arising from the need to seek help is all too often a feeling of guilt on the parents' part. This in turn is responsible for some of the criticism and hostility with which the subject has still occasionally to contend, which is exemplified by the canard that child psychiatrists tend to blame parents for trying to bring their children up properly, to interfere with the normal discipline of the home, and to turn children into unmanageable vagabonds.

In point of fact, one of the cardinal lessons of experience in the wise handling of children is that, if there is one thing more disturbing to a child than rigid rules which may never be broken, it is the complete absence of rules altogether. When a mother discovers that the doctor does not in fact regard her as a criminal because she is having trouble with her child, she is often able to admit that he may not be a crank because he thinks he can help her.

There remain in child psychiatry two other kinds of problem which must be mentioned, although they cannot be much elaborated here. They are the fields of mental deficiency and of the rare psychotic illnesses of childhood; some on the basis of discoverable physical abnormality, and some whose origin is as yet unknown. The teamwork and the approach are the same here as for behaviour disturbances. The nature of mental deficiency makes it inevitable that most people who are affected in this way are discovered to be abnormal during their childhood. The general features of the condition, and the possibilities of special training and treatment, have already been outlined in previous chapters. With the provision of special schools as well as special techniques for training defective patients in colonies and institutions, the contribution of mental hygiene is continuous and increasing.

Psychotic illnesses in children, although rare by comparison with the rest of childhood disorders, are a perennial subject of research and concern. The nature of the illnesses seen bears some resemblance to those of adult life, an example on the organic side being juvenile general paralysis of the insane, which occurs as a result of congenital syphilis; while the functional group are represented mainly by varieties of what appear to be schizophrenic illness. The approach to these illnesses through treatment necessarily follows the same general lines as for adult illness, but here again the results of research are needed to enlarge both range and effectiveness.

Before leaving this subject it is necessary to add that many of the ways of thinking and feeling which are normal in childhood, and to some degree in adolescence, such as a tendency to refer experience to personal feelings (the moon is hiding from me tonight; she usually follows me wherever I go ...), and to credit words and thoughts with magical power, combine to give a schizophrenic flavour to disturbances which may be far more transient and benign than schizophrenia in adult patients usually proves. For this reason the diagnosis of schizophrenia is made only with the greatest reservation during this stage of life; there are for example not a few chaotic behaviour disturbances in adolescence which present typically schizophrenic symptoms, but which prove to have a comparatively direct emotional basis and to respond rapidly and effectively to adjustment of the provocative situation.

●

Psychiatric social work as an essential component of the psychiatry of childhood has already been mentioned. The development of psychiatric social work as a whole is another of the advances of mental hygiene which have enormously increased the range and power of preventive medicine in psychiatry. Social workers who concerned themselves with home conditions, housing, financial and social problems of the patients who attended large hospitals, had proved their value before their special role in psychiatry was fully recognized. In this sense the psychiatric social worker is a descendant of the hospital almoner on the one side and the health visitor on the other; the essential addition to these workers' equipment is the provision of a basic understanding and training in human relationships, and in certain aspects of psychiatry itself.

The role of the psychiatric social worker in psychiatry to-day is that of valued assistant to the psychiatrist in the investigation of psychological and social factors in the home, environment, and work of the patient and his family; such workers may be either men or women, but at the moment women predominate. In the collection of information about these areas of the patient's life, in visiting the home or the place of employment and establishing contact between others interested in the patient's welfare and the clinic where he is being treated, and in helping and advising him in his own relationships at work or in the home, the psychiatric social worker has an important part to play in the practical therapy which so many patients need. But here again popular misconception, where it occurs, is usually based on the natural underlying emotional approach which surrounds mental illness and its treatment, rather than upon the facts. The psychiatric social worker is not a snooper who pops up uninvited in the most delicate areas of the patient's life, to bedevil his relationships and plague or infuriate others in his circle with foolish inquiries. She is rather a trained and competent student of human relationships with the knowledge and experience both of what can be done for individuals in difficult situations, and of what they can do for themselves through the medium of social agencies with which it is her business to be familiar; and all this knowledge and experience is at the service of the patient, whose need of it is recognized by the psychiatrist, and for whose benefit alone it is employed.

The contributions which psychiatry and normal psychology have to make to society as a whole will concern us in wide review towards the end of this book. But during this consideration of mental hygiene, we can follow the implications of social psychiatry, through the role of the psychiatric social worker in the problems of childhood and then of adult practice, to the further areas of human relationships involved in education and in industry. The most obvious relationship between psychiatry, psychology, and education lies in the diagnosis and management of children who are mentally defective. We have already encountered this problem, but it is only a beginning. Throughout the whole of school and university education the problem of human relationships is at least as important as the problems involved in the acquisition of knowledge.

In America, a number of universities have already recognized this to the extent that a counselling service, together with opportunities for consultation with psychiatrists and educational psychologists, are available to undergraduates as part of the structure of a student health service. Some indication of the need for such services during the educational period may be gained from the experience of two leading American universities where a whole time psychiatric service exists for the benefit of the student population. These are the University of Ann Arbor, in Michigan, and the University of Minnesota, at Minneapolis. Taking the average number of undergraduates at a major university as about twenty thousand, they find that they need to cater for about eighty consultations a month. The subject of these may range from concern about examinations, or anxiety about personal health, to major emotional disorders. In view of the stresses imposed by the immense competition for vacancies at universities, by examinations, and very often by associated financial anxieties, all falling upon young people only recently emerged from adolescence, it is perhaps not surprising that the need for a service of this kind should be so great. Nevertheless opposition to it in England remains active. Expense provides the rationalization, but emotional prejudice cannot be excluded as the underlying basis. It would seem an unusually short-sighted economy to neglect the study and early treatment of emotional disturbances among people striving to equip themselves for full citizenship and responsibility, in a community where stability, skill, and productive work were never more necessary than they are to-day.

Social relations and individual human relations in industry, a field of enquiry where the psychiatric social worker can be an invaluable asset, have also a practical importance which has been emphasized by recent research of which the work of Dr Russell Frazer may be taken as an example. He undertook a study on behalf of the Industrial Health Research Board in 1947 into the incidence of neuroses among factory workers. He discovered that neurotic illness caused between a quarter and a third of *all* absence from work due to illness of any kind, and that 10 per cent of the whole group of workers studied, some three thousand men and women selected at random from various factories, had suffered from definite and disabling neurotic illness, and a further 20 per cent from minor forms of neuroses. The connexion between such findings and what is loosely termed 'absenteeism' is one which is beginning to receive serious attention. It should be obvious that the more contented, harmonious, and loyal the relationship between employers and employed, the better will be the output and the greater will be efficiency; what is perhaps more important still from the point of view of the doctor is that work will become a contribution to health, as it should be, rather than a source of conflict or frustration which undermines both health and happiness.

A further aspect of the relation of the individual to society in which mental hygiene is constantly striving to play a part, is in the sphere of criminal behaviour among adults and children, and of the attitude of the law towards such behaviour, its prevention and cure. In the entire history of psychiatry there is no field more embattled, more laden with prejudice and mutual recrimination than this. Yet the stark fact that the problems, which both psychiatry and the law would agree require solution, are so manifestly far from being solved, is one which must in time compel a more fruitful co-operation than has as yet been achieved.

The investigation of human behaviour and of personal relationships cannot be unimportant in the control and prevention of crime, and in the assessment of the effects of punishment both upon the offenders and upon the conscience of society itself. But all too often, as was exemplified in the days of Bodin and Weyer, the judge condemns the psychiatrist as a fool, who waxes sentimental over the fate of the criminal while ignoring that of the victim, whilst the psychiatrist challenges the emotional prejudices of the judge who justifies brutal punishment for brutal offences and can believe that hanging is good for society.

This is one of the vexed questions for discussion in the concluding chapters. Here we are concerned simply to see what contribution mental hygiene claims to make. It is this. At the preventive stage research is needed, and can be planned to relate the disturbances of childhood behaviour and family life to actual law-breaking. The general connexion has already been established and is virtually unassailable. Beyond this the relationship between criminal behaviour and, for example, such abnormalities of mental life as mental defect and psychopathic personality, apart from the more well recognized forms of mental illness, is another line of research which only requires co-operation for its further advance.

Research which *has* already been accomplished has shown, for example, that out of 781 boys and girls studied in the juvenile courts in New York City 70 per cent showed either some degree of mental defect, or emotional disturbance sufficient to have required treatment had it been recognized before the offence was committed; of 608 consecutive admissions to Sing Sing prison 60 per cent were either feeble-minded, mentally ill, or of psychopathic personality. Of these 608 admissions 406, or 66·8 per cent, were recidivists, i.e. men with a record of repeated crime and punishment.

Recent investigations in Great Britain have shown that physiological studies of brain function in prisoners, by means of the electro-encephalogram, reveal an incidence of abnormal records of over 25 per cent, by comparison with about 5 to 10 per cent when random samples of the population as a whole are studied. A particular investigation along these lines, of prisoners charged with murder, showed that, of over 100 cases examined, over 50 per cent had abnormal records, and in those whose crime appeared to have no understandable motive but whose mental state could not be shown to be abnormal afterwards, over 75 per cent gave records which were abnormal and often grossly abnormal.

No one would maintain that *all* criminals are mentally ill or abnormal. Such a proposition is as false as the medieval assumption that all mentally ill people were criminal, or at any rate possessed by devils. But the relationship between crime and mental illness must be fully recognized and its implications properly studied before prevention can be seriously tackled.

At succeeding stages in criminal procedure, both in the assessment of responsibility and in the subsequent management and treatment of the offenders, sound and informed psychiatric opinion, with experimental findings behind it, must be accorded due weight in the deliberations of the law. The object of the proponents of mental hygiene is not to hand over the world to psychiatrists; that would indeed be a grotesque ambition: it is rather to hand over the contributions of psychiatry to the world, to invite their use and to extend their possibilities.

* * *

This chapter and the one immediately preceding it have had as their aim a description of that particular contribution of psychological medicine most likely to commend itself to the general public; the contribution of treatment, in both its curative and its preventive aspects. We have studied a number of methods of treatment and seen something of their application in the various fields of mental illness. It is now time to take stock of their results in so far as these can be expressed in general but not misleading terms.

We began our consideration of treatment with psychotherapy. In assessing the results of psychotherapy, or indeed of any other form of treatment, the most vivid and convincing technique is to compare the recovery rate of patients who have been treated with that of patients who have not. If we could take a series of figures illustrating the percentage of people who recovered from mental illness during, for example, a particular year in the middle of the last century and could compare it with a similar study made within the last five years, on a comparable section of the population matched for age, diagnosis, and number of cases studied, then we might satisfy even the most sceptical critic of the value of the treatment. But in practice, although studies of recovery rates and careful estimations of what happened to people who were mentally ill were made by such pioneers as Pinel and Esquirol 150 years ago, neither their diagnostic categories nor their methods of study are directly comparable with the modern approach. The only comparison we can make is between one kind of treatment and another; and an illuminating example of this kind of study is to be found in the work of Professor Landis,

Assistant Professor of Psychology at Columbia University, which was published in 1938.

Professor Landis worked out what he called the basic ameliora-tion rate for psychoneuroses. This is the proportion of patients with this type of illness who are discharged from hospital as recovered or improved within one year of their admission. He based his figures as far as possible upon hospitals in America where very little active psychotherapy was undertaken and where the care was largely general nursing and supervision. He found that between 62 and 72 per cent of all cases were recovered or improved within a year and were discharged on this basis. The variability of some 10 per cent between the figures is accounted for by the small differences between one year and another, the total study being conducted over seven years. Landis took this to mean that, with the basic minimum of skill, care, and attention, there was a spontaneous tendency for between two-thirds and three-quarters of all psychoneuroses to get very much better within a year. It must be remembered that since the majority of patients with this kind of illness are not admitted to mental hospitals unless their symptoms are fairly severe, the period of a year or less for recovery, even without active treatment, is not as long as it might seem.

Since then Professor Landis has compared the recovery rate claimed by other workers with this basic amelioration rate which we have just described. The important figures in such comparisons are not simply the recovery rate recorded but also the length of time required to produce this rate. Here are some of the com-parisons he made: in every case treatment was carried out by psychotherapy at the institution or clinic named, either on an in-patient or an out-patient basis (see table, p. 224).

These figures of Professor Landis tend to suggest that in the comparatively small number of cases over a ten-year period who were able to benefit from full-scale psycho-analysis, the results were exceedingly impressive. On the other hand we note that no figure is given for the duration of treatment: we have already seen that such treatment is extremely time-consuming, and that a full analysis may take anything from two to four years, or more.

Since this pioneer investigation of Professor Landis other

investigations upon the average duration of treatment by psychotherapy and its results have been undertaken. They have included consideration of those briefer methods which we have encountered in the preceding chapter. The most recent of these was published in April 1951 by Professor Finesinger, recording the results of a follow-up on a small series of cases treated by comparatively inexperienced students under his supervision and by the brief method which he had evolved. His assessment of results was characteristically conservative: the study was based on a follow-up of sixty-two patients with anxiety neuroses, two to twelve years after psychotherapy in hospital.

Fifty-eight per cent of the patients were considered to be definitely improved or recovered, and the total duration of treatment averaged fifty-two days. The average number of interviews given during this time was twenty-seven. The striking thing here is the remarkably short time taken to produce this result, by comparison with that likely to be needed for spontaneous

Hospital or Clinic	Period of Investigation	Total Number of Cases Treated	Average Duration of Treatment	Per cent Recovered or Improved
Maudsley Hospital (England) . .	1931–5	1,531	6 months	67
Cassel Hospital (England) . . .	1921–33	1,186	4·1 months	70
New York Psychiatric Institute (U.S.A.) .	1930–5	119	6·1 months	87
Berlin Psychoanalytic Institute (Germany) } 1920–30 {		*Total Number treated* 312		58
		Total who completed Treatment *200		91

* The difference between 312 and 200 represents the number of patients (112) who, after entering into psycho-analytic treatment, broke it off or gave it up for one reason or another.

recovery, or consumed in some of the other procedures already outlined.

A further factor of importance in assessing the outlook for a particular case is the length of time that the illness had been going on before treatment was begun. Despite the comparatively high basic amelioration rate quoted by Landis, quite a large number of patients with psychoneuroses remain ill or miserable for a long time if they are not treated. They are probably represented by the 30 per cent who do not get well within a year. The average duration of illness in Finesinger's sixty-two patients, *before* treatment was undertaken, was a little over five years. That two-thirds of them should have been well in about three months or slightly less from the time of starting treatment is all the more impressive.

Research upon an accurate statistical basis into the results of psychotherapy is still only in its infancy, but we can sum up the position as it stands at present in this way: the percentage of patients with psychoneuroses who can expect to be restored to health, or relieved in varying degree by psychotherapy, is between 60 and 90 per cent. The time in which this relief will be granted may be as little as a few weeks or, in particularly severe or long-standing cases, as much as several years. In any particular case a large number of factors will necessarily influence the outlook; these will include the basic personality, assets, and liabilities of the individual patient, the length of time for which the illness has been present before treatment as well as its severity, and the external circumstances which are causing or increasing the patient's present difficulties. But in every case help can be offered and at least some degree of relief expected. No patient is beyond aid; many can be cured.

The results of physical treatment can be more easily compared with the outcome of mental illness before such treatment was available, because we have figures from mental hospitals for all the more important types of illness in the days when these could be offered nothing but custodial care. These again have been collected by Professor Landis and will be set out below. They are the average figures for the percentage of patients discharged as recovered or improved between 1926 and 1933 in the United

States of America. They can be taken as representative of the spontaneous amelioration rate for these illnesses.

Diagnosis	Percentage discharged recovered or improved (*Average annual rate for period* 1926–33) *Per cent*
Senile dementia	10–11
General paralysis of the insane . . .	17–25
Schizophrenia	37–45
Involutional depression	43–51
Other forms of depression, including manic depressive	61–67
Psychoneuroses	62–72
Alcoholism	63–76
Psychopathic personality	61–71
Entire mental hospital population under diagnosis	39–41

We have already discussed the implications of the figure of 62 to 72 per cent for psychoneuroses; for the rest, with one exception, these percentages provide us with a base line for comparison with the results of modern methods of treatment.

The exception is that of general paralysis; here the period of 1926 to 1933 included the great improvement in results already produced by malaria therapy in this illness. This form of treatment was introduced in Vienna in 1917 by Professor Wagner-Jauregg, and was the first major advance in physical methods of treatment of mental illness; by 1926 it had revolutionized the outlook for remission of this disease. It had in fact turned an invariably fatal disease into one which could be arrested. The annual discharge rate for general paralysis cases in New York in 1914 was less than 10 per cent. By 1926 it had more than doubled. A large series of patients followed up in Berlin after the adoption of this treatment for nearly 2,000 cases, showed complete remission of the illness in 24 per cent, with a further 17 per cent showing partial recovery. The follow-up extended over four or five years, and later analyses have shown that if cases are secured for treatment at the earliest possible stage in the disease, remission may be hoped for in up to 46 per cent of those given a full course of treatment. We can now compare the results of treatment of some of the other conditions mentioned, with more recent studies.

The treatment of depression by electrical methods yields an average rate of recovery of 80 per cent in involutional depressions and 75 per cent in other forms of depression; moreover these results are achieved within a period of two to three months of starting treatment. The recovery rate has thus been almost doubled in cases of involutional depression and the duration of illness, even in those cases which might have recovered spontaneously, has been cut from months or years to a matter of weeks. It is not too much to say that the entire outlook for this type of illness has been fundamentally changed.

We have already reviewed the treatment of schizophrenia by insulin, and seen how, despite its great importance as an indication of the immense possibilities inherent in an active and bio-chemical approach to the problem of long-term psychotic illness, it was eventually superseded by a combination of electrical treatment and medicines of the chlorpromazine group. In the days before insulin, the outlook for schizophrenia could be summarized by saying that 25 per cent of the patients recovered spontaneously and remained well; 25 per cent were left with what can be described as a residual defect and many even of these remained in hospital for years; while the remaining 50 per cent never regained sufficient health or stability to be discharged from hospital at all, and were regarded by Bleuler, who first described them, as afflicted with dementia. Bleuler gave his patients work to do, including farming and building within the hospital; but even so it was said of him that 'His patients were prisoners, and in a way he himself was a prisoner, caught up in the difficulties of the field in which he had chosen to work. . . .'

The impact of insulin coma treatment and the improvement in results thereby achieved can now be seen in perspective. The remission rate was more than doubled for patients treated in the first year of the illness, but the degree of success fell away steadily if the duration of the illness before treatment was more than two years.

Insulin has been virtually abandoned since 1955, but the overall improvement in the treatment of this chronic illness between

1928 and the present time is indicated in the following figures, collected from a mental hospital close to London, between 1928 and 1957.*

Date	Patients who had been in hospital for more than 2 years at date of survey. Per cent	Patients who were discharged recovered during the current year. Per cent	Duration of admission of patients discharged.
1928	60	20	7 months
1949	30	45	6 months
1957	10	60	9 weeks

Further evidence of the improved outlook for patients with chronic schizophrenia can be deduced from other figures from this hospital: for example, in the thirty years from 1928 to 1958, 42 long-stay patients had been discharged; but 20 of these had been discharged in the three years 1955–8. One implication which must be remembered is that patients with a serious illness of this kind, whose chances twenty-five years ago were only 2 in 5 of ever leaving hospital, are likely from time to time to require periods of readmission now that 4 out of 5 of them spend most of their time at home and often at work. The need for mental hospitals will not therefore wither away entirely, but the estimate of the Ministry of Health now dares to hope for a fifty per cent reduction of mental hospital beds over the next sixteen years.

The most recent of all methods of physical treatment, and the most drastic and irreversible, namely that of leucotomy and similar surgical procedures, has already produced a number of investigations and results, of varying degrees of reliability. Of this method of treatment one thing can be said with virtual certainty. Every case in which recovery or material improvement has been secured is pure gain, since this operation has to all intents and purposes been restricted to cases in which spontaneous recovery appeared out of the question, and which without it seemed to have a steadily worsening or utterly hopeless prognosis.

The investigation undertaken in the United Kingdom by the Board of Control, who analysed the results in 1,000 consecutive cases, 348 men and 652 women, has already been mentioned in Chapter 7. The results in brief were these. Following operation

*Bexley Hospital, Dartford.

25 per cent of the patients recovered sufficiently to be discharged from hospital; 36 per cent, while requiring to be kept in hospital, were regarded as substantially improved both from the point of view of their own well-being and the ease with which they could be nursed and cared for. Five per cent of the patients died as a result of the operation. 599 of these 1,000 cases had been diagnosed as schizophrenia; when the other groups of patients were studied separately, it was found that among the manic depressive, involutional depressive, and obsessional patients the results were proportionately even better than those of the series as a whole. Remember that these were all patients who were specially selected as being otherwise incurable. All of these had been in mental hospitals for several years, many for more than five, some for more than twenty. More recent investigations suggest that very much better results can be hoped for if operation is undertaken within five years of the onset of illness.

A comparable survey conducted in eighteen different clinics in the United States and Canada between 1936 and 1943, over three-quarters of the operations being performed since 1939, gave the following results: total number of patients, 604; died as the result of operation, 11; died subsequently, 18 (2 by suicide); recovered, 213; substantially improved, 188; slightly improved, 106. Of these patients 250 were discharged and are now working part or full time; of those remaining in hospital the majority listed as improved were able to work and take renewed interest in their lives. The implications of these figures in terms of the relief of human suffering and the restoration of productive activity needs no comment. Here again the people for whom this operation was undertaken were people apparently without hope from any other procedure. They include of course patients who had received other forms of physical treatment before operation, either without success or with a response which was too short-lived to be regarded as satisfactory.

The most recent but necessarily more limited survey of the results of the bi-medial leucotomy operation from a single modern psychiatric unit (the York Clinic, Guy's Hospital) reveals that with an average turnover of about 360 patients a year through 44 beds, 58 patients over the last ten years have been selected for this operation and have subsequently been followed up and assessed as follows:

Relieved of symptoms and now well	8
Substantial improvement	37
Relatively unchanged	11
Dead	2*

The range and indications of this operation may yet be further extended as the result of current research and the further study of results. Nevertheless psychiatrists and neuro-surgeons alike remain aware that it cannot be the final answer. No operation which depends for its efficiency in relieving symptoms upon the severance of intact and structurally healthy nerve pathways, can ever be finally accepted as a wholly satisfactory answer to human suffering. But it will continue to be used while it remains the best and sometimes the only answer we have for intractable anguish: and, as I have tried to show, it gained its initial reputation in the treatment of patients for whom hope might otherwise have been abandoned. I can think of no better way of illustrating this than of quoting from two cases mentioned by Dr Partridge towards the end of his book on pre-frontal leucotomy. His purpose in mentioning these two is to introduce a concluding section dealing with speculations as to how the operation works. I quote them for our purpose as examples of what the operation can do:

... when one sees a patient who has been insidiously ill for eight years, and severely so for between three and four years, with an increasing deterioration ... and sees him just over a year after operation, physically robust and singing excellently in a well-known choir which is participating in a choral competition, having taken the bus from his home to get there: when one sees a patient with contractures of the muscles of his thighs from having spent the better part of seven years in fixed attitudes of prayer between bouts of being violent with double incontinence, and sees him within a year of operation making fifty at

*Neither of these deaths was related to the operation. One occurred in a patient in the improved category and the other in the category listed as unchanged.

cricket, having taken the afternoon off work to play for a local side, one feels bound to make some inquiry as to how it is done.

The inquiry is of course vital to progress in the understanding of this method of treatment, but that it has been done at all is perhaps the most striking conclusion to our consideration of the results which it is possible to expect from treatment in psychiatry.

The Place of Psychiatry in Modern Medicine

WE have now reached a stage in our exploration of psychiatry today in which we can begin to take stock of the present position before looking ahead to future promises or possibilities. We have seen how the subject has emerged from the mists of witchcraft and yet has not entirely shaken itself free from the shadows of fear and shame; we have seen too how the age-old dichotomy of mind and matter has at last begun finally to be resolved, at least within the limits of practical possibility in psychological medicine, by an acceptance of the interdependence of one upon the other. It is not surprising that psychiatry has always attracted philosophical speculation as well as provoking emotional heat. For apart from the central question of the relationship between body and mind, its study also confronts the observer with another fundamental source of controversy: the question of the nature of free will, with which is bound up the concept of responsibility for thought or action on the one hand, or their complete dependence upon blind chance operating along mechanically determined lines on the other.

It is with the first of these two questions that this chapter will be largely concerned, because the essential link between psychiatry and the rest of medicine is the ultimate impossibility of treating states of mind apart from states of body, or states of body apart from states of mind. With the second question, around which centre all the legal and ethical disputes in which psychiatry becomes so frequently and sometimes so needlessly and clumsily involved, we shall have to deal in the next chapter. Here our concern is essentially with the modern basis of psychological medicine as a part of the whole field of medical knowledge, and particularly in its relationship to all other forms of illness and their treatment.

We have accepted that the basis of the psychiatric approach to illness is a consideration not simply of the whole person but of all that can be known about his background, heredity, and life history. Psychiatry today is rooted in genetics, in biochemistry, in endocrinology, as well as in anatomy and physiology; it demands moreover a knowledge not simply of normal psychology and psychopathology, but some acquaintance with sociology, anthropology, history, and philosophy. Yet the object of this somewhat formidable and even alarming catalogue is in the end a modest one. It has been expressed with wonderful simplicity by a great physician, Trudeau, in these words: 'To cure sometimes, to relieve often, to comfort always,' and this, after all, is the aim to which every doctor, each in his own way, has to devote his life.

There is nothing exclusive about this: no psychiatrist would claim for one moment that the happiness and peace of mind of sick people is a goal to which he alone is dedicated or one whose attainment he alone understands, but he can point with some assurance now to a growing body of evidence which demonstrates not simply that the happiness and peace of mind of sick people is desirable as an end in itself, but that to a greater or lesser extent in every case it is necessary and even indispensable to healing and recovery.

If we turn aside for a while from the great proportion of sick people whose illness presents mental or emotional symptoms, including in this category those whose complaints may be of bodily pain or weakness but who prove on physical examination to have no structural lesion to account for it, and consider the patients with fractures or ulcers or heart disease or high blood pressure, all sufferers whose disability carrries with it an obvious and indisputable bodily cause, we find that the same careful and patient study of their lives and personality as a whole will reflect yet one more example of the inseparable unity of body and mind. Doctors have known for many years that anxious, miserable, worried, or irritable patients heal slowly and relapse often. With the interest in studying disease as an active continuing process rather than as a static condition of separate bodily organs, medicine in the twentieth century was bound to recognize more and more contributory factors which played their part in varying degree in the course of any particular illness.

The same period has seen a similar development in the study of the mind; no longer was mental disturbance regarded as a subject which defied all but a purely descriptive approach; it became possible to see it as something continuously moving and changing. Psychodynamics on the one hand, and studies of the physiology of emotion on the other, paved the way for the integration of psychiatry and general medicine, when physical illness could be studied from a psychiatric standpoint as well as psychiatric illness from the standpoint of physical change. In this respect both general medicine and psychiatry were only catching up with what is sometimes called common sense or everyday knowledge, although it is unfortunately true that common sense is by no means as common as might be supposed, nor everyday knowledge nearly as widely recognized or understood.

Common sense and everyday knowledge for example tell us that blushing, weeping, laughing, and trembling are all physical states which are produced and maintained by an emotion. When the emotion is continued for a long time the physical changes may themselves become to some degree modified or permanent. After prolonged grief and much weeping you are left with a swollen blotchy face; you do not regard this as an illness, but it is indisputably a physical symptom and it requires time to get well. You may treat it physically with cold water or cosmetics. One thing you will certainly not do is to doubt or deny its emotional origin, at least to yourself.

The study of bodily changes which appear to be due to or at least frequently linked with emotional states has been undertaken by very many investigators. Upon their results has been erected a body of knowledge which at the present time it is fashionable to refer to as psychosomatic medicine. As an adjective 'psychosomatic' is not particularly objectionable, and it certainly has the advantage over many pieces of technical jargon that its derivation is not a mixture of two languages, or quite meaningless in the language from which it is derived. But where we may take exception to it is in its implication that there is something special about those particular illnesses in which the interdependence of emotion and bodily change has been experimentally demonstrated.

A diagram will help to clarify this point. We can picture the mental and physical sides of human life as two aspects of the same whole, and we can draw them as two triangles fitted together to make one simple rectangle. The diagonal line down the middle of the rectangle is a purely arbitrary division between

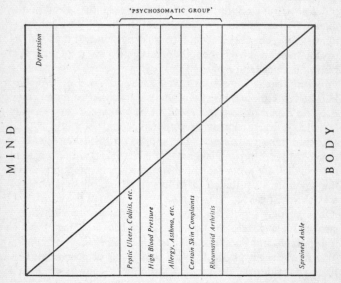

the two, which are really of course inextricably mingled. If we think of any illness or disability we can put it at some point on this arbitrary diagram so that the diagonal line will divide it roughly in the proportions in which the two aspects are involved. If therefore we choose to consider for example a broken leg or a sprained ankle, in most cases this will be almost entirely a physical misfortune with physical causes and physical symptoms; but there will inevitably be an emotional side to it. This may simply be the distress and anxiety caused by the pain and the inconvenience. In this case the symptoms will be purely referable to the initial injury, but it is not impossible that we may have fallen down because we were worried, anxious, impatient, or in a temper, just as Professor Higgins fell upstairs because he was cross with Eliza Doolittle. When we remember how much of our everyday moods, feelings, and behaviour are liable to be dependent upon or at least considerably affected by entirely unconscious mental processes, this is even easier to understand. But there is no need to belabour the point at this stage, and we can be quite content to put the little column representing a sprained ankle at the extreme end of our diagram, so that the area of emotional involvement in the patient is as small as most people would consider it likely to be.

At the other end of the scale we can put for example a severe depression. Here the emotional element is the striking and obvious part of the disability, but the physical changes are represented partly in the symptoms of impaired digestion and elimination, loss of appetite, weight, and speed of muscular response, and partly in the glandular and biochemical changes in the brain which, like the accompanying mood changes, are reversible by specific physical treatment.

The group of illnesses which has been called psychosomatic illnesses can now be seen to be simply those illnesses which happen to fall somewhere about the middle of the scale. They include such conditions as ulcers of the stomach and duodenum, which are sometimes called collectively peptic ulcers, various forms of colitis, many cases of high blood pressure and some forms of heart trouble such as angina, as well as such apparently diverse ailments as certain skin diseases, allergic complaints like asthma and hay fever, and also migraine and rheumatoid arthritis.

On the physical plane the diversity of these illnesses is not really as great as it might seem. Both angina and migraine for example depend for their appearance upon alterations in blood flow through the arteries supplying respectively the heart and certain parts of the brain and its coverings. Moreover all these complaints have in common the importance of the contribution of the autonomic nervous system (that part of the nervous system not directly under conscious control and concerned with the automatic regulation of bodily function) in their development. But the factor they share which from our point of view is the most striking, and incidentally the most recently established, is the large part which continued emotional stress appears to play in producing and maintaining them. It is of course for this reason that they have attracted the most attention when studied by the combined approach to which the name of 'psychosomatic' properly belongs. It is probably better therefore to speak of the psychosomatic approach to an illness as being a desirable one, rather than to call a particular illness psychosomatic simply because in its case the balance between psyche and soma is the most evident and most evenly distributed of those studied so far.

For the rest of this book at any rate, when we talk about psychosomatic medicine, or use the adjective psychosomatic, we shall be referring to a method of approach based upon an acceptance of the body-mind relationship and all it implies, and not to any particular disease or group of diseases, still less to a particular speciality in medicine open only to a particular kind of doctor. It is in fact a method of approach which no good doctor ignores.

However, before the acceptance, now generally agreed, of the value of this method and the principles on which it is based could be won, a great deal of work had to be done. The general nature of this work has already been mentioned; it falls broadly into two groups.

The first contains a number of ingenious experiments devised and conducted in the laboratory and usually involving animals, although sometimes human volunteers could be used. One example was the demonstration of the effect in a cat of sudden emotion upon stomach shape and movement; this was achieved by giving the cat a meal mixed with barium, an entirely harmless element which is opaque to X-rays and constantly in use in hospitals for demonstrating the outline of the digestive organs.

After its barium meal this cat stood upon a platform so arranged that an X-ray picture of its stomach could be projected upon a screen, and the normal outline and churning movements of digestion clearly seen. When a dog was introduced into the room and the cat was gently but firmly prevented from climbing up the curtains it not only displayed considerable and understandable evidence of emotion, but the whole contour and behaviour of its stomach altered completely; the valves at each end closed tight while the rest of the stomach sagged and digestive movements ceased. This is the well-recognized effect of the secretion of adrenalin through the autonomic nervous system, and its purpose would seem to be to damp down secondary functions such as digestion, in preparation for the violent action by which emotion in the cat is commonly followed.

Medical students have long been taught that secretion of adrenalin prepares the subject for 'fight, flight, or fright'. It would be more accurate to say, as this experiment conclusively demonstrates, that the role of fright in this response, and its effect, is to produce the reaction rather than to follow it.

Another experiment of some interest along the same lines, but going considerably further and this time involving a human subject, is that of Dr Harold G. Wolff and Dr Stewart Wolf of Cornell University and the New York Hospital. Employed in their department is a most amiable gentleman called Tom. Owing to an unfortunate accident many years ago he cannot swallow his food in the normal way because his oesophagus, the tube leading from the mouth to the stomach, is blocked; he therefore has to feed himself through a specially constructed opening directly into his stomach through the abdominal wall. Wolff and Wolf have enlisted his aid in studying the direct effect upon the lining of the stomach of emotional changes.

To do this it has of course been necessary to induce such changes in Tom, sometimes without warning him. For example, he was on one occasion told that he was being fired for inefficiency. If this had been true it would have been grossly unjust, and was anyway not the kind of thing which would happen to anybody without warning in that happy and admirable department. Tom's reaction was visible and striking, not simply in his face, manner, and speech, but very much so in his stomach as well. He was bitterly resentful and angry; the lining of his stomach became congested and engorged, even to the point of bleeding at the lightest touch. When the experiment and the trick which it had necessarily involved were explained to him he was at once relieved and reassured, and his stomach rapidly returned to normal.

Further studies on Tom have shown that when he is depressed and dejected his stomach suffers a corresponding change. It becomes pale and grey and covered with mucus. The angry resentful stomach, and above all the stomach in which the owner's emotional drive has been blocked or frustrated, is ready to bleed and, in those particularly susceptible, to develop an ulcer. Such susceptibility itself is neither wholly physical nor wholly emotional; like all else in the study of man it is a combination of both. It seems to occur in about 10 per cent of the population, and it is from this 10 per cent that all cases of peptic ulceration are probably drawn. The pale, grey, miserable, dejected stomach is the one whose owner develops chronic gastritis, that miserable blend of dyspepsia and sadness all too familiar to the general practitioner, who knows full well that it is a complaint of mind at least as much as of body.

Similar changes in response to emotion have been demonstrated in the colon by Dr William Grace, working with Wolff and Wolf, and by other members of the team working on the mucous membrane of the nose. The full details of these experiments which resulted in a tremendous gain in practical knowledge, have been set forth in three monographs which are now well on the way to becoming medical classics. The one which the general reader may find most interesting is that dealing with Tom and his stomach and is called *Human Gastric Function* by Wolff and Wolf.* Much of the work of the team as a whole exemplifies the manner in which experiments of this sort should be planned and undertaken.

The second group of studies consists essentially in the application of psychiatric techniques to the study of patients with predominantly physical illness in general hospitals. Some of the best known work in recent years was performed by Dr Flanders Dunbar over twelve years at the Presbyterian Hospital, New York. The primary object of her research was to discover the nature of the correlation between emotions and bodily changes in particular illnesses, and to discover to what extent such corre-

* Oxford University Press.

lations were specific to the illness in which they appear. She sought also to discover whether apart from emotional changes themselves there were any particular combinations of stress in the patients' lives or aspects of their personality which produced or predisposed to a specific kind of illness. For all this she had to have controls. She chose patients in the fracture wards for this purpose on the assumption that while they could readily be matched for age, sex, and social position with the subjects of her study, and were, like them, in hospital and facing the same general conditions, they were otherwise likely to be within the average limits of normal emotional adjustment and type of personality.

The results of her study led her to a number of very interesting conclusions. Not only was she able to demonstrate conclusively the role of continued tensions, anxiety, and frustration or resentment in many of the illnesses falling into our middle group in the diagram, but she was also led to conclude that her choice of control group had itself been less simple than she had imagined. Many of these patients proved to have a number of personality characteristics in common, among these being a disproportionately high tendency to be involved in accidents, so-called 'accident proneness', impulsiveness, adventurousness, and a fondness for immediate rather than deliberate action. These characteristics occurred far more often in the control group than could be accounted for by chance alone; they formed a striking contrast with the highly developed control of emotional life and behaviour, the restless ambition, strenuous independence, and sustained drive shown by a high proportion of the patients with angina or coronary disease who formed one of the other groups studied.

This has led Dr Dunbar and her disciples to take a rather more definite position with regard to the correlation, not simply of life stress and emotional reaction with bodily illness, but of certain specific types of personality with certain specific physical illnesses. This may well be stretching the whole hypothesis too far; certainly many of her colleagues would consider it unproven; but the general results of her work and their implications are arresting and important and have afforded experimental confirmation of much that had long been the subject of repeated clinical impressions before her studies established it on a scientific foundation.

In Scotland the pioneer studies of Dr Halliday into the relative incidence, in different industries and social groups, of various kinds of illness with a psychogenic basis, led him to the concept of what he has called psychosocial medicine. This is essentially an epidemiological approach to the problem. The clinical approach is exemplified by the work of Dr Wittkower, who has immensely enlarged our understanding of the emotional factors in such illnesses as tuberculosis, and acute and chronic disorders of the skin.

If therefore we now accept the implications of the psychosomatic approach and its particular importance in the treatment and management of those illnesses falling into the middle group of our diagram, the next question which poses itself inescapably is just how this body-mind relationship works in the production of illness. Are the emotional factors underlying an anxiety state essentially the same or essentially different from those contributing to high blood pressure or a peptic ulcer? In this field opinions are divided and we have still a great deal to learn. If we attempt to survey the two main schools of thought on the question we shall discover them to be something like this: one school, in which a number of psycho-analysts and some general physicians with an analytic background or training are to be found, believes that the psychodynamic processes underlying all illnesses, but of course contributing to them in widely varying degree, are essentially the same.

This means for example that conflict, repression, and the operation of unconscious complexes are believed to play as large a part in the emotional contribution to a particular physical illness as they undoubtedly play in the production of hysterical illness or an obsessive compulsive state. In these terms I have heard a colleague describe some forms of physical illness as the alternative to a psychosis for a particular patient; he believes that emotional stress resulting from unresolved conflicts emerges through physical channels in one person and more directly through mental illness in another. Remember that this point of view does not imply that *the whole of the contribution* to the physical illness is emotional; but it does imply that that part of it which is emotional derives from an identical mechanism to that which might otherwise produce a psychosis. He made this observation when discussing a case in which a crippling physical illness had been relieved by a brilliant new method of physical treatment, only to be followed by the development of a very serious psychosis in the same patient within a matter of a few weeks. But there were other possible explanations for this disaster. One, that the actual physical effect upon the brain of the patient, produced by the administration of the physical remedy, had released certain ominous mental changes, just as the physical effect of an acute illness upon the brain can lead to delirium; another, that the complete change in outlook which the promise of cure demanded in a patient who had come to believe that his case was hopeless, had itself disturbed the balance of mind already long distressed.

The other school of thought is less dogmatic. While accepting as highly probable that the psychopathology to be discovered in many patients with physical illness is vitally important to their condition and essentially a target for treatment, this school of thought is also prepared to acknowledge that, in a number of cases where the emotional contribution to physical illness is equally important, its basis does not seem to involve any psycho-pathological process at all.

For example, there are some patients whose skin condition is made worse by anger or resentment. They are perfectly well aware of this connexion, and moreover they are equally aware of the stresses which provoke them to anger. Like everybody else they may well have conflicts and repressed feelings. But it does not always seem necessary to invoke these in the explanation of their symptoms. My own view about such people is that the response evoked in them by direct stress of an emotional kind is discharged in part *directly* through their autonomic nervous system, instead of reaching the surface mainly through consciousness after traversing the higher pathways of the central nervous system in the brain. This response can be thought of simply in terms of energy, whatever that may be. We can detect the passage of such energy in the form of a minute electric current through a nerve fibre, and to this extent the hypothesis is not purely allegorical.

If this is so we have emotion producing symptoms in two rather different ways: directly, by discharge through the autonomic nervous system, so that the normal physical accompaniment of the primary emotion is simply heightened or intensified; or indirectly, by the operation of unconscious mental processes by which, through failure to deal with a conflict or to accept the unbearably painful nature of the emotion, a kind of secondary tension is set up. This may then issue either in a hysterical symptom, a symbolic act, a conscious and unpleasant feeling for which no cause can be found, or once again as a disturbance of bodily function, when this secondary tension is discharged through the autonomic rather than through the central nervous system.

The practical effect of this view, if it is right, is that while we must seek and treat emotional stress in every patient, we are by no means bound to expect that such stress will necessarily be produced *only* by the mechanisms we have come to recognize in mental illness, every time that it is important in bodily disease. Sometimes there will not only be important emotional aspects to physical illness; there will be important unconscious elements in these emotional factors which must be tackled before the emotions themselves can be relieved. In other cases the emotions will be no more and no less complicated than they are in normally adjusted people, but they will owe their particular importance and their need for understanding and relief to the part they are playing in producing or maintaining the illness.

The psychiatrist called in to see the general medical or surgical case does not therefore necessarily prepare himself for a plunge into the unconscious; he does however approach the patient with precisely the same care and general interest which the study of his other patients, and for that matter of human beings in general, seems to him to demand. Furthermore, he accepts what he finds as far as he can on its merits in the particular case. Sometimes his special skill and knowledge are further required, sometimes they are not. If the emotional factors can be relieved by simple direct common-sense methods he may well not seek to do more. Indeed, increasing co-operation between the psychiatrist and his brothers in the profession of medicine is already leading to two very desirable results: the first is that they are far more ready to call him in than their forefathers would have been; the second is that they themselves and their students are studying the psychosomatic approach and practising it in many cases with profound success. The logical outcome of all this is that everybody who follows these principles is thereby enabled to approach more closely the simple modest aim of the good doctor ... 'To cure sometimes, to relieve often, to comfort always.' And, one might add, whenever possible to try to understand.

*

In the sphere of understanding a new and stimulating possibility for research has been opened up by another important development in physiology and general medicine whose applications to psychiatry are only just beginning to be fully realized. This is the theory of what is called by its originator, Professor Hans Selye of the University of Montreal, the general adaptation syndrome. It is concerned with the effects of stress of all kinds upon the living organism.

Professor Selye has been working on this problem for rather more than fifteen years. Only comparatively recently have his discoveries received general recognition and attention, but their probable importance has been dramatically underlined by the use which has been made of the new glandular preparations A.C.T.H. and cortisone, in the relief of a number of serious illnesses. A detailed exposition of Professor Selye's theory would demand a good deal of space. He himself has recently completed his first embodiment of the whole theory and the experimental work upon which it rests in a huge monograph packed with highly technical information and followed by over a thousand references. It is obviously impossible for me to do justice to it here, nor indeed is this the place to try. But a general indication of some of its important and relevant applications in reasonably simple terms is something which the scope of this chapter demands.

Selye was interested in stress as something which tended to produce a change in the organism, a change to which the organism was in turn bound to react. The object of this reaction would seem to be to restore as far as possible the inner equilibrium of

the organism, and this tendency to restoration of inner equilibrium is called homeostasis. A simple example of the process in
action is the way in which we react to the stress of heat by dis-
carding clothing to expose greater areas of skin for cooling, and
by sweating so that the evaporation of the sweat will aid the
cooling process. In this way we maintain a relatively constant
body temperature; and there are of course opposite processes by
which we react to cold, which will readily occur to the reader.

Extremes of heat, cold, physical exhaustion, injury, and infection were among the forms of stress which Selye studied patiently
and exhaustively and with considerable ingenuity for many years.
From his observations he developed the hypothesis that, however
diverse the reactions to stress in a living creature, the same
fundamental principles underlie them all. No matter what the
precise nature of the provocative stress, the response of the
organism is a combination of a general reaction, common to all
forms of stress, and a specific reaction peculiar to the particular
stress which has occurred. Moreover three main stages can be
distinguished in the development of this response.

The first stage Selye called the alarm reaction. This is characterized by relatively violent bodily disturbance, with glandular
and autonomic nervous mechanisms working at high pressure.
It is comparatively short-lived, but while it lasts it bears all the
characteristics of illness. If the creature survives, the next stage is
one of adaptation; the stress has been successfully encountered
by whatever mechanisms were necessary, and, at whatever cost to
the organism as a whole, relative homeostasis has been achieved.
In this stage the creature is comparatively impervious to further
stress of the kind to which adaptation has been secured. For
example, rats exposed to very low temperatures in a refrigerator,
after passing through the first stage in which the effects of the
stress upon their normal habits of feeding and mating are all too
evident, achieve such equilibrium later on that they are able and
willing to raise a family while still in the ice box; but the stage
of adaptation is none the less an abnormal one, in response to an
abnormal situation: the situation of continued stress.

Other dissimilar stresses may find the animal far less prepared
to deal with them. Under such circumstances the apparently

increased hardihood is not general but specific to the stress which produced it. Refrigerated rats have a diminished resistance to infection. But if the severe stress is continued long enough the stage of adaptation will be followed by one of physiological exhaustion under which the homeostatic mechanism breaks down and the animal dies. When the stage of adaptation is itself incomplete, either because it is failing or because the nature of the response called forth is incompatible with normal health to a major degree, symptoms of illness become apparent. These tend to be characteristic and specific. To the whole process from which such symptoms may arise Selye has given the name of the general adaptation syndrome; and those illnesses in which the characteristic and specific symptoms tend to appear he has called the diseases of adaptation.

One element of particular clinical importance in the first stage, or alarm reaction, is the outpouring of glandular secretions, which appear indispensable to the subsequent mobilization of defences constituting the stage of successful adaptation. Inability to maintain these secretions, the exhaustion of their supply, or certain changes in their balance and relative proportions, seem to underlie the failure of this stage, with the production of one or other of the diseases of adaptation. It follows that these diseases ought to respond to treatment with the glandular extracts concerned.

This has been apparently confirmed by the successful use of such extracts as A.C.T.H. and cortisone, in the treatment of such complaints as rheumatoid arthritis, asthma, and certain very serious or otherwise fatal afflictions of the skin, blood vessels, and connective tissues, which have previously been entirely refractory to treatment of any kind.

The whole of this work is still only in its preliminary stages; its implications cannot fully be foretold. Its promises may prove to be exaggerated, its disappointments have already begun to challenge but not to deter the further efforts of clinical and laboratory research, but its particular importance to us in the considerations which are our concern in this chapter is this: the illnesses which Selye has called diseases of adaptation are with very few exceptions the same general group as those which other workers, approaching the problem from an entirely different angle, have called psychosomatic disorders. The stresses which interested Selye, and which formed the basis of his experimental work, were contrived and intended to be physical stresses. The stresses studied in the work of Flanders Dunbar and many others employing the psychosomatic approach are predominantly emotional stresses. It begins to look as though, despite their apparent difference in origin, in effect they may be essentially the same.

There is another small piece of research which seems to drive home this lesson still further. During the war I spent some time in the Royal Air Force as a Unit Medical Officer. A part of my job which I found particularly interesting, although difficult and exacting, was the first-hand study of the effects of the stress of operational flying upon air crew. One had to understand its nature, to predict where possible when and how it would affect a particular individual, to minimize its ravages, and to treat them when they occurred. It had at last come to be generally acknowledged that the supreme operative factor in such stress was fear; natural, normal human fear. From first-hand experience of the conditions involved I can confirm that observation with all my heart. The more imagination you had, the more inwardly terrified you were a great deal of the time; and the more strained, tense, anxious, and apprehensive you were apt to become at the prospect of the job you had to do.

But the men who had volunteered for this job, and had been specially selected and trained to do it, had to be enabled to carry on in the face of this overwhelming stress for far longer than anyone would have wished. Studying over four thousand of them and knowing a great number personally over four and a half years I was able to devise a method of investigation of the effects of this stress which proved to have a certain validity.

The normal tour of operations for the air crew in Bomber Command was thirty trips. It proved possible to predict with some accuracy the phases through which a normal man would go in attempting to complete a tour of this kind. The odds *against* his surviving, uninjured, and not a prisoner-of-war, were about five to one. While everybody hoped to get through, no single individual could reasonably expect to do so. None the less the vast majority maintained sufficient morale to carry on until they either did complete the tour or were killed, injured, or captured in the attempt.

The study was concerned with the phases through which a man went and the fluctuations which occurred in his morale over this period. In essence there were three stages, each with its own characteristics. The first stage occurred during the first three to five trips. Here the initial courage and determination, coupled with a natural desire to find out what it was really going to be like, met the full impact of the waking nightmare which the job was to become. Some people broke down at this stage, and of those who did practically none were able to resume flying. But the majority kept going and the next period of extreme stress came somewhere between the eighth and sixteenth sortie. Everyone encountered this stage, in which even the most phlegmatic and stolid had realized the full nature of what he was up against, while the honourable completion of the tour still seemed almost unattainably far away. In varying degree everyone needed help to get through this stage; some drew upon their resources of courage and determination, many turned to their friends or the inspiration of good leadership, a few came to the doctor who was their friend as well as their physician.

They learned that if they could hang on through this phase, in which physical symptoms of anxiety were so common as to be almost universal, they could expect a relatively stable period until the end of the tour approached, when the cumulative toll of mounting stress, physical exhaustion, and fatigue produced the last of the three critical periods. Then it was that a wise Squadron Commander, in consultation with a doctor who knew his men, might relieve a man here and there before the mathematical total of the tour had been reached, if that man's share of stress or his capacity to bear it made the decision wise and just.

These are the bare bones of a study which at the time was important, conducted in days and under conditions which I hope never to see again. At that time I knew nothing of Selye or of his hypothesis. Yet a comparison of these three stages of response to flying stress, the first an immediate reaction, the second a partial but inevitably abnormal state of adaptation, and the third, in the more vulnerable or severely pressed, a final stage of exhaustion, with Selye's three stages of alarm reaction, adaptation, and exhaustion, suggests an immediate parallel. But while my concern was essentially with emotion as the operative factor, the conclusions worked out in such detail by Selye under very different circumstances were based upon physiological stresses and physiological responses in experimental animals. It would seem that underlying the results in both cases is a single fundamental aspect of the response of living creatures to all they have to endure, whether it be fear or pain, hunger or infection, emotional stress or physical disease.

We know that sudden shock, whether the cause be physical or emotional, will produce sudden and sometimes catastrophic results. We have begun to see now that in a different way the long-continued battle with stress and tension which it is the lot of so many of us to fight, is not a battle in which it is always very profitable to distinguish between hard knocks and hard feelings; nor are the scars borne separately upon the body or upon the mind. They have their being, like those who carry them, somewhere in the tangled, intricate, and mysterious unity of mind and body, spirit and flesh, which is man himself. And he who seeks to cure them must be a whole and tolerably well rounded and well grounded doctor, for it is the whole man or woman with whom he has to deal.

* * *

All that we have now considered about psychiatry to-day can have left us in no doubt that it is in fact inevitably the province of the physician. Yet it must be recorded that Freud himself proclaimed the view that, at least in treatment, the care and management of certain patients could be safely entrusted to laymen whose training need consist simply of a personal analysis, and an adequate knowledge and grasp of the principles underlying the theory and practice of psycho-analytic technique and philosophy. There are in fact people performing this function to-day. It is inevitable that a doctor writing a book of this kind will be suspected of prejudice in his dealing with the question of lay treatment, and particularly lay analysis. It is only right that he should be so suspect, and, moreover, that he should as far as possible accept the probability that his views will be coloured to some extent by a personal bias inherent in his own sincere belief that medical training is an essential prerequisite to the treatment of human beings.

Accepting the implications of this without further dispute I must none the less record my own opinion that the great danger and drawback inseparable from lay treatment is that, however well the mental and emotional mechanisms are understood, the emergence of fresh symptoms, which may often present themselves in the form of physical complaints in the course of treatment, will raise again the problem of diagnosis which no layman can be expected to handle.

This objection is not overcome by having the initial diagnosis firmly established by a competent physician before treatment begins, because patients under analysis or long-term psychotherapy are just as liable to develop acute or insidious illnesses, requiring physical as well as psychological treatment, as anybody else. Nor can the problem be adequately solved by referring the patient back to a physician every time a new complaint is met. This procedure is liable to result in a periodic oscillation between one expert and another, with a consequent division of the patient's confidence and, moreover, a ready-made means of escaping from emotionally disturbing situations which must be handled properly if treatment is to succeed.

Therefore, while I would not deny that in some very special circumstances where the physician who has made the diagnosis knows the patient well, and enjoys a complete understanding with a particularly gifted and sensible lay analyst, valuable and perhaps indispensable work may be achieved through their collaboration, exceptions of this kind are so rare as to be no basis for precedent, and certainly would not justify the training of numbers of lay analysts in an attempt to solve the admittedly difficult problem of providing sufficient therapy for all who need it.

This is not to say, however, that no psychotherapy can be done by anybody except a doctor. If we accept the wide implications of the term set out in the beginning of Chapter 7, any exchange or examination of ideas and emotions with another person, any acceptance of the patient which gives him comfort or security, any inspiration which he may gain from or share with someone else is in one sense a form of psychotherapeutic experience.

There is another form of experience whose value in healing or relieving mental anguish none but the most obtuse or prejudiced would deny. This is religious experience, whether in its mystical form or in the relationship more commonly recognized between the priest and the penitent. Not all psychiatrists are able to accept this point of view; some even maintain sincerely that while it is scientific to explain religion, it is unscientific to believe in it. Here again we encounter at least as much emotional prejudice on one side of the argument as on the other: but once such prejudice has been set aside there remains no logical or reasonable basis for conflict between science and religion, or between the acknow-ledgement of what is unknown and the exploration of what can be known about it. An admirable discussion of one aspect of this question is to be found in the final chapter of Professor Mottram's book, to which I have already alluded.

The psychiatrist, like any other doctor, can often work with the priest, although his goal as a physician is necessarily more limited. It is a psychiatrist's job to help the patient achieve as much of health and happiness as are possible by natural means. The claims and the authority of the priest are vested in something greater and far beyond this.

But while psychiatry cannot and should not claim to be the sole means whereby a man or woman, sick or troubled in mind or body, can achieve peace, neither can medicine as a whole or psychiatry in particular accept the claims of some religious sects that all healing can be achieved by faith and prayer alone, without the use of any of the natural physical or mental processes which science and medicine have developed, and which are as much a part of creation as anything else.

*

The doctor's job is concerned then with the restoration of health and happiness to a sick person, and the prevention of ill health or unhappiness among those who are well. The psychia-trist, as a doctor with a particular interest in the emotional and mental element in the body-mind problem, shares and reflects this concern within his own speciality and in all its contacts with other branches of medicine and surgery and with human existence as a whole. We may ask at this stage, what makes a medical student or a doctor choose the field of psychological medicine for particular study, and once he has so chosen what kind of training does he need before he can practise it with any degree of competence and safety?

The motives which attract or impel a doctor to this kind of work are almost as varied as those which determine a man's choice of medicine as a whole as his profession. We can recognize some of the reasons, both good and bad, which may play a part in shaping such a choice, but we can never know them all. Probably the single most desirable characteristic of a candidate for psychiatric training is a clear and lively mind, and a sincere interest in and affection for the human race, and particularly the individual. This of course is desirable in any doctor, even if his work ultimately takes him into the laboratory or into administration. But to the psychiatrist dealing with human beings in their most vulnerable, and sometimes, at least superficially, their most unattractive aspects, it is indispensable.

There are of course a few recognizably bad reasons for choosing this branch of medicine. One of them is a desire for power; another, comparable to it but perhaps more subtle in expression, is the need to compensate for a personal sense of inadequacy or insecurity by working out one's own difficulties through handling those of other people. Again, there are some men and women who have been attracted to psychiatry on the basis of an entirely mistaken belief that manual clumsiness, or a relative incapacity to master the techniques of clinical medicine, would matter less in a branch in which, to them, salesmanship and a certain garrulousness might seem to compensate for the lack of other qualities. These form a small but unhappy band whose shortcomings in one of the most difficult branches of medicine are all too evident; moreover they provide a ready target for critics of the branch itself. They are probably no more numerous than the vainglorious and superficial minority who have chosen surgery because of an adolescent passion for limelight and adulation, or consulting medicine out of a need to assume a pompous importance and a mantle of infallible wisdom.

Doctors, in fact, like every other group of men and women are a mixed lot, whether they are specialists, research workers, administrators, or general practitioners. It would be as idle to pretend that because their aims are noble none of them is base or frail, as it would be false and unjust to maintain that baseness or inadequacy characterized the group as a whole, or any particular part of it.

Any doctor who can accept with understanding human suffering in its emotional aspects may well feel drawn towards psychiatry. How must he then prepare himself to undertake it? As a student he will begin by paying particular attention to his relationship with the patients, to listening rather than talking, to being ready with attention and modest with advice. He will use his imagination as well as his senses and will accept his own feelings in the face of suffering without shame or dismay. He will be a cautious optimist and a constant friend.

After qualification he will profitably spend a year or so in House appointments, of which at least one should be surgical, and he will use this time and any military service, which in these days it may be his duty to undertake, to develop a sense of perspective and an increased awareness of human beings as a whole in sickness and in health. At the end of this time, and preferably before beginning his specialized training, he will take a higher degree in general medicine to establish both his background and position as a general physician. For the next four or five years he will divide his time between post-graduate study in libraries, laboratories, and specialized hospitals, and intensive and unremitting clinical work with all kinds of patients in psychiatric and neurological wards and out-patient clinics, and if he is fortunate he will spend a part of the time in another country, working as a member of a team or as a junior colleague to some outstanding member of his profession.

His professional aims will be to acquire sound and basic knowledge of psychiatry, neurology, and normal psychology. Included under these headings will be, to a greater or lesser extent, all those other related aspects of medical and scientific knowledge which we have already seen are part and parcel of the subject as a whole. The personal gain of all this work and experience, if it is to bear full fruit in his subsequent career, will be the development of comparative maturity in his attitude towards psychiatry and medicine as a whole, together with a capacity for criticism, most of all of himself and his own work, and that element of courage and responsibility without which the work itself cannot be completed.

There will be some more examinations to take, as evidence of study rather than as any guarantee of knowledge or experience. They will probably include the Diploma in Psychological Medicine of a recognized university and perhaps a Doctorate of Medicine, of Science, or of Philosophy. These will come somewhere in the latter half of his post-graduate work, and unfortunately, although inevitably, they will compete for his diligence and attention with the making of original observations and the approach to research, which are an essential part of adequate specialized training.

If it is his wish to make treatment along primarily psycho-analytic lines his main goal he will also have to find time and money for a process of personal analysis, which will combine training in technique with the experience of the transference situation from the patient's point of view, and that degree of increased awareness which, although not provided always or exclusively by this experience, is none the less always aimed at and often achieved.

From the beginning to the end of these five to ten years of post-graduate study the doctor will have been in constant contact with patients, will have followed many through for months and some for years as their individual physician, will have studied the problems of childhood as well as those of adult life, and will have become acquainted with criminal and abnormal behaviour, as well as the more readily acknowledged kinds of illness. Some doctors will find their vocation in clinical work and practice; some in teaching and research; some in a combination of these activities: for some the desk, for some the laboratory bench, and for others the consulting room will provide the medium for their endeavours. Whatever they do, the more they read outside their subject as well as inside it, the more they meet and study people, the more they love and the less they hate and fear, the better doctors they will be. It is comparatively easy to prescribe a counsel of perfection, as I have done; easier still to fall far short of it as all of us do. But we have within our hearts a noble if a simple ideal: 'To cure sometimes, to relieve often, to comfort always ...'

The Size and Shape of the Social Problem

ANYBODY who has stayed with this book to this point will, I hope, have discerned a semblance of order emerging out of chaos, and picked up a thread which, running through the pages, seeks to link the whole into a co-ordinated picture of psychiatry to-day. It is a subject with an interesting history, a particular way of studying, describing, and seeking to understand and to treat illness; it deals with many different kinds of illness which in turn arise from a multiplicity of causes; it embodies a variety of theories, most of them capable of integration in the whole but some seeming to contradict each other; and it demands from its disciples a standard of training and medical and general knowledge which are higher than we may achieve but no higher than we ought to aim. The object of all this in practice is to promote health and to relieve suffering. It will be the aim of the last two chapters of the book to consider some of the wider implications of the subject: in this chapter we shall be concerned with the size and shape of the problem which confronts psychiatry in this country to-day.

It is indeed a tremendous challenge. We shall get some indication of this by surveying in round figures some of its more important aspects. Taking the then population of England and Wales as approximately 40,000,000, here are some of the figures for patients suffering from various forms of mental illness. At the end of 1949 the mental hospitals of this country contained just under 150,000 people (the exact figure was 147,288). Comparison with other years shows that this is a reasonably consistent number and a sound basis for comparison with other forms of illness. At the same time there were some 300,000 people suffering from mental deficiency of a sufficient degree to warrant their certification. Of these about 45,000 were actually being cared for in institutions, but the estimate of a Committee appointed for this purpose in 1929 was that between two and three times this number required such care.

One way of looking at these figures is to say that out of the total population roughly three in every thousand are in-patients in mental hospitals, and one in every thousand resident in institutions for mental defect. Another way of approaching it, which will perhaps convey even more vividly the actual size of the problem in terms of illness, is to recognize that the number of beds at present required for mental illness in all forms is almost as many as the total number required for all other forms of illness, accident, and injury put together. These figures do not include the incidence of psychoneurotic illness among the general population, which has been calculated as a result of various surveys as falling somewhere between eight and eleven per thousand of the population.

At this point one might be excused for feeling a trifle despondent. But what we have already seen of the progress which psychiatry to-day is making and hopes to continue to make will, if appropriately applied, provide us with very solid grounds for reassurance. In 1946 an eminent English psychiatrist, Dr C. P. Blacker, published a book called *Neurosis and the Mental Health Services*. This dealt with a survey of the existing facilities for the prevention and treatment of neurotic illness, and went on to consider the future needs of the mental health services of this country as a whole. It is a book of some 200 pages, and every page is packed with facts. This is going to be a comparatively short chapter, and it is obviously impossible to endeavour to distil within its compass even in the most condensed form a fully adequate account of the findings and recommendations of Dr Blacker's book.

We can, however, take note at least in outline of the general scope of existing facilities and compare them with that most stimulating part of Dr Blacker's report, which deals with his proposals for mental health services for a population of a million people, this being the size of a unit within the total framework of such services which he considers best suited to their future organization. We have already seen that about 150,000 patients were accommodated in mental hospitals in this country [now over 200,000 in England and Wales and over 27,000 in Scotland]. They were divided between over a hundred separate institutions and the total overcrowding estimated to exist throughout the service was between 12 and 15 per cent. It should be added that ideally, in the view of Dr Blacker and the vast majority of the medical superintendents of mental hospitals with whom this question has been discussed, no such hospital should contain more than 1,000 beds. We have also seen that the provision for mentally defective patients is about one-third of what is considered desirable. It is only fair to add that, apart from the war and its effect upon building and shortages, another important cause for overcrowding and under-provision of in-patient services is the comparatively high standard of efficiency of diagnosis and recognition of mental illness in this country.

In this respect public opinion, and even the recognition by the medical profession as a whole of the importance of this type of prevention, is lagging far behind the possibilities which already exist. We are drawn to the somewhat disappointing conclusion that while the importance of providing adequate care and treatment for established illness is at last recognized, far too little attention is being paid to the preventive aspects of the problem. Some of the more important contributions of mental hygiene to this subject have already been mentioned; in addition to the undoubted need for adequate research into the problems of childhood and their treatment, the full value of early treatment in every branch of psychiatry is constantly being stressed. But before this can be secured the public confidence in this treatment, its integration and acceptance into medicine as a whole, and its final release from the medieval attitude of horror and superstition must be secured.

Blacker's proposals for an adequate mental health service for a specimen population of a million people take all these factors into account. They can be summarized as follows: as a start 100 beds per million population should be provided outside mental hospitals for psychiatric cases, either in teaching psychiatric units which form part of the general teaching hospitals of university medical schools, or in non-teaching units located in key towns. Over and above this provision he suggests that additional psychiatric beds should be made available to deal with the emergency admissions which now tend, except in the larger towns, to go directly to mental hospitals. The provision of observation wards as a part of the general hospitals in the London area and in other large towns in England has amply demonstrated that a considerable proportion of patients admitted for observation as emergencies need never be certified or transferred to mental hospitals at all.

He concludes this section of his report by saying:

The sum total of work would be varied and stimulating; it would hold attractions for a wide circle of potential recruits; and it would offer good prospects to men with clinical interests. Indeed we should think of a mental *health* rather than a mental *hospital* service.

Dealing with the provision for out-patient work he suggests three essential ways of meeting the need for its expansion: by increasing staff at existing sessions; by increasing the number of sessions of existing clinics; and by increasing the number of clinics in the area. The existing material on which this part of the report is based was drawn from a study of 216 clinics in England and Wales. He estimates that they should be expanded by about 75 to 100 per cent in the course of the next five years.

His views on the provision which should be made for children divide facilities under two headings: comprehensive child psychiatric clinics for the diagnosis, classification, and selected treatment of all types of mental illness in childhood, including behaviour disorders as well as the problems of mental defect, organic illness, and psychoses; and child guidance centres largely devoted to the treatment of behaviour disorders on the scale likely to be necessary if all children and their parents who stand in need, however briefly or transiently, of this kind of help are to be offered it and enabled to accept it. On this basis he suggests that three or four child psychiatric clinics, each forming part of a central psychiatric clinic under the mental health services, should be provided for a population of a million. His estimate for the need of child guidance centres, to be established by the education authorities, is that of a minimum requirement of one such centre for every 20,000 children. On this scale, ten child guidance centres would be needed for the 200,000 children who would be included in a population of a million.

He also recommends a hostel for about fifty unstable or defective children who might be referred from the child guidance clinics, and a children's reception centre for the care, sorting, and appropriate disposal of homeless or destitute children, or for children needing immediate care which cannot otherwise be provided.

Following the Report of the Wood Committee (1929) he regards the ideal provision for mental defectives in an area of a million people as being two colonies, each of which should contain a residential school and should be divided into villas containing not more than sixty patients apiece, each colony having a total accommodation of between 1,000 and 1,200 patients. He follows these recommendations with these words:

At first sight the difficulties and costs of such an enterprise will appear staggering: indeed, their dimensions are such as to obscure the very tangible gains which would result from a vigorous handling of this problem. The majority of defectives are trainable and, with proper training, can be turned into socially useful human beings. Many can be taught to do simple repetitive manual work both in agriculture and industry. The task, once mastered, is performed with a thoroughness and fidelity which are a surprise to many. The Colony is the best place for a certain type of defective to be thus trained, and arrangements can then be made for small groups of patients to be boarded out in special hostels under the supervision of the parent Colony, from which they can engage in remunerative work in field and factory. It is better both for the community and the defective that he should be thus stabilized and employed than that he should drift into unemployment or delinquency, becoming in indirect ways a burden on the community. . . The dynamic conception of the Colony outlined and advocated by the Wood Committee is one which, when adopted, transforms the outlook of the staff. Work in residential institutions for defectives is sometimes regarded as the most dismal and uninspiring backwater in medical and social work. This view is quickly dispelled by a visit to an enterprising Colony which aims at training the maximum number of its inmates for specific tasks and at placing them suitably outside.

The provisions of the Mental Health Act which became law in 1959 have gone some way towards paving the way for the kind of organization which Blacker has recommended.

The essential spirit underlying the letter of the Act is that treatment for mentally ill patients should be provided with no more legal formality or social or geographical isolation than that involved in the treatment of any other illness. The Act looks forward to smaller, modernized mental hospitals, each with its own active treatment programme, special psychiatric units in all general hospitals, and the provision of psychiatric out-patient facilities as a routine part of general hospital services.

It also enjoins the co-operation of local authorities in the rehabilitation and domiciliary care of patients discharged from mental hospitals or special units.

Nevertheless these admirable aims are far from achievement, at least as yet. One of the crucial shortages is the lack of adequately trained and suitable men and women available as nurses. At the beginning of 1961 it was estimated that, throughout the National Health Service as a whole, there were some 25,000 unfilled vacancies for nurses and nearly 10,000 hospital beds closed for lack of staff. Even more serious was the shortage of appropriately trained doctors. In many of the ordinary mental hospitals in Britain, the average ratio of patients to doctors is still between 100 and 150 to one. In some hospitals it is over 250 to one. This inevitably means that some patients receive no treatment at all, apart from physical care and supervision, and the casual kindness that an unknown face can expect from a doctor whose time can never stretch to encompass the needs of all the patients nominally under his care.

All this is, of course, directly related to the financial provision for the Mental Health Service. Comparisons in costs between general hospitals and mental hospitals must be treated with some reserve, but the following table, based on the Ministry of Health's Hospital Costing Returns for 1956–7 is striking proof of the difference in standards. The figures refer to general hospitals and mental hospitals, but exclude teaching hospitals.

	Average weekly cost per patient		
	Total	Medical Staff	Nursing Staff
	£ s. d.	£ s. d.	£ s. d.
General hospitals (acute, 300–900 beds)	19 12 0	3 3 4	5 8 0
General hospitals (mainly acute)	17 17 8	2 5 6	4 16 11
Mental hospitals	5 17 8	5 0	1 16 11

So despite the fact that the staff in mental hospitals make the best of conditions which are often far from ideal, show a tremendous enthusiasm and drive towards the cure and relief of all forms of mental illness, and have abolished physical restraint and even, in very many hospitals, all locked doors, they are still working under difficulties which only public interest and an adequate provision of public funds can overcome. What are we doing about it to-day, to improve our hopes for the future?

One thing we have done in this country is to set the highest existent standard for mental hospitals to be found in the world. So that, although there is room for improvement, we are in the lead and are not lagging behind in this respect.

The future provision of really adequate and creditable psychiatric services for the community as a whole inevitably depends upon the quality, inspiration, and scope of the training which can be given to medical students in their undergraduate days, so that those who show an aptitude and interest in this work can receive early encouragement and practical experience. For this to be possible every teaching hospital needs a fully equipped in-patient department as an essential part of its Department of Psychological Medicine. A further step which it is hoped will come in time will be the provision of mental observation wards as units within the psychiatric in-patient department, so that the handling and treatment of psychiatric emergencies will become as much a part of the routine training of the doctor as are the handling and treatment of surgical and general medical emergencies in teaching hospitals at present.

Leaving aside all the figures and virtually all the categories of patients already covered in this chapter it remains to be said that it is the experience of most general practitioners and most consultants in general medicine that at least 30 per cent of all the patients who consult them require some measure of psychiatric understanding and treatment as a part of their general problem, and as a necessary contribution to their full recovery. All this it is within the province of the general medical training to provide, once the necessary time in the curriculum and, be it admitted, the equally necessary emphasis in examinations, which after all inevitably determines much of the attention paid by students to their studies, is allotted to the subject of psychiatry in both its general and specialized applications. The challenge confronts us not simply in the form of numbers of mentally ill patients or patients with mental defect, or children, disturbed, unhappy, or beyond control; nor is it fully represented when we have added to these outstanding problems the need for a better integration of psychiatry within the framework of medicine as a whole: in essence it is still the problem of an attitude of mind on the part of the public, who in turn must look for leadership to members of my own profession, to demand not only that all these needs be met, but above all that men and women be trained, and adequately trained, to meet them.

Acts of Parliament, although they can set standards, cannot always make them work. We need not only ideas but their acceptance; not only goodwill, but the funds from public resources (which after all are ultimately provided by the productive enthusiasm of every single one of us in the country) to go to work to provide the improved conditions. And we need the vastly improved prospects for treatment which lie within our grasp as the result of modern research and our increased knowledge and understanding.

We need in fact to take up the challenge of mental illness, as a part of the whole problem of human sickness and unhappiness, with confidence and vigour and generosity.

We began this chapter by facing something of the nature of the problem; and we began the book as a whole by discovering some of the instinctive elements in ourselves which tend to make us turn away from such problems. But we are not merely animals, largely ruled by instinct: we are men and women with freedom, choice, and power of decision. The size and shape of the problem may be vast, and the size and shape of the answer no less great. But finding and providing the answer is urgent, and with imagination, faith, and energy it is not beyond our grasp.

The Wider Implications of Psychiatry

THIS chapter can do no more than indicate the scope of the approach along psychological lines to three vitally important areas of human existence, outside medicine. These areas, in the order in which we shall encounter them, are those of human society and its laws, of art and its appreciation, and of philosophy and religion.

It is important from the outset to realize that psychiatry cannot under any circumstances claim to propound any final answers to the problems raised by a consideration of these three vast overlapping realms of thought, feeling, and behaviour. But it offers a technique which is always interesting and sometimes indispensable to a clear and balanced understanding of some of their principles, and it is in the value of the psychological approach as a technique that this chapter finds its justification.

That an awareness of unconscious as well as of conscious motives is fundamental to any sincere attempt to understand human behaviour is a proposition which, at this stage in this book, has either been established finally or has failed to overcome the individual prejudices of those who reject it. As a psychiatrist I believe it to be true; I hope I have made its presentation as convincing as possible, but if I have not, I shall not blame those readers who part company with me from now on. We are anyway nearing the final stages of this particular journey, and for my encounter with the law, however brief it may have to be, I need most of all the company of those who have preserved at least an open mind.

The common law of England, based as it is upon the foundations of ancient legal systems and particularly upon Roman law, has a long, complicated, and glorious history. It has never set aside the rights and duties of the individual; nor has it ever abandoned as its central principle the ideal of justice and the concept that innocence must be presumed whereas guilt has to be proved. Whatever some lawyers may say of some psychiatrists, they are bound together by one indissoluble bond which has formed a principle of English law for nearly 800 years: that crime is always and essentially an affair of mind as well as of body, of intention as well as of action. This is embodied in the famous legal tag *Actus non facit reum nisi mens sit rea*. This observation must be almost as familiar to the public, at least in translation, as it is to the legal profession. It means that there cannot be a guilty act unless there is a guilty mind.

The determination of whether the mind of a person is in fact guilty in the legal sense is one which clearly calls for some knowledge of mental processes in general. For example, to assume that because a man commits an illegal action with apparent deliberation he has therefore intended to do wrong, is to risk begging the entire question of the importance of his mental state. The true homicidal maniac is more or less a legal or dramatic fiction; but we have seen that, for example in schizophrenia, it is perfectly possible for a person to make a violent and murderous attack on someone whom he has never seen before and against whom he can have no reasonable grudge or suspicion. It is equally possible for a patient whose mind is disturbed to steal, or commit forgery, or set fire to property; all these are unquestionably wrongful and illegal acts, but their mere commission tells us nothing conclusive about the state of mind of the person who committed them and therefore about whether in fact that person is guilty of a crime or not.

It is in the interpretation of the mental state that the lawyer and the psychiatrist all too often part company. The lawyer is perfectly prepared to admit that somebody who appears to him to be mad is not responsible. He is not only reasonable in his attitude towards such people; he is as just and generous as English law invariably is to those whose guilt cannot fairly be proved. But it is when the person accused of a crime appears on the surface to be perfectly sane that the evidence of the psychiatrist is apt to be not simply challenged, which is fair enough, but occasionally altogether discounted, ridiculed, and regarded as preposterous. Moreover the psychiatrist himself is apt to come in for wholesale condemnation, to a point where it is possible for an exceedingly eminent judge to advise magistrates and probation officers to pay no attention to psychiatric evidence as a matter of general principle. Now psychiatrists occasionally make fools of themselves in court because they endeavour to argue about principles, when the whole structure of legal procedure obliges witnesses to confine themselves to facts. There can be no question that they are foolish to do this. The only people who can effectively change the substance or interpretation of the law by their actions during the course of an actual trial are Her Majesty's Judges themselves. They can establish precedents in this way, but every other citizen who wishes to see the law reformed in a particular aspect must do so by influencing public opinion and ultimately by getting the modifications which he proposes embodied in an Act of Parliament. Every time a psychiatrist tries to argue in court against the law as it stands he puts himself in the wrong from the beginning, but if psychiatrists are sometimes ridiculous in courts of law, this is almost always precisely because they do allow their emotions and their indignation to influence their judgement and their opinions. In court they are nothing but expert witnesses; fully entitled to a hearing, but to no more reverence or respect than the soundness of their evidence can command and their status as citizens entitles them, in common with all the other witnesses who may be called. Outside the court, however, there are a number of pertinent observations which it is their duty to make.

The first of these is that the natural legal presumption that a man is not only innocent until he is proved guilty, but completely sane until he is proved to be in any way of unsound mind, should *not* be taken to mean that the presumption of sanity entitles lawyers or laymen to dismiss evidence which conflicts with their own common sense or observation. If the psychiatrist is going to be believed only when he says something which everybody else can see for himself, his role as an expert witness is a sham and a mockery. We have seen in this book that human beings neither know completely the motives for all their own actions nor are in a position to interpret fully the motives for the actions of others. We tend to fill in the gaps in our knowledge about other people's feelings and motives by ascribing to them those explanations which occur most readily to us. Nearly always these explanations are projections of our own emotional tendencies, often those which we most rigorously repress and deny in ourselves. If somebody else maintains that our explanation is wrong and that the true motives which actuated the person are such as to relieve him of some of the guilt of his actions, our natural response is indignation. We do not want to see him 'getting away with it'. A certain amount of psychiatric evidence about the state of mind of people who steal or who commit violent crime or display sexual perversions, conflicts with the immensely strong but largely subconscious human impulse to punish in others the tendencies which we deny or repress in ourselves. It is for this reason that such evidence all too frequently excites powerful feelings of criticism and hostility in those to whom it is presented.

It is often much easier for a court of law to accept the evidence of a technical expert in some field relatively unconnected with emotion, such as for example engineering, than it is to accept equally valid evidence about states of mind and feeling. Few judges and few juries would commit the gaffe of remarking, on seeing the photographs and drawings of a bridge which an engineering expert has just testified is unsoundly constructed, 'There cannot be much wrong with it; it looks strong enough to me.' But I have heard an experienced, and, I am sure, honest and fair-minded judge say of a prisoner about whose mental state careful and considered evidence had been given by a psychiatrist, 'Well, anyway, he looks sane enough to me.'

The contention here is not that judges are fools or that the law is an ass. It is simply that the very real difficulty of accepting opinions which are occasionally disagreeable or disturbing on an emotional basis is one which must be acknowledged and faced if psychiatric evidence is to be fairly weighed in courts of law, and if psychiatric advice and opinions are to be properly integrated into the reform of legal procedures where this is necessary.

Two concrete examples, one familiar, the other perhaps less well known to the public, will suffice to conclude this section.

The first relates to the present position of the law concerning the mental state of prisoners charged with murder. This is based on the views of Her Majesty's Judges formulated in response to a series of questions from the House of Lords in 1843, after the murder of Mr Edward Drummond, the private secretary of Sir Robert Peel. Drummond was murdered by a man called McNaghten, who was suffering from delusions of persecution and who shot Drummond in mistake for Sir Robert Peel himself. The rules laid down by the judges, which are still binding although they are frequently liberally interpreted, are in essence as follows: In order to establish a defence on the grounds of insanity it must be clearly proved that at the time of committing the act the accused was labouring under such a defect of reason from disease of the mind as not to know the nature and quality of the act he was doing; or if he did know what he was doing, that he did not know that it was wrong. The second important provision is that if the accused commits the act by reason of a delusion, the degree of responsibility which must be attached to him, and therefore in law the degree of culpability which must be attributed, is based upon the justification which the delusion would provide if it were true. This means that if a man suffering, for example, from schizophrenia believes that another man is killing him by electric thought waves, and kills this other man in self-defence, he cannot be punished, although of course, and very properly, he will be detained in a suitable criminal mental hospital at Her Majesty's pleasure. If on the other hand the same patient's delusions were limited to the belief that his victim was depriving him of his reason and his sexual power by magical means, then, since even if this were true it would not justify homicide in self-defence, it cannot be taken as a legitimate basis for a defence against the charge of murder, which is at present punishable by death. In fact, in cases of this kind the law makes very few mistakes. This is because the absurdity of evaluating delusions as if they were true, and then deciding upon the degree of responsibility in which they involve the sufferer, is one which everybody now recognizes.

In cases where obvious delusions can be proved and acknowledged the obsolete clauses of the McNaghten rules are set aside in practice, but where these rules continue to operate in a manner which, from the standpoint not simply of psychiatry but of humanity and justice itself, is palpably absurd, is in their effect upon the estimation of responsibility when the person accused is not suffering from an illness as bizarre and spectacular as schizophrenia, but from an affective disorder such as acute depression. Here it is comparatively uncommon for the honest expert witness to be able to maintain that the prisoner did not know what he was doing, or that he did not know that what he was doing was wrong. On the contrary such a depressed patient will often maintain strenuously that he did know these things, that his guilt is overwhelming, and that he deserves to die. But because the balance of his mind is disturbed along emotional rather than along rational lines, all too often no psychiatric defence is legally possible in such cases.

In the summer of 1950 a man murdered his wife while she slept, by smashing her skull with an axe. He then took his two children down to a south coast town where, after giving them a day on the beach and buying them ice creams, he gave them both some sleeping medicine and then smothered them. He next endeavoured to commit suicide himself by taking the rest of the sleeping medicine and attempting to drown himself. He failed to do so, and after wandering about in a distracted frame of mind for a further forty-eight hours he was arrested by the police. From the evidence of this man's conduct, and his own statements about the hopelessness with which he viewed his own and his family's future, and which had induced him to do what he did, there seemed reasonable grounds for regarding his mental state as a highly significant element in the assessment of his culpability. Yet under the McNaghten Rules it would have been extremely difficult to offer a valid defence in law; in point of fact no such defence was offered and the man was hanged. The inclusion in the Homicide Act (1957), of the concept of diminished responsibility as a potentially mitigating factor, capable of reducing a charge of capital murder to one of culpable homicide, was the first important concession to the advances in our understanding of human mental and emotional processes in the 116 years since these rules were laid down. But it seems clear that as long as capital punishment is retained in this country, judges and juries will continue to lean heavily upon the McNaghten rules in cases where capital murder is charged.

The second example is in the sphere of treatment. The Criminal Justice Act of 1946 has made some notable advances in the provisions under which young criminals and first offenders can be handled. These provisions tend generally in the direction of placing less reliance upon imprisonment and more upon probation and attendance at centres of corrective training which do not deprive the individual of his liberty in the first instance. That they have become law is indeed a notable step forward. That they offend the emotions and prejudices of a number of honest and indignant people is unquestionable. Some of the reasons which permitted these advances have already received support from the results of psychiatric research. But the next and most essential step, if this kind of legal reform is to continue, and a diminution both of the incidence of crime and the very serious overcrowding in all our prisons is to be achieved, is for the scope and facilities of psychiatric research into the attitude and feelings of the young criminal before and after conviction to be immensely widened and encouraged. Psychiatry does not postulate that *all* crime is a form of sickness; nor can the findings of psychopathology explain away the problem of evil. But psychiatric techniques for studying individuals, based as they are upon that interest in the individual in all his aspects which is at the heart of psychological inquiry, have a great deal to offer in the approach to crime, its understanding and prevention as well as its treatment.

*

When we come to the realm of art we may at once feel inclined to breathe a sigh of relief under the impression that we have exchanged the precision and concentration of legal argument for the unfettered freedom of artistic expression. But as every artist knows, no matter what the sphere in which his creative endeavours are exerted, the demands of art are as exacting as those of any activity which man feels impelled to undertake. For art is not simply the fortunate release of an urge to self-expression on the part of those capable of original creation. It is a passionate necessity to reflect and distil in its purest form something within the artist which will not give him peace. Moreover, there is something desperate and merciless about this necessity; it drives the bad artist as well as the good: and sometimes it drives him even harder. There are a number of people who conceive and produce in considerable anguish works of an appalling mediocrity, whether it be in verse, in painting, in sculpture, or in any other field. They are perpetually unsuccessful and yet they strive without ceasing, without encouragement, and often without hope of reward. Why do they do it? This is a question to which psychiatry might be expected to give an answer. It has given an answer; the only trouble about the answer, or perhaps I should say its one great redeeming feature, is that there is nothing final about it.

However, the type of inquiry which has led to the answer, and indeed the nature of the answer itself, is illuminating and not without interest. Like many other inquiries in psychiatry it began with a study of the abnormal and expanded to include those aspects of the normal which had never previously been recognized in their full significance.

Some of the most productive artists, in terms of sheer output, are to be found in mental hospitals. Reams of verse, volumes of remarkable prose, paintings and drawings and modellings, sometimes of an extraordinary power, are to be found in the collections of those mental hospitals where someone has been interested enough to study this aspect of abnormal mental life. Some of the most striking work is done by schizophrenics, who are particularly apt to convey, through the medium of artistic expression, something of the fantastic world in which they live. In the last twenty years a great deal of interest has been taken in work of this kind and all manner of interpretations have been placed upon the productions of such patients. Some of these productions are of very high artistic quality, as judged by any available standards; others are poorly conceived and executed, but although they may have little technical merit, they are rarely banal. The consensus of opinion of those who have studied these things in detail is that such writing and painting seek to convey experiences in the emotional life of these patients which are in turn derived from those deeper conflicts and frustrations which enter into the psychopathology of the illnesses from which the patients suffer.

Freud was one of the first to seek to apply the implications of this approach to art as a manifestation of conflict, to a much wider study of art as a whole. He wrote a number of deeply interesting monographs upon the problem of genius and its relationship to mental illness. He was fascinated by the personality of Leonardo da Vinci and by the works of Shakespeare. His followers were not slow to set about the holiday task of analysing the great masters and their works. We saw in Chapter 3 and again in Chapter 6 something of the derivation of the term Oedipus conflict or Oedipus situation to describe that mixture of respect and rivalry, admiration and rebellion, love and hatred, which the child tends to feel for his father in the early years of life; and we noted too how powerful is this theme to move and hold us when it appears in literature or drama. The tragedy of *Oedipus Rex* itself is perhaps one of the greatest in literature. The tragedy of Hamlet provides a later and marvellously complex example of the same theme. It is not surprising therefore to learn that the character of Hamlet has been studiously dissected along psycho-analytic lines by more than one disciple of Professor Freud.

Freud himself wrote one book in which he analysed the dreams of a character in a novel. He records his delight but not surprise at the realization that the content, mechanisms, and meaning of the dreams attributed to this character fitted perfectly with the psychopathology revealed by the character's actions and experiences throughout the novel as a whole. He maintained steadfastly that the artist was able, and in one sense was bound, to reflect with fidelity and precision those workings of the mind of which he might know nothing from a scientific standpoint, but which his heightened sensitivity enabled him to discover on an intuitive basis. In this way a true artist could create characters of a depth and complexity which was all the more striking and impressive because their analysis along strictly scientific lines proved them to have as consistent and valid a relationship with psycho-analytic theory as had the psychopathological structure of living people.

Now all this makes very stimulating reading and adds a whole chapter of possibilities to the scope of literary criticism, but on the purely scientific basis on which Freud took his stand it has always seemed to me to contain one monumental inescapable fallacy. For in the analysis of dreams of living people it is a cardinal principle of the Freudian school that only the free associations of the patient, and not the projections and interpretations of the analyst, can lead to a full understanding of the case. Neither Hamlet, nor the character in *Gradiva* whose dreams Freud analysed, were available to offer free associations on anything they said or dreamt: the whole stupendous creation of Hamlet's character, and every word he uttered, has remained unaltered and unalterable from the time that Shakespeare finished the play. The more penetrating our speculations, the more profound our understanding of such a character, the more deeply moved we are by all he says and does, the more inevitably do we introduce our own responses to the genius behind the play, and our own projections of the feelings which he continues to evoke in us. The fallacy of analysing the creation of an artist's imagination is that one's own imagination inevitably fills in the gaps which genius always leaves in a character for that very purpose. To attempt to analyse a human being we need all the help that human being can give us; and no analysis which rested purely upon a study of the dreams or the history of the person, without his association or comments upon them, could claim to be complete. None the less, as a technique for literary criticism which is often productive of an original and provocative treatment, and as a refreshing form of relaxation for psychiatrists themselves, there is a great deal to be said for this procedure, provided always that we do not take its results or ourselves unduly seriously. That is why I have called it a holiday task.

Another and in some ways even more absorbing result of studying some of the implications of psychiatric study of art is the insight which it is apt to give us into the well-established connexion between conflict and creativeness in artists themselves. This is a theme which has intrigued a number of medical writers, including Dr Lange-Eichbaum and Professor Kretschmer, of Marburg. Its most recent exponent is Sir Russell Brain, a former President of the Royal College of Physicians of London. His essay contained a list, which he remarked was certainly not comprehensive, of some great writers who were sufficiently mentally unbalanced to have been notorious in this respect as well as for the greatness of their artistic achievements. He mentioned Beddoes, Blake, Boswell, Bunyan, Burns, Byron, Chatterton, Clare, Coleridge, Collins, Cowper, Crabbe, De Quincey, Dickens, Donne, Gray, Johnson, Lamb, Rossetti, Ruskin, Shelley, Smart, Swift, Swinburne, Tennyson, and Francis Thompson. He added . . . 'and to show that English literature is not exceptional in this respect let me add a few from other nations: Baudelaire, Dostoyevsky, Flaubert, Goethe, Gogol, Hölderlin, Nietzsche, Poe, Rimbaud, Rousseau, Strindberg, Swedenborg, and Verlaine.' He proceeded in this essay (published in the *British Medical Journal* of 24 December 1949) to consider in some detail a selection of the authors he had just mentioned, recounting how Donne was constantly preoccupied with thoughts of the body's dissolution, of how he wrote in his *Devotions on Emergent Occasions*, not only reflexions upon mortality of a kind which have become immortal, but also some penetrating observations upon the frailty of physicians:

> . . .The patient takes to his bed. The Phisician is sent for. The Phisician comes. The Phisician is afraid. The Phisician desires to have others joyned with him. The King sends his own Phisician. Upon their consultation they prescribe . . .

Donne was all too well aware that the physician fights but a delaying action with death. His own attitude to it remained morbid and obsessional. He could distil some of this into exquisite poetry, for example, the sonnet which begins with the words 'Death be not proud . . .' but in its effect upon his own conduct the more pathological side of his nature was revealed. He preached his last sermon, when he was dying, upon the subject of death. It was believed by many of his hearers to be his own funeral sermon. He insisted upon posing for the monument which was to commemorate him, standing upon a wooden urn and wrapped in his own winding sheet. Sir Russell Brain quotes Gosse in ascribing this obsession with death as part of 'the morbid and fantastic character of his genius'.

Other writers of genius whom the author selects for special attention in his essay include Jonathan Swift, whose emotional immaturity, particularly in his attitude towards bodily functions and sexual relationships, he discusses, taking vivid examples from the text of *Gulliver's Travels*. The unabridged version of this famous and remarkable satire is perhaps less familiar than the various bowdlerized versions which have appeared from time to time; for these largely omit the vivid evidence of the author's extreme horror of physical contact, of the touch and smell of human beings, and of his fascinated disgust with their excretion and its possibilities.

Samuel Johnson is another great man whose bizarre obsessional characteristics attracted the attention of his contemporaries and the interest of all who have followed him. He suffered, too, in his own words, from 'a morbid melancholy'. Like Donne he had what he called 'a secret horror of the last' which he felt was inseparable from any thinking being. Dr Brain remarks that evidence of Johnson's mental state which suggests morbid traits can be obtained at three levels; his compulsive gestures, which involved him in performing the most spectacular and alarming antics whenever he crossed a threshold, his obsessive fears and deep sense of guilt, and once again his preoccupation with the evils of life which from time to time reduced him to a state of severe depression, accompanied by disturbance of sleep, by agitation, and profound gloom. Dr Brain concludes his essay with an examination of the manic-depressive features in the character of Dickens, whose son is quoted in support of this diagnosis. Once again disorder of sleep, of appetite, and of mood were characteristic. The son, Sir Henry Dickens, spoke of his father's 'heavy moods of deep depression, of intense nervous irritability, when he was silent and oppressed'. Dr Brain also refers to the study of Dickens by the American author, Mr Edmund Wilson, who has drawn attention to the sadistic and masochistic trends in Dickens's stories; the fascination mingled with repugnance with which Dickens describes violence and cruelty, particularly by treacherous brutal bullies like Bill Sikes, against helpless lovable victims like Nancy in *Oliver Twist*. It seems clear that while Dickens himself hated cruelty he was none the less aware of those instincts in himself and in others which demand that cruelty be cruelly punished. Sometimes he could resist them, at others both his own feelings and his flair for driving home a point and bringing a final satisfaction and catharsis to his readers impelled him to bring a savage and revolting character to a savage and revolting death. The end of Bill Sikes is not simply poetic justice in the superficial meaning of the word. It offers that deep but dangerous release to passionate feelings of revenge which Dickens himself knew were ultimately as cruel as the actions which had inspired them.

It would be to lose entirely the underlying theme of the author of this essay if one were to imagine for a moment that because he can illustrate the abnormalities of the mental state of men of genius, he believes or in any way seeks to persuade his readers that such signs or symptoms lessen the power and character of genius itself. On the contrary he quotes one poet, Christopher Smart, whose only truly great and poetic work was done during a period of frank insanity.

The connexion between mental anguish or abnormality, and creative work, is far more subtle and complex than would be explained either by supposing that it is a necessary handicap which genius overcomes, or that it is an indulgence which genius may be permitted. Its simplest explanation along psychodynamic lines would seem to be that the tremendous emotional tensions which inner and largely subconscious conflicts and frustrations can produce, are themselves powerful sources of stimulation. Those who suffer them are aware of an urge to seek release and expiation; to communicate something of the source and nature of their feelings, and thereby in some degree to gain peace. This as we have seen is precisely the kind of tension which drives many people to their doctor or confessor: it may well drive others to write, or to paint, or to sculpt, or to compose, with varying degrees of talent.

But when, in addition to these tensions and their demand for release, there exists a rare and wonderful capacity for sustained effort and brilliant communication in one medium or another, there is always the chance that these tensions will be discharged through channels which are not only creative but almost intolerably moving and inspiring. When this happens the result is work of genius.

The partial recognition of this has sometimes led to the grossly over-simplified view that all art is nothing but the artist's attempt at a sort of public solution of his own conflicts; that the sources of creative work exist entirely in the psychopathology of the individual, just as his values are presumed to have no more sure foundation than the trends and customs of his environment. This point of view has been expressed by the editor of an anthology of modern poetry who claims for the particular school of modern poets whom he favours a number of advantages derived from this point of view. He says:

> . . .It prevents them from that poetic inflation, which follows when a poet mistakes the product of the conflicts in himself for the gift inspired in him, mysteriously, by some outside agent. . . . It is a very good thing for writers to be subjecting themselves in this way to a discipline of objects, and events. They deal once more with an explicable, if not with a calculable and an orderly universe . . . I think it is possible to trace in the poems as they come out in *New Verse* this gradual emergence of a criterion, formed by an amalgam of science (in scraps), Freudian theory (in scraps), Marxist thought (in scraps), the political and economic situation in the world, the practice and precept and perspicacity of Mr Auden (and Mr MacNeice and Mr Spender) and the load of reaction and attraction which the time I belong to has inherited. . . .
>
> And whatever may be the quality of our best poems now in the highest kind of poetry, I am sure of one thing: we know with more exactitude, with more health, and less pretentiousness and priggishness how poems come about and how poets should be related to people . . .

This was written by Geoffrey Grigson in his Preface to the anthology called *New Verse* in 1939. That of course was twenty-four years ago, and there are few of us who might care to be quoted, particularly out of context, from what we said or wrote at that time. If I reproduce those words with all their suggestion of complacent smugness, hiding under that pretence of humility which materialism so frequently assumes, it is because I believe that this rather naive assumption that a materialist psychology and a materialist politico-economic theory can between them supply the answer to what Thomas Browne once called 'the alphabet of man', is an assumption which is still made by a number of sincere and honest people. They are of course entitled to their opinions, but in so far as they imagine them to rest upon the established tenets of modern psychology or psychiatry, it is time that such misleading over-simplification was exposed as the fallacy which it is.

We know a good deal about the way in which conflicts between fundamental feelings and impulses come about. We know nothing of the original source of those feelings and impulses themselves. We know something about the power of genius to transform the expression of such conflicts so as to convey with astonishing force that extraordinary blend of love and hatred, violence and compassion, beauty and horror, and pity and despair, which strives for mastery within us all, when we become aware of our lives and the world in which we live them; but we know nothing of the source and origin of that power which we call genius, which works such miracles with our imagination; and to say that it comes not from inspiration from without, but from conflict from within, is in the last analysis an entirely meaningless observation. Man has not made himself, nor has he made the conflicts he encounters or the aspirations with which he is born.

*

Freudian philosophy bears, like all systems of philosophy to some degree, the imprint of its author's necessity. Freud saw in the idea of God the illusion created by humanity to comfort them in the face of their helplessness when they had outgrown their parents. He ascribed their sense of guilt and shame to an original primitive act of murder or rejection when the sons of the tribe rebelled against the father. Despite this sudden excursion into imaginative mythology he claimed and believed that this thesis provided a rational basis for the abandonment of religion; while at the same time in the book in which he first explained these ideas in full he concluded, frankly and reluctantly, that mankind was not yet strong enough to accept this rational liberation from belief, and that therefore the worship of God and belief in an absolute system of values belonging to Him was a necessary fiction to preserve some semblance of law and order until the human race advanced sufficiently in wisdom to do without any of the illusions to which it clung.

Freud was himself a sincere agnostic who wrote like an atheist and behaved with some of the characteristics of a saint and a martyr. If we permit ourselves the same speculations about him that he, much to our edification and instruction, has permitted himself about Moses and Leonardo da Vinci, we may wonder whether his own unresolved conflict and feeling about his father was perhaps at least as much responsible for his views about conscience, guilt, and religion, particularly as exemplified by the Jewish and the Christian idea of the personal God, as were any of his scientific abilities.

We may also observe something else of considerable interest. When to his own satisfaction Freud had destroyed the temples of the existing God, as he saw Him, he was faced with the ultimate necessity to set up something else in His place: for the idea of evil as the enemy of good, he had to substitute a postulated death instinct at war with the life instinct in every living creature. For the idea of God Himself he had to substitute a tyrannical primeval patriarch murdered by his anthropoid sons. For the commandment 'Thou shalt love thy neighbour as thyself', which he considered frankly impracticable, he was compelled to suggest as an alternative only the somewhat arid proposal that each individual should become as fully aware of himself as possible, thereafter pursuing a policy of that enlightened self-interest which ultimately would enable him to live at peace with others; although his instinctual urge to dominate and attack them would have no greater deterrent than the general undesirability of this action taking place on all sides.

It is small wonder then that the philosophy, and one might almost say the system of ethics and values, which some disciples of Freud claim to regard as new and specific to psycho-analysis, is the one part of the whole system which will not stand up to one moment's serious consideration. Psycho-analysis regarded either as a method of study, a technique for treatment and research, or as the body of knowledge which this method and technique have uncovered, has certain solid claims which cannot be ignored. Moreover, as a method which has produced results, it can claim an empirical justification and a scientific respectability. Its philosophical aspects have always appeared to me to be the projections of its originator, based upon his own conflicts and feelings, conveyed with considerable force and energy and eminently worth reading for the sake of the light which they shed upon the personality of Freud himself; but they remain purely notions and speculations. Moreover, they try to go further than science itself can ever go, by seeking to give an answer to the question Why? when the whole aim and purpose of science is to answer the question How? It is the confusion between those two questions, and the failure to perceive their essential difference, which has for so long been responsible for the fundamental fallacy implicit in the whole idea that science and religion are really in conflict at all.

We saw a little way back that Freud, the iconoclast, had to give way to Freud, the designer of new beliefs. This appears to be an inescapable necessity which eventually confronts all who seek to destroy the belief which men feel and need in something greater and beyond themselves. It is brilliantly illuminated from two apparently widely different standpoints in the writings of Professor Jung on the one hand and of Rex Warner on the other. In one passage in his book, *Psychology and Religion*, Jung is discussing the gradual development of man's understanding of himself and his world, together with the dangers as well as the possibilities towards which such understanding may lead him, if he mistakes its inevitable incompleteness for finality. At first, as we saw in the opening chapters of this book, man projected all his feelings on to nature. He peopled his world with gods and spirits and believed them responsible for everything that happened both in his world and in his mind. Later he came to realize how much greater was the complexity of his mind than he had previously understood, and to withdraw many of the projections which up to now had seemed absolute. Jung's own words about this are striking:

The gods first lived in superhuman power and beauty on the top of snow-clad mountains or in the darkness of caves, woods, and seas. Later on they drew together into one god, and then that god became man. But the gods in our time assemble in the lap of the ordinary individual and are as powerful and awe-inspiring as ever, in spite of their

new disguise — the so-called physical functions. Man thinks of himself
as holding the psyche in the hollow of his hand. He dreams even of
making a science of her. But in reality she is the mother and the maker,
the psychical subject and even the possibility of consciousness itself. . . .
At first the materialistic error seems to be inevitable; since the throne
of God could not be discovered among the galactic systems, the inference was that God had never existed. The second inevitable mistake is
psychologism; if God is nothing, He must be an illusion derived from
certain motives, from fear, for instance, from will to power, or from repressed sexuality. The arguments are not new. Similar things have
already been said by the Christian missionaries who overthrew the idols
of the pagan gods. But whereas the early missionaries were conscious of
serving a new god by combating the old ones, modern iconoclasts are
unconscious of the one in whose name they are destroying the old
values. . . .

The tragedy of Zarathustra is that, because his god died, Nietzsche
himself became a god; and this happened because he was no atheist, He
was too positive a nature to content himself with a negative creed. For
such a man it seems to be dangerous to make a statement that God is
dead. He becomes instantly the victim of 'inflation'. . . . If he declares
God to be dead, then he should find out at once where this considerable
energy, which was first invested in an existence as great as God, has disappeared to. It might reappear in another name, it might call itself
'Wotan' or 'the State' or something ending with -ism, even atheism, of
which people believe, hope, and expect just as much as they formerly
did of God.

Happily enough for the rest of mankind there are not many individuals as sensitive and as religious as Nietzsche. If dull people lose the
idea of God nothing happens — not immediately and personally at least.
But socially the masses begin to breed mental epidemics, of which we
have now a fair number.

These words were written in 1938. They are no less true to-day.

Rex Warner, in a book called *The Cult of Power*, deals in the
title essay with the same theme. Writing of the rebel, the moral
anarchist, whose sincerity and courage are admirable qualities,
but whose end is all too often to lead his fellows into a greater
subjection and even more appalling degradation than that from
which he liberated them, he has this to say:

What in our present situation would strike one as most remarkable,
if one had not observed the same thing happening before in history, is

the rapidity with which generally accepted ideals of the early twentieth century, such as toleration, kindliness, objective truth, freedom, have been replaced in many people's minds by their exact opposites . . . The more successful the moral anarchists are the greater is the feeling of uncertainty in the minds of everyone, including, in the end, the moral anarchists themselves.

He goes on to develop this idea to the point where the leader finds that:

There is one way of escape, and that is by giving to the mass of people, for whom he has so often expressed such contempt, what they want – a system of ideas by which they can regulate and give meaning to their lives (indeed, this is something which, by this time, he needs himself). But the old idols are smashed and to resuscitate them would be to admit failure. There is only one thing for it – after having rejected God to make himself God and to cause it to be generally believed that those characteristics by which he won his first eminence – and perhaps these have been self-assertion, violence, brutality, amongst others – are the characteristics of Godhead. The old faith, the old system of values, must have very thoroughly disintegrated to make such a plan possible. That is an indispensable condition.

We can all recognize that it is none the less a condition which has been fulfilled more than once in the twentieth century; a condition whose ultimate effects we have not seen the last of yet. In a later and perhaps the most powerful essay in the book, he makes a telling analysis of the contradictions involved by taking man's moral and religious instincts for granted, while ignoring the problem of their source. He is comparing the approach of Karl Marx to the problems of human existence with that of Dostoyevsky: he writes:

Dostoyevsky's view of the world may be to us, perhaps, more enlightening than is that of Marx, for Dostoyevsky's psychological insight is directed just towards those fundamental aspects of human nature which Marx consistently ignores. Indeed, on all problems of morality and psychology Marx is strangely muddled and inconsistent. Here is the great gap in his theory which stares one in the face and yet over which his disciples somehow skip, hop or jump, to the great prejudice of their own cause. Why do men act in ways which are socially 'good' or 'bad'? Why should they wish to subscribe to a general brotherhood of man? What indeed is 'goodness'? To all these questions Marx is either deaf or else returns unsatisfactory answers. Sometimes it is the forces of history which will force men to unite in brotherliness. Sometimes it is men who will force the forces of history in the 'right' direction. Sometimes it is economic self-interest which will drive the majority to come together into the classless society. But then what about the minority? Why did the well-to-do Engels act so strikingly against his own economic interest?

The fact is that on these and kindred questions Marx is all the time assuming that his readers share his own moral sense, though he gives them no justification for doing so. His and their moral senses have been developed and conditioned by the effects of centuries of Jewish history, of Greek philosophy, of Christianity, and his revolt against the conditions of his time is, whether he likes it or not, largely dependent upon the moral insight which has been developed from the past. He attacks the organization of religion because it is, in his view, inextricably concerned in the maintenance of economic privilege. (Here, incidentally, he is at one with Tolstoy.) But with the actual claims of religion, as apart from the hypocrisies of this or that church, he hardly deals at all. Indeed he attacks the hypocrisies from the ground of the ethics of religion itself, and seems not to observe that this is what he is doing. . . . He does not observe how vague and barren for most people is the idea of 'humanity' once the psychological support of religion or 'mysticism' is withdrawn. He urges his followers to ethics of world-brotherhood, indeed the ethics of Christianity, but the sanction for this is in the bleak operation of economic laws rather than in any psychological or spiritual conviction. But man is neither so rational nor so irrational as Marx would have him. On the one hand he looks for something more than the consciousness that he is living in accordance with history. . . . On the other hand, once the traditional supports for his conventional morality have been withdrawn he will not continue to act as though they were still there.

Dostoyevsky, as we have seen, would certainly maintain that this conviction of brotherhood and feeling for mankind which is assumed as a concomitant of international socialism or, for that matter, of the 'classless society' anywhere, is an impossibility unless it is based on a 'mystical' religious view of the whole universe. He would regard as altogether too naive the assumption of the 'scientific' socialists that all you have to do is to remove inhibitions and organize production 'sensibly', and that then the native goodness of man will blossom like the rose. He would insist that in man evil as well as good is 'native'. Sin is a fact of nature and not merely the result of unscientific organization of society. The optimism of the socialist is to him either sentimental or pedantic, based on an inadequate or too rigid view of both the heights and depths of nature.

To-day it would seem that, if Dostoyevsky realized insufficiently the necessity of an economic reorganization, Marx was most certainly too little occupied with the spirit in which this reorganization was to be carried out. Dialectical materialism, whatever its merits as a guide to the interpretation of history, is no substitute for either religion or philosophy.

And if dialectical materialism is no substitute for religion or philosophy, neither is psychiatry, nor the special pleading of the philosophical structure of psycho-analysis.

*

We have seen that the principles underlying all forms of psychotherapy which have insight as their aim, including psycho-analysis itself, rest upon a number of hypotheses which can be regarded as pretty well established. The first of these is that behaviour is prompted chiefly by emotional considerations, but that understanding is necessary to modify and control such behaviour and the emotions behind it. The second is that a very significant proportion of human emotion, together with the action to which it leads, is not accessible to personal introspection, being rooted in areas of the mind which are beneath the surface of consciousness. The third hypothesis is logically derived from the first two, as well as being supported empirically by the result of experiment: it is that any process which makes available to individual consciousness the true significance of those emotional conflicts and tensions hitherto repressed will thereby produce a heightened awareness and with it an increased stability and emotional control. This in turn will lead not simply to improved health in its widest sense, but also to a more mature and developed personality.

From the religious standpoint there is nothing exceptionable in this – as far as it goes. But it remains evident that even after complete and successful analysis the subject has still no more than his own individual human resources upon which to rely. And in fact these are not always enough. Herein lies the fallacy at the heart of the philosophical and anti-religious claims of some ardent disciples of materialistic psychology.

Sometimes the conflicts of which the subject becomes aware remain insoluble for him. Thrown back upon himself he finds no comfort and no solace in this final attempt at self-sufficiency. This is the crisis in analysis; and within its own framework analysis has no answer. The patient, groping beyond himself for the final answer, cannot get it from the analyst; for the transference, even were it sufficient, cannot be maintained for a lifetime. In one of his last essays, *Analysis Terminable and Interminable*, Freud himself is most explicit on this point.

Where then can a man turn? If full self-awareness and self-realization are not by themselves enough, what is? As a psychiatrist I know of no answer to this question: as a man I can only say with all humility that I believe in God.

Freud and Marx had this in common; that they rejected belief in God while clinging implicitly to the system of ethics whose basis they had explicitly denied. Seen in this light it is not religious belief whose future is an illusion, but belief in science which seeks to deny its own ultimate source.

It seems to me a vital necessity if psychiatry is to play its proper part in society that it should avoid making claims which it cannot fulfil. In particular it would do well to cease suggesting that it can replace moral standards by theoretical expediency, or provide its own basis for human ethics and values. It can answer a number of questions about the way in which things happen; it cannot begin by itself to answer a single question as to why man is so constructed that they should happen in this way.

Freud himself, for all his passionate and sincere renunciation of religious belief and of the religious basis for ethical behaviour, none the less acted in his own life as though loving one's neighbour as oneself was indeed the key to happiness. He devoted himself tirelessly and often without regard to self-interest to the discovery of truth as he saw it, and to the application of his discoveries to the relief of suffering. It is not surprising that he was persecuted; understandable that the advent of Nazism in Austria compelled him to take refuge in England. But for a man who prided himself on the materialist and deterministic nature of his methods and discoveries it might perhaps seem to be surprising that he should continue to act, to paraphrase Rex Warner, as though the spiritual supports of love and of morality were still guiding him. It might have seemed to him a final and supreme irony that his system of psychiatric procedure, rooted in his own view in deterministic materialism, should have been so uncompromisingly rejected by the disciples of political materialism in Communist societies.

*

Before attempting to draw the threads of this somewhat complicated discussion together we should perhaps examine for a moment one further aspect of the problem, apparently inherent in any psychiatric theory which rests upon a search for causes of present attitudes and behaviour in the details of previous existence. If childhood emotional conflicts do in fact produce complexes which in turn influence adult behaviour powerfully but unconsciously, does this mean that there is no such thing as free will? Does it mean that we are creatures running helplessly along pre-determined lines, like the man who compared himself to a tram in the famous limerick? There is one indisputable scientific test which we can apply to answer this question: the test of prediction.

If psycho-analysis is really an argument for a wholly deterministic approach to human behaviour, one might expect that success in treatment would be evidence in favour of a deterministic point of view. But this would be to confuse the validity of the method *in treating patients*, with its validity in predicting their future behaviour, on the basis of the information obtained through treatment. It is the transference which plays an incalculable part in treatment; and this is in essence an emotional exchange.

If the deterministic basis of psycho-analysis is to be taken seriously, its capacity to predict future behaviour in some detail must be seriously examined. Freud himself gives us, however unwillingly, our answer. It is an example of his scientific honesty and objectivity at its best, inasmuch as it contains no speculation, no special pleading, and no tendency to gloss over a failure, which he himself could have found no satisfaction in acknowledging. He is writing of a particular case:

But at this point we become aware of a state of things which also confronts us in many other instances in which light has been thrown by psycho-analysis on a mental process. So long as we trace the development from its final stage backwards, the connexion appears continuous, and we feel we have gained an insight which is completely satisfactory and even exhaustive. But if we proceed the reverse way, if we start from the premises inferred from the analysis and try to follow these up to the final result, then we no longer get the impression of an inevitable sequence of events which could not be otherwise determined. We notice at once that there might have been another result, and that we might have been just as well able to understand and explain the latter. The synthesis is thus not so satisfactory as the analysis; in other words, from a knowledge of the premises we could not have foretold the nature of the result.

In the far more exact science of physics the wholly deterministic view has been finally abandoned. Indeed the principle of uncertainty has been enthroned as an inevitable concomitant of human observation. For when measurements are sufficiently accurate the actual effect of the observer upon the phenomenon observed always weighs in the scales and cannot be precisely estimated. Contemporary writers who have been concerned with the failures of absolute determinism as a scientific principle include C. S. Lewis, Kenneth Walker, and, once again, Professor Mottram.* At one time it used to be argued that although free will was almost certainly an illusion, on a day-to-day basis it paid to act as though it existed; to-day in the realm of human behaviour, arguments about free will have become essentially obsolete.

Human behaviour is so complicated and so variable that prediction as the basic empirical argument in favour of determinism cannot be admitted. Moreover, the feeling common to us all, that at least in most of the more personal aspects of our life we have a certain freedom of choice about our behaviour, is

*C. S. Lewis: *Miracles*. Kenneth Walker: *Meaning and Purpose*. Professor Mottram: *The Physical Basis of Personality*.

a real feeling. It emerges ultimately as no less valid than any of the hypotheses that have been brought forward to explain it away. And real feelings have a prima facie claim upon our attention in psychiatry to-day.

* * *

We can now attempt a synthesis and crystallization of the essential ideas touched upon in this chapter. Psychiatry embodies methods of study which are in part scientific and in part intuitive. The more exact and consistent they are the better; but they aim not simply at providing knowledge, but also at providing help to those in need. As an aspect of medicine which is in turn a branch of human knowledge, psychiatry has certain scientific claims to put forward, and is entitled, as a study of man's mental and emotional life, to offer contributions to many other aspects of human existence wherein such a study is relevant. Of these some of the more important include the law, particularly in its relation to crime and punishment; art, where psychiatric insight can fill some but by no means all the gaps in our knowledge of creative activity; and philosophy and religion, where the knowledge gained from psychiatric study can be added to those other sources of human experience which must be included in any consideration of man in his relationship to the universe, and of the ultimate nature of reality.

Psychiatry can help us to break bonds which have hitherto confined our knowledge, but it cannot really set a limit to what we can know or believe. Freud, dealing with one piece of evidence which had been offered to him as the ultimate source of religious sentiments, namely, a subjective sense of awareness of eternity, of something limitless and unbounded, of some indissoluble connexion with the nature of reality itself, remarked,

These views ... put me in a difficult position. I cannot discover this oceanic feeling in myself. But I cannot on that account deny that it in fact occurs in other people.

Such a denial would have been unwise and moreover impossible to sustain, because this subjective experience is a recurrent and undeniable reality for a great number of people. It seems to bc at the core of all mystical experience, and whatever its nature it is not something which psychiatry or any other scientific procedure can explain, still less explain away. Jung has written of it:

> ... I must point out that there is no question of belief, but of experiences. Religious experience is absolute. It is indisputable. You can only say that you have never had such an experience and your opponent will say, 'Sorry, I have.' And there your discussion will come to an end. No matter what the world thinks about religious experience, the one who has it possesses the great treasure of a thing that has provided him with a source of life, meaning, and beauty and that has given a new splendour to the world and to mankind ... where is the criterion by which you could say that such a life is not legitimate and that such experience is not valid ... ? Is there, as a matter of fact, any better truth about ultimate things than the one which helps you to live?

It is this which links the discussion of psychiatry in relation to art, and particularly to genius in art, to the discussion of its relationship with religion and philosophy. For there is a part of genius which would appear to be abnormal only in the sense that it is super-normal, or, if you like, supernatural. It is the revelation which corresponds in the artist to the experience of supreme awareness in the mystic. Where the person who receives this gift or inspiration is an artist as well as a mystic, as were, for example, Blake and Emily Brontë, the outcome is not only genius but genius with a particularly passionate and deeply religious aura. It would perhaps be possible for a psychiatrist to approach and to understand the human element in this kind of creation; but he would be no better and no worse placed than anyone else to appreciate that other than human element which many will call divine. Nor has he any right whatever to pretend that anything he knows casts reasonable doubt upon such divinity. There is nothing about a belief in psychiatry which makes impossible a belief in God; and nothing about a belief in God which makes impossible a belief in psychiatry. The part is not greater than the whole.

Psychiatry To-day and To-morrow

THIS has been a book about psychiatry to-day. Yet to give this conception of the present condition of the subject its full depth and meaning it has been necessary to go far back into the past, the better to understand the trends and implications and advances of the present. And just as the present has its roots in the past, so also does it contain the seeds of the future. If psychiatry is to fulfil the promise which it holds for medicine and for mankind, it has two most urgent tasks, transcending in their ultimate importance even the day-to-day care of all the people who stand in need: these tasks are teaching and research.

We have already discussed teaching, particularly in regard to the training of competent and well-rounded doctors to provide the next generation of psychiatrists. But this is only one of the aspects of teaching which are important. The public as a whole need to be taught the truth about psychiatry. They need to know something of its practical possibilities, something of the size of the problem, something of the spirit in which the psychiatrist approaches it, and something of the solid and sensible help which it is his aim and duty to provide. They need to be helped to overcome the shame and fear which have dogged the whole concept of mental illness for centuries and which are to some extent inherent in the instinctive attitude of us all. Like the patient who is actually under treatment, they need to become a little more aware of the nature of their own feelings, a little more able to accept them for what they are, and a little more ready to recognize them and to make allowance for them in others.

To understand and even to be able to accept one's feelings and one's problems is not always to solve them. But it is often an indispensable prerequisite to their solution. Psychiatry can never claim to create either the capacity for awareness or the capacity for acceptance of what is made aware, any more than surgery can claim to create the capacity of severed tissues to unite and heal. In both cases the method relies upon something which is innate in all living creatures; but while men and women have learnt to take the power of bodies to heal almost for granted, they have still much that is comforting to learn of the power of minds to do the same.

Psychiatry has much to offer, as we have seen, in the sphere of human relations; it has contributions to make to man's happiness and security in childhood, in adolescence, in work, in marriage, in sickness, and in health. It is a useful tool in sociology and in anthropology, it has something to bring to the appreciation of art and literature, and to the interpretation of some aspects of philosophy and religion. To learn about these possibilities is stimulating; moreover it is something which is open to the intelligent layman just as much as to the doctor. But it is in the training of the doctor, whatever the branch of medicine in which he is going to interest himself, that psychiatry has a particular responsibility to teach something of the elements of human relationships and human feelings, for as we have seen, everyone who needs a doctor is to some extent disturbed and unhappy, and unless the patient can be understood as a person his chance of being helped is poor indeed.

The actual proportion of time in the medical curriculum which ought to be devoted to the teaching of psychiatry, particularly in its wider implications throughout the whole of medicine, is not something with which we can be concerned in detail here: but if it were to approach in proportion the size of the problem which the qualified doctor will meet in his practice, a great deal of the existing balance and emphasis in medical training and in medical examinations would have to be changed.

Meanwhile research in psychiatry continues to link many of its special problems and techniques with the wider understanding of man and medicine as a whole. Studies in human biochemistry and the function of the endocrine glands have begun to lead us to an understanding of the way in which physical treatment works in altering states of depression and withdrawal. It seems as though mood is indeed bound up to a great extent with the balance of glandular secretions, a balance which appears to be alterable by the direct effect upon the brain and the pituitary glands of electric treatment and other methods of temporarily intense stimulation, but this is still very much a matter of speculation. We do not know whether, for example, the physical and glandular changes seen in depression are primarily causal, or whether they have a common origin with the depression itself. We do know that physical methods of treatment for mood disturbance seem to have in common a capacity to alter both the metabolism of the brain and the output of the endocrine glands; and we see for ourselves the remarkable changes which follow in the mood of the patient.

Other pathways of research into the interrelationship of body and mind have been opened up by the discovery of ways of recording electric activity in brain cells, and oxygen saturation in the circulating blood. We now know something of the physical accompaniment of changes in consciousness and something too of the way in which oxygen exchange is related to states of sleeping and waking, awareness or withdrawal. We know too something of the relationship between the concentration of adrenalin in the brain, in states of anxiety and alertness, and the corresponding diminution of that concentration in states of withdrawal, or in sleep and dreaming.

Some of our knowledge overlaps, some dovetails neatly into the over-all pattern which we are striving to build, some seems obstinately contradictory. For example, while we know that the level of oxygen saturation in the blood of the patient in catatonic stupor resembles remarkably that of a normal person who is asleep and dreaming, we also know that it may be exactly paralleled by that of a patient suffering from congenital heart disease who shows no evidence of mental change whatever. Again, while there is a consistent correlation between certain patterns of abnormal rhythm in the brain waves of psychopaths and their clinical state and history, this is neither absolute nor specific as far as the nature of the abnormality is concerned; and it therefore remains impossible in our present state of knowledge to say that a particular record must denote a particular type of personality, or vice versa. In fact, some of the most strikingly disturbed psychopaths I have ever seen have proved on examination to have perfectly normal records on the electro-encephalogram.

Yet all the time we are narrowing the gap between results and their explanation, between pure speculation and a series of working hypotheses. It seems certain that further advances in psychiatry will be made along lines of research directed towards an even closer integration of mental and physical processes. These are the lines which at present seem at any rate to provide the most stimulating possibilities for further research. There is room in the study of psychophysical relationships, as they are called, for every doctor, from whatever aspect he approaches the problem, provided only that he has an open mind, patience, and a capacity for awareness and acceptance of feelings as well as physical states.

Another aspect of the study of psychophysical relationships is concerned with the connexion which seems to exist between certain types of body structure and certain temperamental characteristics: while both of these appear to be associated with the kind of mental illness which the subject will display, if he should become mentally ill at all. This has always been a relatively popular idea, and gained some notoriety when Lombroso described the 'criminal or degenerate type' on a physical basis which was subsequently completely discredited. Work of a more enduring kind along these lines has been done by Professor Kretschmer of Marburg, and Professor Sheldon of New York. Kretschmer's work takes the over-all gross physical proportions of the individual as the basis for classification, and the main division he makes is into three groups to which he gives special names. They correspond in everyday language to the stout or sturdy, the weedy, and the athletic. Affective disorders are more common among the first group, and schizophrenic among the second two.

Professor Sheldon's approach depends on extremely detailed and careful measurements, but his classification, while not the same, is comparable. Both methods provide a valuable set of data for correlation with the results of psychiatric studies, and Sheldon's work has been particularly helpful in recent studies of neurosis and of criminal behaviour in children.

*

Psychiatry to-day remains a study whose boundaries seem all the wider because of the mystery and deliberate obscurity in which the subject was for so long confined. It is a difficult subject and yet a tremendously fascinating one: and its disciples are at heart explorers rather than rulers within its domain. We can liken the whole development of psychiatry, and its impact upon ordinary men and women, to the discovery and exploration of a volcano upon a desert island. For a very long time the islanders have lived with the volcano in their midst. They have become familiar with its presence, but they are always disturbed by its possibilities. They have seen it erupt and destroy; they fear it and hate it, but it is one of the most powerful images and experiences which they have, and there are times when they feel impelled to worship it and ascribe to it magical powers which must be propitiated. All this men have in their time felt about mental illness.

In the course of time the threat and the mystery of the volcano have been claimed by the priests and seers as their particular province, and have come to underline much of the mythology of the people. Eventually explorers reach the island and seek to penetrate and understand the mystery of the destroying mountain. For so long have men hated, feared, and worshipped its manifestations that the early attempts of the explorers are regarded with considerable hostility. But the explorers go ahead and in time they produce a reasonable map and chart of the mountain and its activities. This is the era of descriptive psychiatry.

Later they find ways of studying the actual processes of eruption and learn something of the nature of the lava which, at first molten and burning, later solidifies and preserves even the forms it took as it pursued its destructive course. Here belong the dynamic studies of Freud, of Adler, of Jung, and of those who have come after them. Examination of all the data revealed by these explorations leads in time to contributions by the explorers to a number of allied fields of knowledge; for example, excavations which have been conducted in lava beds surrounding great volcanoes have told us much of what we know about archaeology and geology, and have even provided confirmation of some geographical theories. In the same way the exploration of psychological and psychodynamic studies has led to a wider understanding of the meaning of primitive rites and myths, in tribes studied by anthropological methods, as well as widening our grasp of some of the underlying principles of modern political and social theory.

The explorers on the volcano have in time developed instruments to record the very quakings and pulsings of the mountain itself; and these in turn can be developed and refined to provide evidence of earthquakes and approaching storms. So too in medicine we have our recording instruments, which reflect with varying degrees of precision the activity of those cells in our brains and nerves which somehow mediate our consciousness and form the link between experience and awareness. To the untrained observer there is even a certain resemblance between the tracings made by the seismograph and by the electro-encephalogram.

But all the while the explorers are diligently clambering and searching about on the mysterious and apparently dreadful mountain, the islanders are regarding them and their work with exceedingly mixed feelings. They show a very natural tendency in the face of this apparent conquest of their mystery, a conquest which they partly desire and partly dread, to transfer a good deal of their mingled feelings of hate and fear and worship from the volcano itself to the explorers. So it is, perhaps, that the current public attitude to psychiatry and psychiatrists to-day reflects a mixture of just these apparently contradictory feelings.

My own view, which I invite you to share, is that the psychiatrist is a doctor with a difficult but immensely worthwhile job to do. In a world in which evil exists, he can neither deny it nor explain it away; but surrounded by the suffering which it causes, as well as by the sickness to which all life is heir, he has his part to play in seeking to understand and to relieve it. I began this book by remarking that in the face of physical disease man has a precious natural humility. This is a characteristic which never leaves the greatest surgeon or physician; through it he can inspire the hope and confidence which it is his aim to deserve. In the face of all unhappiness, and particularly that associated with mental illness, the psychiatrist must experience the same feeling, and strive humbly and faithfully to perform the same service.

GLOSSARY

GLOSSARY

A number of technical terms have of necessity been employed in this book: it was the author's intention to define each one on its first appearance. He is sincerely grateful to those friends who, after reading the finished draft, pointed out that one or two words had escaped this treatment, and that several others might gain from a re-statement of definition apart from the text. The following nine are perhaps the most important of these and they receive a working definition here. In each case the definition is the author's own, and must remain his responsibility.

DYNAMIC (adjective; as applied to psychology). A way of considering mental life which makes use of the analogy of forces in motion (*e.g.* mental strife, conflict, stress, resistance, inertia, retardation, rejection, etc.).

HYPNOSIS. A condition of increased suggestibility accompanied by a diminished awareness of events outside the area of suggestion.

HYPNOTISM. The production of a heightened degree of suggestibility by influencing areas of the mind not normally under the conscious control of the subject.

PSYCHIATRIST. A qualified doctor with an additional specialized training in psychiatry.

PSYCHIATRY. That aspect of medicine which is concerned with the mental element in health and sickness, including mental illness and abnormality.

PSYCHOLOGIST. One who has been trained in psychology.

PSYCHOLOGY. The science of mental life, including the study of intelligence, emotion, and behaviour.

SUGGESTIBILITY. The capacity for accepting or responding to suggestion.

SUGGESTION. A method of conveying ideas or attitudes of mind on an emotional rather than a rational basis in such a way that the ideas or attitudes shall not be criticized by the person to whom they are suggested.

INDEX

INDEX

MORE ABOUT PENGUINS
AND PELICANS

If you have enjoyed reading this book you may wish to know that *Penguin Book News* appears every month. It is an attractively illustrated magazine containing a complete list of books published by Penguins and still in print, together with details of the month's new books. A specimen copy will be sent free on request.

Penguin Book News is obtainable from most bookshops; but you may prefer to become a regular subscriber at 3s. for twelve issues. Just write to Dept EP, Penguin Books Ltd, Harmondsworth, Middlesex, enclosing a cheque or postal order, and you will be put on the mailing list.

Some other books published by Penguins are described on the following pages.

Note: *Penguin Book News* is not
available in the U.S.A., Canada or Australia

FREUD AND THE POST-FREUDIANS

J. A. C. Brown

Freud and the Post-Freudians explains the main concepts of Freudian psychology and goes on to review the theories of Adler, Jung, Rank, and Stekel. Later developments in the orthodox Freudian school are also discussed, as are those of the American Neo-Freudians and the Post-Freudians in England.

This is the first book published in Britain to bring together all these psychological and sociological schools and criticize them, both from the Freudian standpoint and that of the scientific psychologists.

ALSO AVAILABLE

The Social Psychology of Industry
Techniques of Persuasion

THE PSYCHOLOGY OF PERCEPTION

M. D. Vernon

When we look at the world with our eyes, do we see it *as it really is*? In this authoritative study the Professor of Psychology at the University of Reading shows how, behind the retina of the eye, many more fallible mental processes cause errors and inconsistencies to creep into our perceptions. We are seldom aware of these.

Here then is a non-technical outline of the psychological processes which have been shown to be involved in our visual perceptions of things around us. These perceptions of shape, colour, movement, and space develop gradually from infancy upwards. Special processes also emerge to enable us to deal with symbolic material such as printed words and diagrams, for the purpose, in particular, of reading.

Finally this book, which is based on over thirty years of psychological research at Cambridge and elsewhere, shows how the perceptions of different people are not always alike: they vary with attention, interest, and individual personality factors.

CHILD CARE AND THE GROWTH OF LOVE

John Bowlby and Margery Fry

Among the most remarkable results of the work of the new school of psychologists is the realization that mother-love is, perhaps, the greatest influence in the formation of character and personality. In 1951 Dr John Bowlby issued a report on *Maternal Care and Mental Health* of which a leader in *The Times* said, 'it does for the western nations what the Curtis report did for England and Wales.' It was prepared under the auspices of the World Health Organization and summarizes expert world opinion on this question and the important issues that arise from it – the prevention of juvenile and adult delinquency, the problem of the 'unwanted child', the motherhood training of women, and the best methods of supplying the need of maternal love for the child who is deprived of his natural mother.

This book is a summary of Dr Bowlby's report, freed from many of its technicalities and prepared for the general reader. It explains how the capacity for love and sympathy in adult life has its roots in early childhood, and how a lack of motherly care may permanently stunt the growth of love; and suggests practical steps to prevent the neglected children of today from becoming the neglectful parents of the future.

Another Pelican by David Stafford-Clark

WHAT FREUD REALLY SAID

The name of Freud is used (often by those who have never read a word he wrote) to excuse any and every licence, from anarchy to sex-worship. Yet, as a writer, the founder of psychoanalysis deployed over three million words in order to state, very clearly and simply, what he had concluded from his clinical experience with patients.

This first brief summary of Freud's theories has been made by Dr Stafford-Clark, the director of the York Clinic and author of *Psychiatry To-day*. Here the general reader will find the core of Freud's own pronouncements about hysteria and anxiety, the interpretation of dreams, the unconscious mind, sexuality, the nature of the neuroses and the technique of psychoanalysis, as well as his speculations on art, literature, and life.

Dr Stafford-Clark's exact recital of Freud's revolutionary concepts is an essential corrective to almost half a century of misrepresentation.